StatClass

Second Edition

Revised Printing

Dawn E. Holmes
Lubella A. Lenaburg

University of California – Santa Barbara

 **Learning Solutions**

Boston Burr Ridge, IL Dubuque, IA New York San Francisco St. Louis
Bangkok Bogotá Caracas Lisbon London Madrid
Mexico City Milan New Delhi Seoul Singapore Sydney Taipei Toronto

StatClass, Second Edition
Revised Printing

10 11 12 13 14 15 DIG/DIG 16 15 14 13

ISBN-13: 978-0-07-339175-5
ISBN-10: 0-07-339175-1
part of
ISBN-13: 978-0-07-335340-1
ISBN-10: 0-07-335340-X

Editor: Nicole Schmitt
Production Editor: Nicole Baumgartner
Cover Design: Maggie Lytle
Printer/Binder: Digital Impressions

TABLE OF CONTENTS

Unit 1	**Probability**	**1**
Lesson 1.1	Probability for All Events	3
	Exercises for Lesson 1.1	14
	Answers to Exercises for Lesson 1.1	16
Lesson 1.2	Probability for Independent and Mutually Exclusive Events	18
	Exercises for Lesson 1.2	21
	Answers to Exercises for Lesson 1.2	23
Lesson 1.3	More Practice in Solving Probability Problems	25
	Exercises for Lesson 1.3	33
	Answers to Exercises for Lesson 1.3	34
	Avoiding Common Mistakes	35
	Unit 1 Summary	36
	Self-Assessment Quiz	37
	Answers to Self-Assessment Quiz	39
Unit 2	**Discrete Probability Distributions**	**41**
Lesson 2.1	Discrete Random Variables and their Probability Distributions	43
	Exercises for Lesson 2.1	49
	Answers to Exercises for Lesson 2.1	51
Lesson 2.2	Finding the Mean and Standard Deviation of Discrete Random Variables	52
	Exercises for Lesson 2.2	58
	Answers to Exercises for Lesson 2.2	59
Lesson 2.3	More Practice in Solving Discrete Probability Distribution Problems	60
	Exercises for Lesson 2.3	69
	Answers to Exercises for Lesson 2.3	70

	Avoiding Common Mistakes	71
	Unit 2 Summary	72
	Self-Assessment Quiz	74
	Answers to Self-Assessment Quiz	75

Unit 3	**The Binomial Distribution**	**77**
Lesson 3.1	Counting and Binomial Probabilities	79
	Exercises for Lesson 3.1	88
	Answers to Exercises for Lesson 3.1	90
Lesson 3.2	Finding the Mean and Standard Deviation of a Binomial Random Variable	92
	Exercises for Lesson 3.2	95
	Answers to Exercises for Lesson 3.2	96
Lesson 3.3	More Practice in Solving Binomial Distribution Problems	97
	Exercises for Lesson 3.3	106
	Answers to Exercises for Lesson 3.3	107
	Avoiding Common Mistakes	108
	Unit 3 Summary	109
	Self-Assessment Quiz	110
	Answers to Self-Assessment Quiz	111

Unit 4	**Continuous Distributions**	**113**
Lesson 4.1	Continuous Random Variables and the Uniform Distribution	115
	Exercises for Lesson 4.1	121
	Answers to Exercises for Lesson 4.1	122
Lesson 4.2	The Normal Distribution	123
	Exercises for Lesson 4.2	131
	Answers to Exercises for Lesson 4.2	132
Lesson 4.3	More Practice in Solving Continuous Distribution Problems	133
	Exercises for Lesson 4.3	151
	Answers to Exercises for Lesson 4.3	152
	Avoiding Common Mistakes	153
	Unit 4 Summary	154
	Self-Assessment Quiz	156
	Answers to Self-Assessment Quiz	157

Unit 5	**Sample Statistics**	**159**
Lesson 5.1	Descriptive Statistics	161
	Exercises for Lesson 5.1	176
	Answers to Exercises for Lesson 5.1	178
Lesson 5.2	Sample Statistics as Random Variables	179
	Exercises for Lesson 5.2	186
	Answers to Exercises for Lesson 5.2	187
Lesson 5.3	More Practice in Solving Sample Statistics Problems	188
	Exercises for Lesson 5.3	198
	Answers to Exercises for Lesson 5.3	199
	Avoiding Common Mistakes	200
	Unit 5 Summary	201
	Self-Assessment Quiz	203
	Answers to Self-Assessment Quiz	205
Unit 6	**Inference on a Sample Mean**	**207**
Lesson 6.1	Confidence Intervals for a Population Mean	209
	Exercises for Lesson 6.1	218
	Answers to Exercises for Lesson 6.1	220
Lesson 6.2	Hypothesis Testing for a Population Mean	221
	Exercises for Lesson 6.2	229
	Answers to Exercises for Lesson 6.2	230
Lesson 6.3	More Practice in Solving Inference Problems	231
	Exercises for Lesson 6.3	244
	Answers to Exercises for Lesson 6.3	246
	Avoiding Common Mistakes	248
	Unit 6 Summary	249
	Self-Assessment Quiz	251
	Answers to Self-Assessment Quiz	252
Unit 7	**Inference on a Sample Proportion**	**253**
Lesson 7.1	Confidence Intervals for a Population Proportion	255
	Exercises for Lesson 7.1	260
	Answers to Exercises for Lesson 7.1	261

Lesson 7.2	Hypothesis Testing for a Population Proportion	262
	Exercises for Lesson 7.2	268
	Answers to Exercises for Lesson 7.2	269
Lesson 7.3	More Practice in Solving Inference Problems	270
	Exercises for Lesson 7.3	283
	Answers to Exercises for Lesson 7.3	285
	Avoiding Common Mistakes	287
	Unit 7 Summary	288
	Self-Assessment Quiz	290
	Answers to Self-Assessment Quiz	292

Unit 8   **Inference on Two Sample Proportions**   **295**

Lesson 8.1	Confidence Intervals for Comparing Two Population Proportions	297
	Exercises for Lesson 8.1	303
	Answers to Exercises for Lesson 8.1	304
Lesson 8.2	Hypothesis Testing for Comparing Two Population Proportions	306
	Exercises for Lesson 8.2	314
	Answers to Exercises for Lesson 8.2	315
Lesson 8.3	More Practice in Solving Inference Problems	316
	Exercises for Lesson 8.3	333
	Answers to Exercises for Lesson 8.3	335
	Avoiding Common Mistakes	337
	Unit 8 Summary	338
	Self-Assessment Quiz	340
	Answers to Self-Assessment Quiz	341

Unit 9   **Correlation between Two Variables**   **343**

Lesson 9.1	Scatterplots	345
	Exercises for Lesson 9.1	348
	Answers to Exercises for Lesson 9.1	350
Lesson 9.2	Correlation Coefficient and Coefficient of Determination	351
	Exercises for Lesson 9.2	356
	Answers to Exercises for Lesson 9.2	357

Lesson 9.3	More Practice in Solving Correlation Problems	358
	Exercises for Lesson 9.3	365
	Answers to Exercises for Lesson 9.3	367
	Avoiding Common Mistakes	368
	Unit 9 Summary	369
	Self-Assessment Quiz	371
	Answers to Self-Assessment Quiz	373
Unit 10	**Simple Linear Regression**	**375**
Lesson 10.1	Determining the Best-Fitting Line	377
	Exercises for Lesson 10.1	380
	Answers to Exercises for Lesson 10.1	381
Lesson 10.2	Confidence Interval for the Slope	382
	Exercises for Lesson 10.2	385
	Answers to Exercises for Lesson 10.2	386
Lesson 10.3	More Practice in Solving Simple Linear Regression Problems	387
	Exercises for Lesson 10.3	393
	Answers to Exercises for Lesson 10.3	394
	Avoiding Common Mistakes	395
	Unit 10 Summary	396
	Self-Assessment Quiz	398
	Answers to Self-Assessment Quiz	399
Appendix	**Tables**	**401**
	Binomial Table	403
	Standard Normal Table	408
	t-Table	410

Unit 1
Probability

Lesson 1.1 Probability for All Events
Exercises for Lesson 1.1
Answers to Exercises for Lesson 1.1

Lesson 1.2 Probability for Independent and Mutually Exclusive Events
Exercises for Lesson 1.2
Answers to Exercises for Lesson 1.2

Lesson 1.3 More Practice in Solving Probability Problems
Exercises for Lesson 1.3
Answers to Exercises for Lesson 1.3

Avoiding Common Mistakes
Unit 1 Summary
Self-Assessment Quiz
Answers to Self-Assessment Quiz

LESSON 1.1
PROBABILITY FOR ALL EVENTS

1.1.1   INTRODUCTION

Whether we realize it or not, we use probabilities all the time. We have all thought about what our chances were of getting into the college of our choice, or how likely we are to do well on the SAT's, or the chance that the person we like will agree to go on a date with us. These are all examples of how we use probability to help us make decisions. Each individual makes their own judgment on these types of probabilities based on their own experiences, and so there is no consistency in the results. In this unit, we will learn techniques to find probabilities in a more formal way using formulas.

1.1.2   BASIC CONCEPTS OF PROBABILITY

Before you reach for a formula, just STOP and THINK about what you are being asked to do. It is difficult to decide which formula you should use if you do not understand the problem. Even if you do choose the correct formula, you might not use it correctly. There may be more than one way of solving a probability problem, so the best approach is to THINK, look at what information is given, and decide how you can use it to solve the problem. The best way to learn how to solve problems is to do a lot of them.

Calculating probabilities requires you to use your reasoning skills. However, since many real life situations are extremely complex due to the numerous factors that are involved, we will focus on some simple experiments. For example, consider rolling a fair six-sided die. Knowing the die is fair means that all faces are equally likely to occur. If you were asked to find the probability of rolling a 3 with a fair six-sided die, you would say 1 in 6, and the reasoning behind your answer is that there is only one favorable outcome out of the 6 possible outcomes. Another way of saying this is that the probability of rolling a 3 with a fair six-sided die is 1/6, as illustrated in Figure 1.1.

Figure 1.1

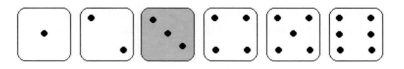

Now suppose you have 10 candies in a bag, 4 red and 6 green, as shown in Figure 1.2. You put your hand into the bag without looking, and pick one candy. What is the probability that the candy you pick is red? Apply the reasoning you used in the dice problem to this problem.

Figure 1.2

As we see in Figure 1.2, there are 4 favorable outcomes out of 10 possible outcomes. Therefore, the chance of picking a red candy from this bag is 4/10.

To generalize the above results, we notice that we are taking the number of outcomes favorable to the experiment and dividing that by the total number of possible outcomes. This result is called the classical definition of probability and states that:

Classical Definition of Probability

$$\text{Probability of an event} = \frac{\text{Number of favorable outcomes}}{\text{Total number of possible outcomes}}$$

This method works for situations when you can count outcomes and the outcomes are all equally likely.

Important Idea

You can think of the classical definition of probability as a *PROPORTION*.

We will be using proportions throughout the course, so be sure you are comfortable with the concept.

Using the classical definition of probability, we can deduce certain facts. Consider throwing a fair six-sided die. What is the probability that the die would show a 7?

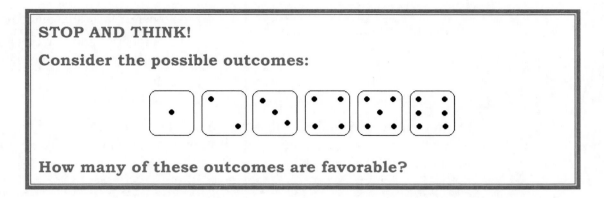
We can find the probability of rolling a 7 by taking the number of favorable outcomes and dividing them by the total number of possible outcomes:

$$\text{Probability of rolling a 7} = \frac{\text{Number of 7's on the die}}{\text{Total number of possible outcomes}}$$

$$= \frac{0}{6}$$

$$= 0$$

A probability of 0 indicates that the event can never happen. Since a fair six-sided die has only the numbers 1-6 on it, it is impossible to get any other number when you roll the die. Therefore:

> When you know an event is impossible,
> this means the probability that the event occurs is 0.

Again, consider throwing a fair six-sided die. What is the probability that the die would show a 1 or 2 or 3 or 4 or 5 or 6?

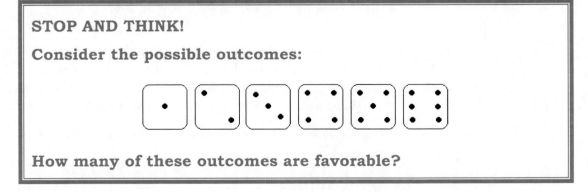
Again, we can consider the number of favorable outcomes out of the total number of possible outcomes:

Probability of rolling a 1, 2, 3, 4, 5 or 6 $= \dfrac{\text{Number of favorable outcomes}}{\text{Total number of possible outcomes}}$

$$= \dfrac{6}{6}$$

$$= 1$$

A probability of 1 indicates that the event will always happen. Since a fair six-sided die has only the numbers 1-6 on it, one of these numbers is certain to occur when you roll the die. Therefore:

> When you know an event is certain,
> this means the probability that the event occurs is 1.

If an event is neither impossible nor certain, then the probability of the event must be between 0 and 1. Furthermore, the closer to 0 the probability of an event is, the less likely it is to occur and the closer to 1, the more likely it is to occur.

Think back to the candy example, where we had a bag with 10 candies, 4 red and 6 green. We found the probability of choosing a red candy from this bag to be 4/10. Similarly, the probability of choosing a green candy from this bag is 6/10. When you pick a candy from this bag, it must be either red or green. That is certain and so has a probability of 1. Notice that if you add the probability of a picking a red candy to the probability of picking a green candy, you also get 1.

Consider another example where we have a bag with 12 candies: 3 red, 5 blue, and 4 green, as shown in Figure 1.3.

Figure 1.3

Three out of the 12 candies are red, so the probability of choosing a red candy is 3/12. Five of the 12 candies are blue, so the probability of choosing a blue candy is 5/12. Four of the 12 candies are green, so the probability of choosing a green candy is 4/12. What would you get if you added all three probabilities together?

> **STOP AND THINK!**
>
> **Add the probabilities for the three colors together. Why do you get 1?**

You get one because you are certain to pick a candy that is either red or blue or green. The results of the candy experiments can be generalized:

> The sum of the probabilities of *all* events
> in a sample space must equal 1.

We now introduce some terminology that is useful when discussing probability experiments in general. Each probability experiment has a certain number of *possible outcomes*; for example, the total number of candies in the bag. A description of all these possible outcomes is called the *sample space*. An *event* is whatever part of the sample space you are interested in.

Suppose you pick one candy from the bag depicted in Figure 1.3. Consider the event R = 'picking a red candy'. All other events remaining in the sample space make up the *complement* of the event, denoted by R^c. For example, the complement to event R is event R^c = 'picking a candy that is NOT red'. Remember that we found the probability of picking a red candy to be 3/12, which we can write as P(R) = 3/12. What is the probability of event R^c, that is, what is $P(R^c)$?

Each of the 12 candies is either in event R or in event R^c, as shown in Figure 1.4.

Figure 1.4

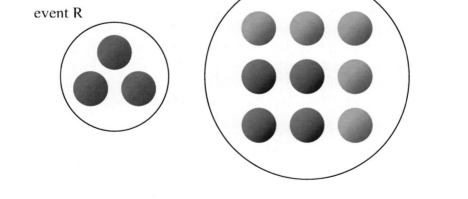

We can see that $P(R^c)$ = 9/12, because there are 9 candies that are NOT red out of the 12. Notice that the probabilities of event R^c and event R add to 1. This result can be generalized for any event A, where P(A) denotes the probability of event A:

$$P(A) + P(A^c) = 1$$

From this equation, we can see that:

$$P\left(A^{c}\right)=1-P\left(A\right)$$

1.1.3   **CONDITIONAL PROBABILITIES**

Suppose your friend rolls a fair six-sided die and wants you to guess the number that is rolled. We have discussed previously that the probability for each face of the die is 1/6. Since only one of the six faces is possible when your friend rolls the die, the probability that you guess the number correct is also 1/6. However, suppose that when your friend rolls the die, he tells you that the number rolled is even, and wants you to guess the number.

STOP AND THINK!

If the number rolled was even, the possible outcomes are:

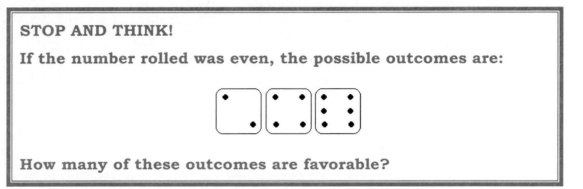

How many of these outcomes are favorable?

You are no longer considering all 6 faces of the die because you are *given* the additional information that the number is even. Hence, you can eliminate three faces from the sample space: 1, 3, and 5. Out of these three even faces, your friend only rolled one. Therefore the probability that you guess correctly *given* the face is even, using the classical definition of probability is:

$$P(\text{you guess correct } given \text{ the face is even})=\frac{\#\text{ of favorable outcomes}}{\text{Total }\#\text{ of possible outcomes}}$$

$$=\frac{1}{3}$$

This idea of finding the probability of event B *given* additional information, event A, is called *conditional probability*. Notice that you can find conditional probabilities using the classical definition of probability. However, instead of considering all possible outcomes, you only consider the outcomes that satisfy the *given* information, event A. The favorable outcomes must satisfy both event A and event B.

Using the Classical Definition of Probability to find Conditional Probabilities

Probability of event B *given* event A $= \dfrac{\text{\# of outcomes in event A and B}}{\text{Total \# of outcomes in event A}}$

Example: Consider the following chart depicting attendance versus GPA for 100 college students.

	High GPA	Low GPA	Total
Regular attendance	60	15	75
Sparse attendance	10	15	25
Total	70	30	100

Question 1
Find the probability that a randomly selected student attends class regularly.

Solution: Notice that the probability that a student attends class regularly is not conditional on any other information. In other words, we do not know whether the student has a high or low GPA, and therefore we must consider all 100 students. As we see in the chart below, 75 out of the 100 students attend class regularly.

	High GPA	Low GPA	Total
Regular attendance	60	15	75
Sparse attendance	10	15	25
Total	70	30	100

We can use the classical definition of probability to get the answer:

$$\text{Probability a student attends regularly} = \dfrac{\text{\# of students that attend regularly}}{\text{Total \# of students}}$$

$$= \dfrac{75}{100}$$

Question 2
Find the probability that a randomly selected student attends class regularly *given* that they have a high GPA.

Solution: Because we are now *given* extra information about the student, we can restrict the sample space to only those students that have a high GPA, as shown below. So we are only considering 70 students. Out of these 70 students, 60 have attended regularly.

	High GPA	**Low GPA**	**Total**
Regular attendance	60	15	**75**
Sparse attendance	10	15	**25**
Total	**70**	**30**	**100**

$$P(\text{student attends regularly } given \text{ they have a high GPA}) = \frac{60}{70}$$

Let's define:

Event A = 'high GPA'
Event B = 'regular attendance'

Then the 'Probability that a student attends regularly *given* they have a high GPA' is written as P(B|A).

How to read P(B|A)

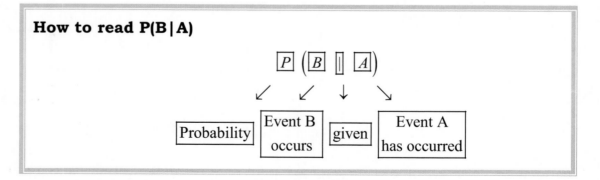

Using the classical definition of probability, we see that:

$$P(A) = \frac{70}{100}$$

$$P(A \; and \; B) = \frac{60}{100}$$

Now, if we divide P(A *and* B) by P(A), we get P(B|A).

$$\frac{P(A \; and \; B)}{P(A)} = \frac{60/100}{70/100} = \frac{60}{70} = P(B|A)$$

We can now generalize the idea of conditional probability:

Finding Conditional Probabilities

$$P(B|A) = \frac{P(A \; and \; B)}{P(A)}$$

From this equation, we get the general relationship for joint probabilities:

Finding Joint Probabilities

$$P(A \; and \; B) = P(A)P(B|A)$$

In Question 2, we found the probability that a student has a high GPA *and* attends regularly using the classical definition of probability:

$$P(A \; and \; B) = \frac{60}{100}$$

However, unless you know how many outcomes are favorable and how many are possible, you cannot use the classical definition of probability. In such cases, you would use the general relationship for joint probabilities, as we will illustrate next in Question 3.

Question 3
Find the probability that a student has a high GPA *and* attends class regularly.

Solution: Notice that we are not *given* any information about the student. We do not know for a fact that the student attends class regularly, or that the student has a high

GPA. Therefore, we cannot reduce our sample space and must consider all 100 students. In order to use the relationship $P(A \text{ and } B) = P(A)P(B|A)$, we need to first find $P(A)$ and $P(B|A)$ using the information in the chart below:

	High GPA	Low GPA	Total
Regular attendance	60	15	75
Sparse attendance	10	15	25
Total	70	30	100

Using the classical definition of probability, we get:

$$P(A) = \frac{70}{100}$$

$$P(B|A) = \frac{60}{70}$$

Now if we multiply $P(A)$ by $P(B|A)$, we get $P(A \text{ and } B)$.

$$P(A)P(B|A) = \left(\frac{70}{100}\right)\left(\frac{60}{70}\right) = \frac{60}{100} = P(A \text{ and } B)$$

Question 4
Find the probability a student has a high GPA *or* attends class regularly.

Solution: Notice that we are not *given* any information about the student. We do not know for a fact that the student attends class regularly, or that the student has a high GPA. Therefore, we cannot reduce our sample space and must consider all 100 students. We want to see how many students have either a high GPA *or* attend class regularly.

	High GPA	Low GPA	Total
Regular attendance	60	15	75
Sparse attendance	10	15	25
Total	70	30	100

We are going to use the classical definition of probability. Look at the chart. The total number of possible outcomes is 100. We need to find the number of favorable outcomes:

Total # of students with a high GPA = 70
(including the 60 with regular attendance)

Total # of students with regular attendance = 75
(including the 60 we already counted with a high GPA)

These 60 students have been counted twice, so:

# of students who have a high GPA or attend class regularly = $70 + 75 - 60$

$$= 85$$

Hence:

P(A or B)= probability a student has a high GPA or attends regularly

$$= \frac{\text{\# of favorable outcomes}}{\text{Total \# of possible outcomes}}$$

$$= \frac{85}{100}$$

■

To derive a more general relationship, we can make use of some probabilities we have already found:

$$P(A) = \frac{70}{100}$$

$$P(B) = \frac{75}{100}$$

$$P(A \ and \ B) = \frac{60}{100}$$

Notice that if you add P(A) to P(B) and subtract P(A and B), you get P(A or B):

$$P(A) + P(B) - P(A \ and \ B) = \frac{70}{100} + \frac{75}{100} - \frac{60}{100} = \frac{85}{100} = P(A \ or \ B)$$

We can therefore generalize the relationship:

$$P(A \ or \ B) = P(A) + P(B) - P(A \ and \ B)$$

LESSON 1.1 EXERCISES
PROBABILITY FOR ALL EVENTS

1. A fair six-sided die is thrown. Find the probability that the number obtained is:
   a) a four.
   b) odd.
   c) multiple of 2.

2. A fair coin is tossed. Find the probability of obtaining:
   a) a head *or* a tail.
   b) *neither* a head *nor* a tail.

3. A fair coin is tossed until a tail has been obtained. Find the probability that exactly 3 tosses are required.

4. A fair six-sided die is thrown twice. Find the probability that:
   a) the sum of the scores obtained is a multiple of 5.
   b) *neither* throw results in a 4.

5. A bag contains 3 yellow candies, 7 red candies and 5 brown candies. If you pick one candy from this bag, find the probability that the candy picked is:
   a) red.
   b) red *or* yellow.
   c) orange (Think carefully!)
   d) red *or* yellow *or* brown.

6. A bag contains 5 yellow candies, 10 red candies and 5 green candies. For each of the following events, state whether it is impossible, certain or probable.

   A candy picked from this bag is:
   a) yellow, red or green.
   b) red.
   c) brown.

7. The probability that Event A will occur is 0.45, the probability that Event B will occur is 0.65 and the probability that Event (A and B) will occur is 0.2. Find:
   a) $P(A^c)$
   b) $P(B^c)$
   c) $P(A \text{ } or \text{ } B)$

8. The probability that a married man will attend church on Sunday is 0.65, the probability that a married woman will attend church on Sunday is 0.7, and the probability that a married man will attend church on Sunday given his wife attends is 0.9.

   What is the probability that:
   a) a wife and her husband both attend church on Sunday?
   b) a wife will attend church on Sunday, given that her husband attends?
   c) at least one member of a married couple will attend church on Sunday?

9. The annual call for blood donors at UCSB resulted in 500 students coming forward. Their blood types were as follows:

	Female	Male	Total
Blood Type A	120	105	**225**
Blood Type B	100	75	**175**
Blood Type AB	60	40	**100**
Total	**280**	**220**	**500**

   Find the probability that a chosen student:
   a) has blood type B.
   b) is female.
   c) is male with blood type A.
   d) is female with blood type AB.

10. Customers at Pizza Parlor can choose a side salad or garlic bread free when they order a large pizza. Experience has shown that 80% of customers order a large pizza. Out of these, 25% will choose a free side salad. 60% of customers will order a large pizza and the free garlic bread.

    Find the probability that a customer:
    a) will order a large pizza and a side salad.
    b) will *not* order a large pizza.
    c) will order the free garlic bread *given* they ordered a large pizza.

ANSWERS
LESSON 1.1 EXERCISES
PROBABILITY FOR ALL EVENTS

Below are the answers to the exercises for Unit 1, Lesson 1.1.
For full solutions, please refer to the CD included with this textbook.

1. a) $P(\text{roll a 4}) = \dfrac{1}{6}$

    b) $P(\text{roll an odd face}) = \dfrac{3}{6}$

    c) $P(\text{roll a multiple 2}) = \dfrac{3}{6}$

2. a) $P(\text{coin lands on heads or tails}) = 1$

    b) $P(\text{coin lands on } neither \text{ heads } nor \text{ tails}) = 0$

3. $P(\text{H } and \text{ H } and \text{ T}) = \dfrac{1}{8}$

4. a) $P(\text{roll a sum that is a multiple of 5}) = \dfrac{7}{36}$

    b) $P(4^c \text{ 1st } and \text{ } 4^c \text{ 2nd}) = \dfrac{25}{36}$

5. a) $P(\text{choose red}) = \dfrac{7}{15}$

    b) $P(\text{choose red or yellow}) = \dfrac{10}{15}$

    c) $P(\text{choose orange}) = 0$

    d) $P(\text{choose red or yellow or brown}) = 1$

6. a)   This event is ***certain***.
    b)   This event is ***probable***.
    c)   This event is ***impossible***.

7. a) $P(\text{A}^c) = 0.55$

    b) $P(\text{B}^c) = 0.35$

    c) $P(\text{A } or \text{ B}) = 0.9$

8. a) P(wife *and* husband attends) = 0.63

   b) P(wife attends|husband attends) = 0.969

   c) P(wife *or* husband attends) = 0.72

9. a) $P(\text{blood type B}) = \dfrac{175}{500}$

   b) $P(\text{female}) = \dfrac{280}{500}$

   c) $P(\text{male } and \text{ blood type A}) = \dfrac{105}{500}$

   d) $P(\text{female } and \text{ blood type AB}) = \dfrac{60}{500}$

10. a) P(large pizza *and* side salad) = 0.2

    b) $P(\text{large pizza}^c) = 0.2$

    c) P(garlic bread|large pizza) = 0.75

LESSON 1.2
PROBABILITY FOR MUTUALLY EXCLUSIVE AND INDEPENDENT EVENTS

1.2.1   **INTRODUCTION**
The relationships you learned in Lesson 1.1 apply to all events. However, sometimes events have specific properties that allow simplification of these relationships.

1.2.2   **MUTUALLY EXCLUSIVE EVENTS**
The first simplification arises when we are considering two events that cannot both occur at the same time. Consider the experiment 'rolling a fair six-sided die one time'. Define the events:

$$A = \text{'rolling a 4'}$$
$$B = \text{'rolling a 3'}$$

In this experiment, the events A and B cannot both occur at the same time and are said to be *mutually exclusive*.

> Events A and B are mutually exclusive
> if they cannot both occur at the same time.

Consider finding $P(B|A)$, that is, the probability that in *one toss* you roll a 4 *given* you have rolled a 3. Since you have already rolled a 3, it is impossible that the die is showing a 4. Therefore, $P(B|A) = 0$. This is always true when events A and B are *mutually exclusive*.

> **Finding Conditional Probabilities**
> **when Events A and B are Mutually Exclusive**
> $$P(B|A) = 0$$

Now consider P(A *and* B) ; that is, the probability that in *one toss* you will roll both a 4 *and* a 3. When you toss the die once, it is impossible to get two numbers at the same time, thus P(A *and* B) = 0. This is always true when events A and B are *mutually exclusive*.

**Finding Joint Probabilities
when Events A and B are Mutually Exclusive**

$$P(A \text{ } and \text{ } B) = 0$$

Next, consider P(A *or* B); that is, the probability that in *one toss* you will roll a 4 *or* a 3. We have already established that P(A *and* B) = 0 for mutually exclusive events. Therefore, the probability of event A or B occurring is found simply by adding P(A) to P(B). So in this example:

$$P(A \text{ } or \text{ } B) = P(A) + P(B) = \frac{1}{6} + \frac{1}{6} = \frac{2}{6}$$

We can generalize this result:

When Events A and B are Mutually Exclusive

$$P(A \text{ } or \text{ } B) = P(A) + P(B)$$

1.2.3   **INDEPENDENT EVENTS**
The second simplification arises when we notice that the occurrence of event A does not affect the probability of the occurrence of event B. For example, say you are rolling a fair six-sided die one time and flipping a fair coin once. Consider the following events:

A = 'die shows a 2'
B = 'coin shows a tail'

In this experiment, the events A and B are said to be *independent* because if the die shows a 2, the probability of the coin showing tails remains unchanged.

Independent Events

Events A and B are *independent* if the occurrence of one event does not change the probability of occurrence of the other event.

Events that are *not* independent are said to be *dependent*.

Consider finding P(B|A), that is, the probability the coin shows a tail *given* the die shows a 2. Rolling a die does not affect the outcome of flipping a coin. Therefore, P(B|A) = 1/2 = P(B). This is always true when events A and B are *independent*.

**Finding Conditional Probabilities
when Events A and B are Independent**

$$P(B|A) = P(B)$$

Now consider P(A *and* B); that is, the probability the die shows a 2 *and* the coin shows a tail. In Lesson 1.1, we established P(A *and* B) = P(A)P(B|A). When events A and B are *independent,* we have determined that P(B|A)=P(B), so the relationship for the joint probability of *independent* events A and B can be generalized as:

**Finding Joint Probabilities
when Events A and B are Independent**

$$P(A \text{ } and \text{ } B) = P(A)P(B)$$

Next, consider P(A *or* B); that is, the probability the die shows a 2 *or* the coin shows a tail. In Lesson 1.1, we showed that:

$$P(A \text{ } or \text{ } B) = P(A) + P(B) - P(A \text{ } and \text{ } B)$$

We have already established that P(A *and* B) = P(A)P(B) for *independent* events. Therefore:

$$P(A \text{ } or \text{ } B) = P(A) + P(B) - P(A)P(B) = \frac{1}{6} + \frac{1}{2} - \left(\frac{1}{6}\right)\left(\frac{1}{2}\right) = \frac{7}{12}$$

We can generalize this result:

When Events A and B are Independent

$$P(A \text{ } or \text{ } B) = P(A) + P(B) - P(A)P(B)$$

Finally, we note that the definition of independence implies that mutually exclusive events are *dependent*.

LESSON 1.2 EXERCISES
PROBABILITY FOR INDEPENDENT AND MUTUALLY EXCLUSIVE EVENTS

1. a) If two events are independent, are the events mutually exclusive?
   b) Are complementary events independent or mutually exclusive?

2. Suppose you roll a pair of fair six-sided dice.
   a) What is the probability that the sum of the two numbers is greater than 9?
   b) What is the probability that the number showing on one die will be twice the number showing on the other die?

3. A two-person team is being chosen from two different groups. Group 1 has 5 males and 3 females, and Group 2 has 7 males and 8 females. One person is chosen at random from each group.
   a) What is the probability the team consists of two females?
   b) What is the probability the team consists of one male and one female?

4. You have two bags of candies. Bag 1 has 3 red candies, two orange candies, and 5 purple candies. Bag 2 has 5 red candies, 3 orange candies, and seven yellow candies. You select one candy from each bag.
   a) Is the selection from the first bag independent or dependent on the selection from the second bag? Explain.
   b) What is the probability that you pick a red or purple candy from Bag 1?
   c) What is the probability both candies are the same color?

5. Suppose there are two smoke alarms in your dorm hallway, each of them independently has a 95% chance of alerting you in case of a fire. What is the chance at least one alarm will alert you if there is a fire?

6. You flip a coin and roll 2 dice.
   a) What is the probability that the coin will show tails and the sum of the two dice will be 7?
   b) What is the probability that the coin will show heads and the sum of the two dice will be less than 4?

7. A study shows that 25% of high school students enjoy statistics and 45% of high school students enjoy media studies. The same study also showed that 15% of high school students enjoy both statistics and media studies. Can you conclude from these figures that whether a high school student enjoys statistics is independent of whether they enjoy media studies?

8. Two fair coins are tossed. Find the probability that the result is two heads *given* that at least one of the coins shows a head.

9. In a group of 50 adults, 12 out of the 30 women are overweight and 6 out of the 20 men are overweight.
   a) What is the probability that a person chosen from the group is an overweight woman?
   b) What is the probability that a person chosen from the group is a woman *or* someone who is overweight?

10. Two fair dice are rolled. Find the probability that:
   a) the sum rolled is at most 4 *given* the sum is even.
   b) at most one die comes up six.

ANSWERS
LESSON 1.2 EXERCISES
PROBABILITY FOR INDEPENDENT AND MUTUALLY EXCLUSIVE EVENTS

Below are the answers to the exercises for Unit 1, Lesson 1.2.
For full solutions, please refer to the CD included with this textbook.

1. a) No, events that are independent are NOT mutually exclusive.
    b) Complementary events are mutually exclusive.

2. a) $P(\text{sum greater than 9}) = \dfrac{6}{36}$

    b) $P(\text{number on one die is twice as much as the other}) = \dfrac{6}{36}$

3. a) $P(\text{F group 1 } and \text{ F group 2}) = \dfrac{24}{120}$

    b) $P(\text{pick one male and one female}) = \dfrac{61}{120}$

4. a) The selection from the first bag is *independent* of the selection from the second bag.

    b) $P(\text{red or purple}) = \dfrac{8}{10}$

    c) $P(\text{both candies the same color}) = \dfrac{21}{150}$

5. $P(\text{Alarm 1 } or \text{ Alarm 2 works}) = 0.9975$

6. a) $P(\text{Tails } and \text{ sum is 7}) = \dfrac{6}{72}$

    b) $P(\text{Heads } and \text{ sum} < 4) = \dfrac{3}{72}$

7. The events 'a high school student enjoys statistics' and 'a high school student enjoys media studies' are NOT independent. (You need to prove this with the use of relationships for independent events, not argue it. See solutions for details.)

8.   P(two heads|at least one head) $= \dfrac{1}{3}$

9. a) P(overweight woman) $= \dfrac{12}{50}$

     b) P(woman *or* overweight) $= \dfrac{36}{50}$

10. a) P(sum is at most 4|sum is even) $= \dfrac{4}{18}$

     b) P(at most one 6) $= \dfrac{35}{36}$

LESSON 1.3
MORE PRACTICE IN SOLVING PROBABILITY PROBLEMS

The best way to learn how to solve probability problems is to do a lot of them! In this lesson we look at some more examples, with full solutions, and introduce some new techniques for solving them.

Example 1: An experiment consists of rolling a six-sided die twice.
a) Describe the sample space using a *list*.
b) Describe the sample space using a *tree diagram*.
c) Describe the sample space using a *grid*.

STOP AND THINK!

There are several different ways to describe a sample space which we will show here. You should choose the method that makes most sense to you. You do not need to do all the methods every time you approach a problem.

Solution: a) *Method 1.* Make a list.

This is easy to do but you have to be careful not to miss out any possible combinations.

$$(1,1) \quad (1,2) \quad (1,3) \quad (1,4) \quad (1,5) \quad (1,6)$$
$$(2,1) \quad (2,2) \quad (2,3) \quad (2,4) \quad (2,5) \quad (2,6)$$
$$(3,1) \quad (3,2) \quad (3,3) \quad (3,4) \quad (3,5) \quad (3,6)$$
$$(4,1) \quad (4,2) \quad (4,3) \quad (4,4) \quad (4,5) \quad (4,6)$$
$$(5,1) \quad (5,2) \quad (5,3) \quad (5,4) \quad (5,5) \quad (5,6)$$
$$(6,1) \quad (6,2) \quad (6,3) \quad (6,4) \quad (6,5) \quad (6,6)$$

Solution: b) *Method 2.* Draw a tree.

This can be very useful when you have to keep track of a lot of different things because it ensures you do not miss any combinations. After drawing a tree, you can use it to make a list of the possible outcomes, if you like.

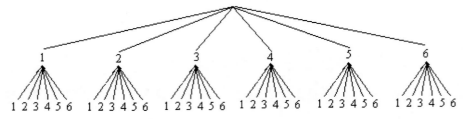

Solution: c) *Method 3.* Draw a grid.

Grids are particularly useful if you need to consider the sum of the 2 numbers.

	1	2	3	4	5	6
1	1,1	1,2	1,3	1,4	1,5	1,6
2	2,1	2,2	2,3	2,4	2,5	2,6
3	3,1	3,2	3,3	3,4	3,5	3,6
4	4,1	4,2	4,3	4,4	4,5	4,6
5	5,1	5,2	5,3	5,4	5,5	5,6
6	6,1	6,2	6,3	6,4	6,5	6,6

Important Idea

Grids are only helpful in situations involving two objects, such as two coins or dice. For three or more objects a tree diagram or list is more appropriate.

Example 2:   A fair coin is flipped three times. Find the probability that it will come up tails at most twice.

STOP AND THINK!

First you need to describe the sample space. What would be the best way to do this?

Solution: We can describe the sample space using a list or a tree. Let's use a tree. We cannot use a grid for this problem.

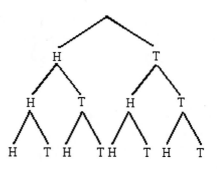

The classical definition of probability tells us that:

$$P(\text{coin comes up tails at most twice}) = \frac{\text{\# of favorable outcomes}}{\text{\# of possible outcomes}}$$

The tree shows us all the possible outcomes. There are 8 of them:

$$\text{HHH} \quad \text{HHT} \quad \text{HTH} \quad \text{HTT} \quad \text{THH} \quad \text{THT} \quad \text{TTH} \quad \text{TTT}$$

The favorable outcomes are given by those branches of the tree where you have either 0 tails, 1 tail, or 2 tails. (This is what 'tails at most twice' means). Count them. There are 7.

So, applying the definition of classical probability we see that:

$$P(\text{coin comes up tails at most twice}) = \frac{7}{8}$$

■

Example 3: A fair coin is flipped four times. If the coin lands with the head up on the first three tosses, what is the probability that the coin will land with the head up on the fourth toss? Explain.

> **STOP AND THINK!**
>
> **What strategy are you going to use to solve this problem?**
>
> **How do the results of the first three flips affect the fourth flip?**

Solution: We are told that the *first* flip came up heads.
We are told that the *second* flip came up heads.
We are told that the *third* flip came up heads.
The *fourth* flip can be a head or a tail, and we want to know how likely it is to come up heads.

The probability that the fourth flip comes up heads *given* that the first three flips came up heads is 0.5. This is because each toss of the coin is independent of the previous one, so the probability of observing heads on any flip is always 0.5.

■

Example 4:   If P(E) is the probability that an event will occur, which of the following must be false? Explain.

A. P(E)=1
B. P(E)=1/2
C. P(E)=1/3
D. P(E)= –1

> **STOP AND THINK!**
>
> **Can probabilities be any value, or are they limited to certain values?**

Solution: Choice D is false because a probability must always be between 0 and 1; you cannot have a negative probability. All the other options are possible values for P(E) because they are between 0 and 1.

■

Example 5:   A box of chocolates contains 21 chocolates: 7 chocolate almonds, 7 white chocolate macadamia nut, and 7 chocolate caramel.
a) Keith closes his eyes and picks a chocolate. What is the probability that he picks a chocolate almond?
b) After Keith has eaten his first chocolate, he picks another. Assuming that Keith *did* take a chocolate almond from the box, what is the probability that he will *not* pick a chocolate almond the second time?

> **STOP AND THINK!**
>
> **What method are you going to use to solve this problem? How is part (a) different from part (b)?**

Solution: a) We can find the probability Keith picks a chocolate almond using the classical definition of probability.

$$P(\text{Keith chooses chocolate almond}) = \frac{\text{\# of chocolate almonds}}{\text{Total \# of chocolates in the box}}$$

$$= \frac{7}{21}$$

Solution: b) We are trying to find the probability that Keith does *not* pick a chocolate almond, *given* that he already picked one from the box. This is a *conditional* probability.

Keith has taken a chocolate, so there are only 20 left in the box. It was a chocolate almond, so there are only 6 left in the box. This means there are 14 chocolates that are *not* a chocolate almond. So we can find the probability by the classical definition:

$$P(\text{Keith does } not \text{ pick a chocolate almond } 2^{nd} \mid \text{he picked one } 1^{st}) = \frac{14}{20}$$

■

Example 6:   A die is rolled. What is the probability that the number rolled is greater than 2 and even?

STOP AND THINK!

How can you solve this problem?   Think of the steps that would lead you to the solution:

1. **Describe the sample space.**
2. **Count the number of possible outcomes.**
3. **Count the number of favorable outcomes.**
4. **Use the classical definition of probability to find the answer.**

Solution: Now let's complete each of these steps in turn:

1. Describe the sample space. We will use a *list*.

$$1 \qquad 2 \qquad 3 \qquad 4 \qquad 5 \qquad 6$$

2. Number of possible outcomes = 6
3. To count the number of favorable outcomes, we must count the number of outcomes that are greater than 2 *and* even. The only faces on the die that meet this criteria are the 4 and the 6. So the number of favorable outcomes = 2
4. Using the classical definition of probability:

$$P(\text{number rolled is greater than 2 and even}) = \frac{2}{6}$$

■

Example 7: A cola drink manufacturer hopes to boost its sales by the following promotion; when you buy a 20 ounce bottle of its cola, you stand a 1 in 4 chance of instantly winning a free bottle. What is the probability that you win at least one free bottle of cola given that you buy two bottles?

> **STOP AND THINK!**
>
> Is the chance of winning for each bottle independent or dependent?

Solution: You are interested in the probability that *at least* one of the bottles you buy will say you win a free bottle. This means that one or both bottles are winners, so we can find the probability that the first bottle is a winner *or* the second bottle is a winner. Recall that the word *or* implies that one or *both* may occur.

Each bottle has a 1/4 chance of being a winner and we are told that these events are independent. We can use the relationship for *or* for independent events:

$$P(1st\ or\ 2nd\ wins) = P(1st\ wins) + P(2nd\ wins) - P(1st\ wins)P(2nd\ wins)$$

$$= \left(\frac{1}{4}\right) + \left(\frac{1}{4}\right) - \left(\frac{1}{4}\right)\left(\frac{1}{4}\right)$$

$$= \frac{7}{16}$$

■

Example 8: Given $P(A) = 0.4$, $P(B) = 0.5$, and $P(A\ and\ B) = 0.2$, find:
a) $P(A^c)$
b) $P(B^c)$
c) $P(A\ or\ B)$
d) $P(A^c\ and\ B^c)$

> **STOP AND THINK!**
>
> What relationships do you need to know to answer these questions?
>
> Do you know for sure if the events are independent? If not, do not use these relationships.
>
> Do you know for sure if the events are mutually exclusive? If not, do not use these relationships.

Solution: a) Remember A^c is the complement of A, and therefore their probabilities should add to one. We can use this to find $P(A^c)$:

$$P(A^c) = 1 - P(A)$$
$$= 1 - 0.4$$
$$= 0.6$$

Solution: b) Remember B^c is the complement of B, and therefore their probabilities should add to one. We can use this to find $P(B^c)$:

$$P(B^c) = 1 - P(B)$$
$$= 1 - 0.5$$
$$= 0.5$$

Solution: c) To find $P(A \text{ or } B)$ we should use our generalized relationship from Lesson 1.1:

$$P(A \text{ or } B) = P(A) + P(B) - P(A \text{ and } B)$$
$$= 0.4 + 0.5 - 0.2$$
$$= 0.7$$

Solution: d) $P(A^c \text{ and } B^c)$ means we want the probability that *neither* event occurs. When we found $P(A \text{ or } B)$ in part (c), we were finding the probability that at least one of these events occurs. Therefore, these two probabilities are complementary and should add to one. We can use this to find $P(A^c \text{ and } B^c)$:

$$P(A^c \text{ and } B^c) = 1 - P(A \text{ or } B)$$
$$= 1 - 0.7$$
$$= 0.3$$

■

Example 9: The probability that a new car has a defective gearbox is 0.2. Independently, the probability that it has a paintwork defect is 0.02. Find the probability that a car chosen at random has both a defective gearbox and defective paintwork.

> **STOP AND THINK!**
>
> **You are told the events are independent. How does that help you solve the problem?**

Solution: You are trying to find the probability that a car chosen at random has *both* a defective gearbox *and* defective paintwork. We know the probabilities for each of these events, and are told the events are independent. We can use the relationship joint probabilities for independent events:

$$P(\text{defective gearbox } and \text{ paint}) = P(\text{defective gearbox})P(\text{defective paint})$$
$$=(0.2)(0.02)$$
$$= 0.004$$

■

Example 10: Two dice are rolled. What is the probability that the sum is less than 5 *given* that the first die was a 1?

> **STOP AND THINK!**
>
> **How can you solve this problem?   Think of the steps that would lead you to the solution:**
>
> 1. **Describe the sample space.**
> 2. **Count the number of possible outcomes.**
> 3. **Count the number of favorable outcomes.**
> 4. **Use the classical definition of probability to find the answer.**

Solution: You can use a grid to describe the sample space, but notice that you are interested in the sum of the scores of the two dice. You can enter these sums in your grid. So, for example, instead of writing 1,1 to represent the score of a 1 on both dice, you can write 1+1=2. Here it is:

Die 1

	1	2	3	4	5	6
1	2	3	4	5	6	7
2	3	4	5	6	7	8
3	4	5	6	7	8	9
4	5	6	7	8	9	10
5	6	7	8	9	10	11
6	7	8	9	10	11	12

Die 2

You have been *given* the information that the first die shows a 1. This means we have narrowed down the possible outcomes to the 6 that are highlighted in the grid. Out of these six outcomes, three of the sums are less than 5. Therefore, we can use the classical definition of probability:

$$P(\text{sum} < 5 \text{ } given \text{ } 1^{st} \text{ die shows } 1) = \frac{\# \text{ of sums} < 5 \text{ where } 1^{st} \text{ die shows } 1}{\text{Total \# sums where } 1^{st} \text{ die shows } 1} = \frac{3}{6}$$

■

LESSON 1.3 EXERCISES
MORE PRACTICE IN SOLVING PROBABILITY PROBLEMS

1. Describe the sample space for the following experiments:
    a) One fair coin is flipped and one die is thrown.
    b) Two fair coins are flipped and one die is thrown.

2. a) What is the probability of scoring a sum of 8 when you roll two dice?
    b) What is the probability of scoring a sum of *at least* 8 when you roll two dice?
    c) What is the probability of scoring a sum of 13 when you roll two dice?

3. You begin a new job selling magazine subscriptions door to door. You know that there is a 6% chance that a household will buy a subscription from you. You decide to go to three houses on a particular street. Assuming the households are independent, find the probability you will not sell a subscription at any of these three houses.

4. Suppose we have 5 candies in a bag: 3 red and 2 blue. We shake the bag and choose a candy with out looking. We make a note of its color, replace it and repeat the experiment. Find the probability that you chose 2 red candies.

5. a) A fair coin is tossed until you get a head. Find the probability that exactly 3 tosses are required.
    b) A fair coin is tossed until you get one head and one tail. Find the probability that exactly 3 tosses are required.

6. The probability that Event A occurs is 0.4.   The probability that Event B occurs is 0.8.   The probability that both events A and B occur is 0.2. Find:
    a) P(B|A)
    b) P(A|B)

ANSWERS

LESSON 1.3 EXERCISES

MORE PRACTICE IN SOLVING PROBABILITY PROBLEMS

**Below are the answers to the exercises for Unit 1, Lesson 1.3.
For full solutions, please refer to the CD included with this textbook.**

1. The sample spaces listed below were obtained using trees and grids. See the solutions on the CD for more details.

    a) H, 1   H, 2   H, 3   H, 4   H, 5   H, 6
        T, 1   T, 2   T, 3   T, 4   T, 5   T, 6

    b) H, H, 1   H, H, 2   H, H, 3   H, H, 4   H, H,5   H, H, 6
        H, T, 1   H, T, 2   H, T, 3   H, T, 4   H, T, 5   H, T, 6
        T, H, 1   T, H, 2   T, H, 3   T, H, 4   T, H, 5   T, H, 6
        T, T, 1   T, T, 2   T, T, 3   T, T, 4   T, T, 5   T, T, 6

2. a) P(scoring 8 when you roll two dice) $= \dfrac{5}{36}$

    b) P(scoring *at least* 8 when you roll two dice) $= \dfrac{15}{36}$

    c) P(scoring 13 when you roll two dice) $= 0$

3. P(will not sell a subscription at any of the three houses) $= 0.8306$

4. P(both candies are red) $= \dfrac{9}{25}$

5. a) P(you do not get heads until the third flip) $= \dfrac{1}{8}$

    b) P(it takes 3 flips to see one head and one tail) $= \dfrac{2}{8}$

6. a) P(B|A) $= 0.5$
    b) P(A|B) $= 0.25$

AVOIDING COMMON MISTAKES

☺ Remember that probabilities are always between 0 and 1. If you ever calculate a probability and it is outside of this range, you did not do the problem correctly.

☺ Unless you are sure that your events are either mutually exclusive or independent; you should always use the relationships in Lesson 1.1 to solve probability problems.

☺ When you use your calculator to multiply fractions, be sure to put each fraction in parentheses so that your calculator will multiply them correctly.

☺ Do not try and guess what formula to use. Think through the problem logically.

☺ When you finish solving a problem, re-read the question to make sure you really answered it.

UNIT 1 SUMMARY

The following facts are always true:

- All probabilities must be between 0 and 1.
- An event that is impossible has a probability equal to 0.
- The closer a probability is to 0; the less likely it is to happen.
- The closer a probability is to 1; the more likely it is to happen.
- An event that is certain to occur has a probability equal to 1.
- The sum of probabilities of all possible outcomes in a particular situation must equal 1.
- $P(A) + P(A^c) = 1$

When all outcomes are equally likely, you can find the probability of an event using the classical definition of probability:

- Probability of an event $= \dfrac{\text{Number of favorable outcomes}}{\text{Total number of possible outcomes}}$

The following relationships are true for any events A and B:

- $P(B|A) = \dfrac{P(A \text{ and } B)}{P(A)}$
- $P(A \text{ and } B) = P(A)P(B|A)$
- $P(A \text{ or } B) = P(A) + P(B) - P(A \text{ and } B)$

The following relationships are true only when events A and B are mutually exclusive, that is, when events A and B cannot occur at the same time:

- $P(B|A) = 0$
- $P(A \text{ and } B) = 0$
- $P(A \text{ or } B) = P(A) + P(B)$

The following relationships are true only when events A and B are independent, that is, when the occurrence of one event does not change the probability of occurrence of the other event:

- $P(B|A) = P(B)$
- $P(A \text{ and } B) = P(A)P(B)$
- $P(A \text{ or } B) = P(A) + P(B) - P(A)P(B)$

SELF-ASSESSMENT QUIZ

1. For events A and B, we are told that $P(A) = 0.4$, $P(B) = 0.3$, and $P(A \text{ and } B) = 0.3$. Are events A and B independent? Explain.

2. The table shows the results of a study in which a pet rescue service specializing in bunnies, hamsters and rats monitored popularity for adoption.

	Bunny	Hamster	Rat	Total
Adopted	27	15	8	**50**
Not Adopted	16	18	16	**50**
Total	**43**	**33**	**24**	**100**

A pet is chosen at random. Find the probability that
   a) it is a rat.
   b) it is adopted given that it is a bunny.
   c) the pet is not a hamster given that it was not adopted.

3. The probability that Event A occurs is 0.87. The probability that Event B occurs is 0.35. The probability that *both* Events A and B occur is 0.22. Find the following:
   a) $P(A^c)$
   b) $P(B|A)$
   c) $P(A|B)$

4. A fair coin is tossed three times. If the coin comes up heads on the first two tosses, what is the probability that it will also show a head up on the third toss?

5. Two dice are rolled. Let event A be 'scoring a total of 7'. Find:
   a) $P(A)$
   b) $P(A^c)$

6. A fair coin is flipped three times. Find the probability that it will come up tails *at least* twice.

7. Alex gets 10 plain cards and writes one number (1,…,10) on each one. She then shuffles them and picks out a card randomly.
   a) What is the probability that the chosen card shows the number 7?
   b) She returns the chosen card to the pack and shuffles them again. She pulls out one card. Find the probability that the card shows the number 2, given that it shows an even number.

8. A bag contains 4 yellow candies, 10 red candies and 6 green candies. If you pick one candy from this bag, find the probability that the candy picked is:
   a) red.
   b) red *or* green.
   c) *not* orange. (Think carefully!)
   d) red *and* yellow. (Think carefully!)

9. All we know about Event A is that it is certain to occur.
   a) What is the probability of Event A?
   b) What is the probability of Event A^c?

10. Which of the following events is more likely to occur?
    Event A: Tossing a fair coin and getting a head.
    Event B: Rolling a fair die and getting a six.
    Event C: Rolling a fair die and not getting a two.

ANSWERS

SELF-ASSESSMENT QUIZ

Below are the answers to the exercises for Unit 1, Self-Assessment Quiz. For full solutions, please refer to the CD included with this textbook.

1. No, events A and B are *not* independent because if you multiply P(A) by P(B) you do not get P(A *and* B).

2. a) $P(\text{Rat}) = \dfrac{24}{100}$

    b) $P(\text{Adopted} \mid \text{Bunny}) = \dfrac{27}{43}$

    c) $P(\text{Hamster}^c \mid \text{Adopted}^c) = \dfrac{32}{50}$

3. a) $P(A^c) = 0.13$
    b) $P(B|A) = 0.2529$
    c) $P(A|B) = 0.6286$

4. $P(\text{Heads on third toss} \mid \text{Heads on first two tosses}) = \dfrac{1}{2}$

5. a) $P(A) = \dfrac{6}{36}$

    b) $P(A^c) = \dfrac{30}{36}$

6. $P(\text{Tails } at \ least \text{ twice in three flips}) = \dfrac{4}{8}$

7. a) $P(\text{card shows a 7}) = \dfrac{1}{10}$

    b) $P(\text{card shows a 2} \mid \text{card shows an even number}) = \dfrac{1}{5}$

8. a) $P(\text{red}) = \dfrac{10}{20}$

    b) $P(\text{red } or \text{ green}) = \dfrac{16}{20}$

    c) $P(\text{orange}^c) = 1$

    d) $P(\text{red } and \text{ yellow}) = 0$

9. a) $P(A) = 1$

    b) $P(A^c) = 0$

10. Event C is most likely to occur.

UNIT 2
DISCRETE PROBABILITY DISTRIBUTIONS

Lesson 2.1 Discrete Random Variables and their Probability Distributions
Exercises for Lesson 2.1
Answers to Exercises for Lesson 2.1

Lesson 2.2 Finding the Mean and Standard Deviation of Discrete Random Variables
Exercises for Lesson 2.2
Answers to Exercises for Lesson 2.2

Lesson 2.3 More Practice in Solving Discrete Probability Distribution Problems
Exercises for Lesson 2.3
Answers to Exercises for Lesson 2.3

Avoiding Common Mistakes
Unit 2 Summary
Self-Assessment Quiz
Answers to Self-Assessment Quiz

LESSON 2.1
DISCRETE RANDOM VARIABLES AND THEIR PROBABILITY DISTRIBUTIONS

2.1.1 INTRODUCTION

In this unit we continue our study of probability. Probability is important because it provides the foundation for much of the statistics we will study later. Once you have grasped the concepts in Units 1 and 2 you will find the rest of the book easier to understand. In Unit 1 we learned how to calculate the probability that an event occurs. Recall the classical definition:

$$\text{Probability of an event} = \frac{\text{Number of favorable outcomes}}{\text{Total number of possible outcomes}}$$

where the list of possible outcomes defines the *sample space*. We will now show how to summarize the probabilities associated with the sample space in a table called the *probability distribution function*, or *pdf* for short. Before explaining how to construct a *probability distribution function* (*pdf*) we need to define some important terms.

2.1.2 RANDOM VARIABLES

What is a random variable? The *outcome of interest* of a probability experiment is called a *random variable*. It is a variable because it has more than one possible value and it is random because its actual value is a matter of chance. Random variables are either discrete or continuous.

Let's look at discrete random variables first. For example, consider tossing a coin twice. Now suppose we are interested in the number of heads obtained. This identifies the outcome of interest and hence defines the random variable. Since we can *count* the number of heads obtained, the random variable is *discrete*. Generally, if the outcomes of a probability experiment can be counted, then our random variable is *discrete*.

What are *continuous* random variables? If the outcomes of a probability experiment can be *measured* rather than counted, then our random variable is *continuous*. Height, weight, time, and temperature are all examples of continuous random variables. We will discuss continuous random variables further in Unit 4.

Example: Use your understanding of discrete and continuous random variables to answer the following questions.

> **Question 1**
> Is the random variable 'X = Number of puppies in a litter' discrete or continuous?

Solution: You can count the number of puppies in a litter. The key word here is 'count', so this is a *discrete random variable*.

> **Question 2**
> Is the random variable 'X = Time it takes you to walk to school' discrete or continuous?

Solution: If you wanted to time how long it takes you to walk to school, you would use a watch to measure the time, so this is a *continuous random variable*.
■

2.1.3   DISCRETE RANDOM VARIABLES AND PDF'S
We will now define discrete random variables:

> **Discrete Random Variables**
>
> A random variable is *discrete* if all its possible outcomes can be counted.

We use upper case letters to denote discrete random variables and lower case letters to denote their value. Usually, we use X to denote discrete random variables and x to denote its value.

Consider the experiment of tossing a coin twice. The sample space is:

$$HH \quad HT \quad TH \quad TT$$

We may be interested in the number of tails that are obtained, or the number of heads, or some other property of the sample space. Each of these properties defines a random variable. Now suppose the property we are actually interested in is the number of heads obtained, then we can define the random variable X as follows:

$$X = \text{Number of heads obtained}$$

and we can find the probabilities associated with X. Each outcome in the experiment corresponds to a value of X, as shown in Table 2.1.

Table 2.1

Outcome	HH	HT	TH	TT
x	0	1	1	2

Using the classical definition of probability:

$$P(HH) = 1/4$$
$$P(HT) = 1/4$$
$$P(TH) = 1/4$$
$$P(TT) = 1/4$$

and you can add these to the table, as shown in Table 2.2:

Table 2.2

Outcome	HH	HT	TH	TT
x	0	1	1	2
$P(X = x)$	1/4	1/4	1/4	1/4

How to read P(X = x)

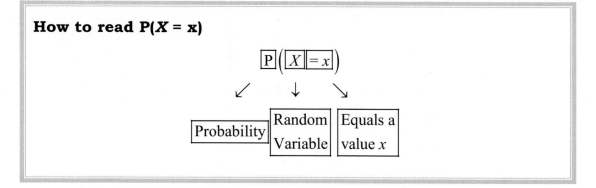

Table 2.2 can be summarized further, as Table 2.3:

Table 2.3

X	0	1	2
$P(X = x)$	1/4	1/2	1/4

We call Table 2.3 the *probability distribution function (pdf)* of X. It shows all the probabilities of the random variable of interest, X, and so these probabilities must add up to 1. If they do not, you have made a mistake!

Important Idea

The values of X in a *pdf* are always mutually exclusive.

You can use the *pdf* to read off probabilities. For example:

$$P(X = 0) = \frac{1}{4}$$

You can also use the *pdf* to calculate other probabilities. For example, to find the probability that you get at least 1 head.

> **STOP AND THINK!**
>
> **Which values of X satisfy this condition?**

If you get at least 1 head, this means $X = 1$ *or* $X = 2$. Since these events are mutually exclusive,

$$P(X \geq 1) = P(X = 1) + P(X = 2) = \frac{1}{2} + \frac{1}{4} = \frac{3}{4}$$

2.1.4

FINDING A MISSING PROBABILITY

If we have all the probabilities except one in a *pdf*, we can always find the missing probability by noticing that it will be the complement of the sum of the probabilities you do have. Consider the following situation:

A researcher is interested in the number of cars people park in their driveways in Isla Vista. The researcher conducted a survey and constructed a *pdf* for the random variable:

$$X = \text{Number of cars in a driveway}$$

You have been provided with the *pdf* that shows all the probabilities except $P(X = 3)$, as shown in Table 2.4:

Table 2.4

x	1	2	3	4	5
$P(X = x)$	0.03	0.07	a	0.30	0.40

Since we know that this is a *pdf*, the probabilities must add up to 1 and so we can find the missing probability as follows:

$$0.03 + 0.07 + a + 0.30 + 0.40 = 1$$
$$a + 0.80 = 1$$
$$a = 0.20$$

So we can complete the *pdf*, as shown in Table 2.5:

Table 2.5

x	1	2	3	4	5
$P(X = x)$	0.03	0.07	0.20	0.30	0.40

We can now use this *pdf* to find probabilities, as shown in the previous section.

2.1.5   CUMULATIVE DISTRIBUTION FUNCTION (CDF)

The cumulative distribution function (*cdf*) is a convenient way of summarizing the information given in the *pdf* and shows $P(X \le x)$, the probability that X is less than or equal to some value x.

How to read P($X \le$ x)

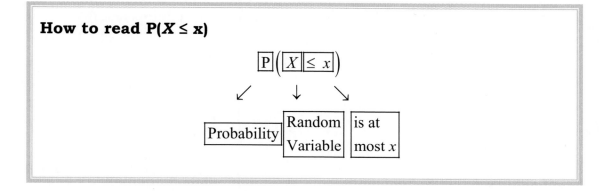

We will now show how to construct a *cdf* from a *pdf*.

Consider the following *pdf* from Table 2.5:

pdf

x	1	2	3	4	5
$P(X = x)$	0.03	0.07	0.20	0.30	0.40

Important Idea

When you construct a *cdf* from a *pdf*, you must list the values of X in increasing order.

Then the *cdf* is constructed from the *pdf* as follows:

$P(X \le 1) = P(X = 1) = 0.03$
$P(X \le 2) = P(X = 1) + P(X = 2) = 0.10$
$P(X \le 3) = P(X = 1) + P(X = 2) + P(X = 3) = 0.30$
$P(X \le 4) = P(X = 1) + P(X = 2) + P(X = 3) + P(X = 4) = 0.60$
$P(X \le 5) = P(X = 1) + P(X = 2) + P(X = 3) + P(X = 4) + P(X = 5) = 1$

We can now put these probabilities in a table, called the *cdf*.

cdf

x	1	2	3	4	5
$P(X \leq x)$	0.03	0.10	0.30	0.60	1

Important Idea

The final probability in a *cdf* must always be 1 since the probability that X is less than or equal to its largest value is a certainty.

As with the *pdf*, we can use the *cdf* to find probabilities. For example, the probability that there are at most 3 cars in a driveway is 0.30.

LESSON 2.1 EXERCISES
DISCRETE RANDOM VARIABLES AND THEIR PROBABILITY DISTRIBUTIONS

1. The University records the number of courses taken per quarter by students registered at UCSB. This information has been summarized in the following *pdf*, where the random variable X is defined as follows:

    X= Number of courses taken per quarter by students registered at UCSB

x	3	4	5	6
$P(X=x)$	0.45	0.35	0.15	0.05

    a) Find the probability that a chosen student is taking *fewer than* 3 courses.
    b) Find the probability that a chosen student is taking *exactly* 3 courses.
    c) Find the probability that a chosen student is taking *more than* 3 courses.

2. An experiment was conducted to find the number of chocolate chips in a certain kind of cookie. Students were each given 10 cookies; they crumbled the cookies, separated out the chocolate chips and counted them. The class then constructed the following *pdf*, summarizing their results:

x	10	11	12	13	14
$P(X=x)$	0.25	0.40	0.25	0.10	0.00

    where the random variable X = Number of chocolate chips in a cookie.

    a) Find the probability that a chosen cookie contains 10 or more chocolate chips.
    b) Find the probability that a chosen cookie contains *exactly* 14 chocolate chips.
    c) Can you remove the entry for X = 14? If so, why?
    d) Construct the *cdf* for this experiment.
    e) Using the *cdf*, find the probability that a chosen cookie contains *fewer than* 12 chocolate chips.

3. A fair coin is tossed three times. We are interested in the number of tails obtained.
    a) Define the random variable of interest X.
    b) Construct the *pdf* for this experiment.
    c) Construct the *cdf* for this experiment.

4. Define the random variable of interest for each of the following situations. Is the random variable discrete or continuous? Explain how you know.
   a) A study on college students investigates how many textbooks they buy each quarter.
   b) The humane society sends a survey to households in the community asking how many pets they have.
   c) A gas station wants to know how much gas each of its customers buys every time they fill up.

ANSWERS

LESSON 2.1 EXERCISES

DISCRETE RANDOM VARIABLES AND THEIR PROBABILITY DISTRIBUTIONS

Below are the answers to the exercises for Unit 2, Lesson 2.1.
For full solutions, please refer to the CD included with this textbook.

1. a) $P(X < 3) = 0$
    b) $P(X = 3) = 0.45$
    c) $P(X > 3) = 0.55$

2. a) $P(X \geq 10) = 1$
    b) $P(X = 14) = 0$
    c) Yes, because the only values of X that *must* be included in a *pdf* are those that are possible to observe.
    d) The *cdf* is:

x	10	11	12	13
$P(X \leq x)$	0.25	0.65	0.90	1

    e) Using the *cdf*, $P(X < 12) = 0.65$

3. a) $X =$ Number of tails obtained from three fair coin flips
    b) The *pdf* is:

x	0	1	2	3
$P(X = x)$	1/8	3/8	3/8	1/8

    c) The *cdf* is:

x	0	1	2	3
$P(X \leq x)$	1/8	4/8	7/8	1

4. a) $X =$ Number of textbooks a student buy each quarter.
        X is a discrete random variable because you can count how many textbooks you buy.
    b) $X =$ Number of pets in a household.
        X is a discrete random variable because you can count how many pets each household has.
    c) $X =$ How much gas a customer buys when they fill up.
        X is a continuous random variable because you can measure how much gas is purchased.

LESSON 2.2
FINDING THE MEAN AND STANDARD DEVIATION OF DISCRETE RANDOM VARIABLES

2.2.1

INTRODUCTION

In Lesson 2.1 we showed how to derive the probability distributions for discrete random variables. In this lesson, we show how to use these probability distributions to find the mean and standard deviation of discrete random variables.

2.2.2

FINDING THE MEAN OF A DISCRETE RANDOM VARIABLE

It is common to hear statements like "The average American family has 2.3 kids" or "College students take an average of 14.6 units each quarter". Statements like these help us understand what is average, or what we *expect* to see. For this reason, the average is also called the *expected value*. Another name for the average is the *mean*. These terms are interchangeable, although they are represented by different symbols.

Important Idea

'Average', *'mean'*, and *'expected value'* are all interchangeable terms.

For Discrete Random Variables:

The symbol for *'average'* and *'mean'* is μ, pronounced 'mu', as in 'music'.
The symbol for *'expected value'* is E(X), read as 'expected value of X'.

To find the mean of a discrete random variable, we need to take into account not only the values of X, but also how likely each value is to occur. For this reason, we find the mean of a discrete random variable with the following formula:

The Mean of a Discrete Random Variable

$$\mu = \sum_{\text{for all x}} xp$$

How to read it:

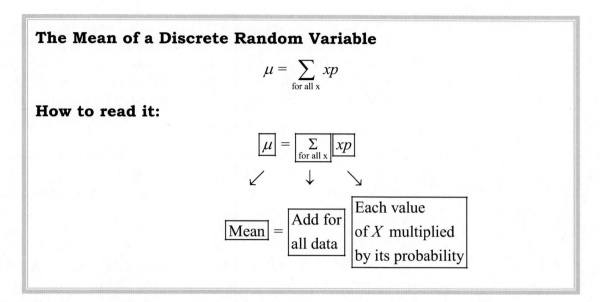

This formula introduces summation notation, denoted by the capital Greek letter Σ, which is pronounced "sigma". Whenever you see this symbol, you will be adding. In this case, you will multiply each value of X by its probability and then add them all up.

Example: Recall the *pdf* from Table 2.5, shown below, for the random variable

$X =$ Number of cars in a driveway

x	1	2	3	4	5
$P(X = x)$	0.03	0.07	0.20	0.30	0.40

Question
What is the mean of X?
Another way to ask this is "What is the expected value of X?"

Solution: Since X is a discrete random variable, we can use the *pdf* of X to find the mean using the formula:

$$\mu = \sum_{\text{for all x}} xp$$
$$= 1(0.03) + 2(0.07) + 3(0.20) + 4(0.30) + 5(0.40)$$
$$= 3.97$$

Lesson 2.2: Finding the Mean and Standard Deviation of Discrete Random Variables

This tells us that the average number of cars in a driveway in Isla Vista is 3.97. Notice that the mean is not a whole number and in fact, it is not even one of the values of *X* listed in the *pdf*. This is often the case as the mean is representative of all the data and does not necessarily reflect individual values. For this reason, DO NOT round the mean to the nearest whole number.

■

To illustrate this further, consider an exam where the average was 78.2. This does not necessarily imply that anybody got a score of 78.2 and it may not have even been possible to receive such a score. The mean is simply representative of how the class did overall.

2.2.3   FINDING THE STANDARD DEVIATION OF A DISCRETE RANDOM VARIABLE

While it is common for us to see averages reported, simply knowing the mean does not always give us a good picture of how the data is behaving. For example, suppose that you take a midterm in one of your classes, and the professor reports that the mean was 78.2. Although this value gives you an indication of how the class did on average, it provides no information as to how spread out the scores were from the mean. Perhaps the scores were not very spread out at all, indicating that most scores were close to 78.2. Or perhaps there was a lot of variability in the scores, indicating that there were some scores near the mean, and some scores that were much lower or much higher than the mean. It is therefore useful to have a measure of spread, which indicates how spread out the data is from the mean. One such measure is the *standard deviation*, which is obtained by taking the square-root of the *variance*.

Important Idea

'Standard deviation' and *'variance'* are related measures, but NOT interchangeable. You find the standard deviation by taking the square-root of the variance.

For Discrete Random Variables:

The symbol for *'standard deviation'* is σ, pronounced 'sigma'.
The symbol for *'variance'* is σ^2, pronounced 'sigma-squared'.

To find the standard deviation of a discrete random variable, we must first find the variance:

The Variance of a Discrete Random Variable

$$\sigma^2 = \left(\sum_{\text{for all x}} x^2 p \right) - \mu^2$$

How to read it:

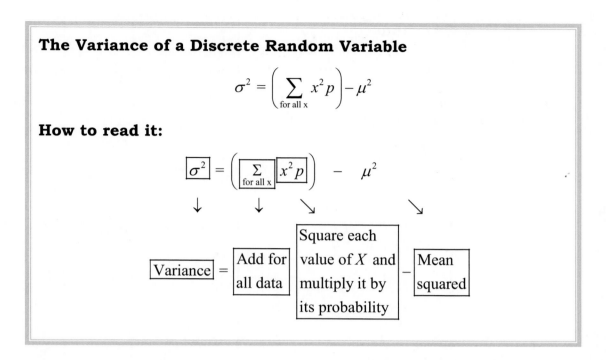

We can then take the square-root of the variance to obtain the standard deviation:

The Standard Deviation of a Discrete Random Variable

$$\sigma = \sqrt{\sigma^2}$$

How to read it:

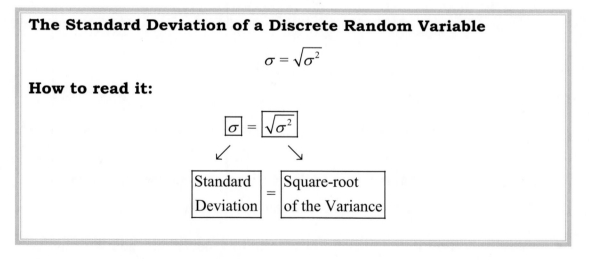

Example: Recall again the probability distribution from Table 2.5, shown below, for the random variable:

$$X = \text{Number of cars in a driveway}$$

x	1	2	3	4	5
P($X = x$)	0.03	0.07	0.20	0.30	0.40

Lesson 2.2: Finding the Mean and Standard Deviation of Discrete Random
Variables

Question

What is the standard deviation of X?

Solution: Since X is a discrete random variable, we can use its *pdf* to find the standard deviation. First we find the variance, using the formula:

$$\sigma^2 = \left(\sum_{\text{for all x}} x^2 p \right) - \mu^2$$

This formula requires that we know the mean, which we found in the previous example to be 3.97. Thus,

$$\sigma^2 = 1^2(0.03) + 2^2(0.07) + 3^2(0.20) + 4^2(0.30) + 5^2(0.40) - 3.97^2$$
$$= 1.1491$$

So the variance of X is 1.1491. We take the square-root of the variance to obtain the standard deviation:

$$\sigma = \sqrt{\sigma^2}$$
$$= \sqrt{1.1491}$$
$$= 1.072$$

So the standard deviation of X is 1.072.

■

Here are some important properties of variance and standard deviation.

Properties of Variance and Standard Deviation:

- Neither variance nor standard deviation can ever be negative.

- If the variance and standard deviation equal 0, this means there is no variability in the data, which indicates there is only one value of X.

- If the variance and standard deviation are positive, this means there is variability in the data, which indicates that there is more than one value of X.

- The larger the variance and standard deviation, the more variability there is in the data, which indicates there are values of X that are much larger or much smaller than the mean.

Knowing both the mean and the standard deviation of a discrete random variable can be particularly useful when comparing two or more variables. For example, say you are considering two different vacation sites. Cabo San Lucas has an average temperature of 86°F and a standard deviation of 2.6°F. Las Vegas has an average temperature of 86°F and a standard deviation of 15.4°F. What can we learn from these values?

STOP AND THINK!

What information is given to us by the average?

What information is given to us by the standard deviation?

Although the *average* temperature is 86°F in both places, the temperature does not behave the same in the two cities. You can expect larger differences in temperature in Las Vegas than in Cabo San Lucas. This is because Las Vegas has a larger standard deviation, meaning that the temperature there is more variable. You can expect temperatures in Cabo San Lucas to stay closer to 86°F than in the Las Vegas.

LESSON 2.2 EXERCISES
FINDING THE MEAN AND STANDARD DEVIATION OF DISCRETE RANDOM VARIABLES

1. When computing the mean and standard deviation of a discrete random variable, does it matter whether you use the *pdf* or the *cdf*? Explain your answer.

2. Parking lots in Santa Barbara let you park for free up to 75 minutes. After that, any hour or part of an hour will cost you $1.50. You need to park in a Santa Barbara lot once a week for a meeting, and you know that there is an 80% chance you will be able to get out of the lot in less than 75 minutes. You will definitely be able to leave in 90 minutes.
    a) Define the random variable of interest.
    b) On average, how much do you expect to pay each week?

3. Recall the cookie experiment from Lesson 2.1, Exercise 2: An experiment was conducted to find the number of chocolate chips in a certain kind of cookie. Students were each given 10 cookies. They crumbled the cookies, separated out the chocolate chips and counted them. The class then constructed the following *pdf*, summarizing their results:

x	10	11	12	13
$P(X = x)$	0.25	0.40	0.25	0.10

    where the random variable X= Number of chocolate chips in a cookie.

    a) What is the average number of chocolate chips in a cookie?
    b) What is the variance for the number of chocolate chips in a cookie?
    c) What is the standard deviation for the number of chocolate chips in a cookie?

ANSWERS

LESSON 2.2 EXERCISES
FINDING THE MEAN AND STANDARD DEVIATION
OF DISCRETE RANDOM VARIABLES

Below are the answers to the exercises for Unit 2, Lesson 2.2.
For full solutions, please refer to the CD included with this textbook.

1. Yes, it does matter which you use. These calculations require the probabilities
    listed in a *pdf*.

2. a) X = The amount of money you have to pay when you park in the lot.
    b) On average you will pay $0.30 per week.

3. a) The average number of chocolate chips per cookie is 11.2.
    b) The variance is 0.86.
    c) The standard deviation is 0.9274.

LESSON 2.3
MORE PRACTICE IN SOLVING DISCRETE PROBABILITY DISTRIBUTION PROBLEMS

In this lesson we look at some more examples with full solutions. You are encouraged to work through these problems yourself if you need extra practice.

Example 1: Which of the following random variables is *discrete*?
   a) X = The number of flavors of ice cream sold at Nibbles Ice Cream Parlor.
   b) X = The number of customers who buy strawberry flavor ice cream at Nibbles Ice Cream Parlor.
   c) X = The time a student spends studying statistics.
   d) X = The number of hours per week a student spends studying statistics.

> **STOP AND THINK!**
>
> **How do you know if a random variable is *discrete*?**

Solution: a) This is a discrete random variable because it is possible to count all the values of X.

Solution: b) This is a discrete random variable because it is possible to count all the values of X.

Solution: c) This is NOT a discrete random variable because it is NOT possible to count all the values of X. Time is an example of a *continuous* variable.

Solution: d) This is a discrete random variable because it is possible to count all the values of X.

■

Example 2: Students conducted a survey to investigate the number of different plant species found in selected 1 meter square plots on Ellwood bluffs. They counted the number of different plant species in 100 plots and found that 23 plots had 10 different plant species, 27 had 11 different plant species, 30 plots had 12 different plant species, and the remaining 20 plots had 13 different plant species. Define the random variable of interest in this experiment.

> **STOP AND THINK!**
>
> **We are provided with a lot of information. What do we need to look for in the problem to identify the random variable of interest?**

Solution: The problem states that the students are interested in the number of different plant species found in selected 1 meter square plots on Ellwood bluffs. Therefore, we can define the random variable of interest:

X = Number of different plant species found in selected 1 meter square plots on Ellwood bluffs.

Example 3:   Use the scenario and random variable described in Example 2 to construct the *pdf* for the number of different plant species found in selected 1 meter square plots on Ellwood bluffs.

> **STOP AND THINK!**
>
> **What are the possible values of X?**
>
> **How likely are you to observe each of these values?**

Solution: We are told that the number of different plant species found in selected 1 meter square plots on Ellwood bluffs is 10, 11, 12, and 13. Using the random variable we defined in Example 2, this indicates that the possible values of X are 10, 11, 12, and 13.

We are told that there were 23 plots with 10 different plant species. Since 100 plots were examined:

$$P(X = 10) = \frac{23}{100} = 0.23$$

We are also told that there were 27 plots with 11 different plant species. Since 100 plots were examined:

$$P(X = 11) = \frac{27}{100} = 0.27$$

We are also told that there were 30 plots with 12 different plant species. Since 100 plots were examined:

$$P(X=12) = \frac{30}{100} = 0.30$$

We are also told that there were 20 plots with 13 different plant species. Since 100 plots were examined:

$$P(X=13) = \frac{20}{100} = 0.20$$

We can display this information in a *pdf*:

x	10	11	12	13
P($X=x$)	0.23	0.27	0.30	0.20

Example 4:   Use the scenario and random variable described in Example 2, along with the *pdf* in Example 3, to construct the *cdf* for the number of different plant species found in selected 1 meter square plots on Ellwood bluffs

> **STOP AND THINK!**
>
> **You have already constructed the *pdf* in Example 3. How can you use this to construct the *cdf*?**

Solution: Once we have the *pdf* of a random variable, we can use it to construct the *cdf*.

The values of X are 10, 11, 12, and 13. So to construct the *cdf*, we find $P(X \leq 10)$, $P(X \leq 11)$, $P(X \leq 12)$, and $P(X \leq 13)$.

First find $P(X \leq 10)$. Since there are no values of X less than 10:

$$P(X \leq 10) = P(X=10) = 0.23$$

Then find $P(X \leq 11)$. The values of X less than 11 are 10 and 11, so:

$$P(X \leq 11) = P(X=10) + P(X=11)$$
$$= 0.23 + 0.27$$
$$= 0.50$$

Next find $P(X \leq 12)$. The values of X less than 12 are 10, 11, and 12, so:

$$P(X \le 12) = P(X = 10) + P(X = 11) + P(X = 12)$$
$$= 0.23 + 0.27 + 0.30$$
$$= 0.80$$

Finally, find $P(X \le 13)$. The values of X less than 13 are 10, 11, 12, and 13, so:

$$P(X \le 13) = P(X = 10) + P(X = 11) + P(X = 12) + P(X = 13)$$
$$= 0.23 + 0.27 + 0.30 + 0.20$$
$$= 1$$

We now display the above information in a *cdf*:

x	10	11	12	13
$P(X \le x)$	0.23	0.50	0.80	1

Example 5: Use the scenario and random variable described in Example 2 to find the probability that a chosen plot contains:
a) *exactly* 11 different species of plant.
b) *fewer* than 11 different species of plant.
c) *at most* 11 different species of plant.
d) 14 different species of plant.

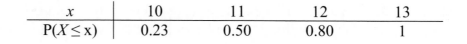

> **STOP AND THINK!**
>
> **When can you use the *pdf* and when can you use the *cdf*?**

Solution: a) To find the probability that a chosen plot contains *exactly* 11 different species of plants, we find $P(X = 11)$. This is a probability given in the *pdf* in Example 3. If we look at this *pdf*, we see that:

$$P(X = 11) = 0.27$$

Solution: b) To find the probability that a chosen plot contains *fewer than* 11 different species of plants, we find $P(X < 11)$. The only value of X that is less than 11 is $X = 10$. So:

$$P(X < 11) = P(X = 10)$$

This probability is easiest to obtain from the *pdf* in Example 3. Looking at this *pdf*, we see that:

$$P(X < 11) = P(X = 10) = 0.23$$

We could also arrive at the answer by using the *cdf* in Example 4 and looking at $P(X \leq 10)$, which is equivalent to $P(X < 11)$.

Solution: c) To find the probability that a chosen plot contains *at most* 11 different species of plants, we find $P(X \leq 11)$. This probability is easiest to obtain from the *cdf* in Example 4. If we look at this *cdf*, we see that:

$$P(X \leq 11) = 0.50$$

We could also arrive at the answer by using the *pdf* in Example 3.

$$P(X \leq 11) = P(X = 10) + P(X = 11) = 0.23 + 0.27 = 0.50$$

Solution: d) To find the probability that a chosen plot contains 14 different species of plants, we find $P(X = 14)$. Notice that according to both the *pdf* and the *cdf* of X, $X = 14$ is not possible. Therefore:

$$P(X = 14) = 0$$

■

Example 6:   You have the opportunity to play one of two lottery games. The first game has expected winnings of $22.50, with a standard deviation of $5.42. The second game has expected winnings of $22.50 with a standard deviation of $14.98.
a) If you are only going to play one time, which game would you rather play?
b) If you have the opportunity to play one game 1,000 times, which game would you rather play?

> **STOP AND THINK!**
>
> **How does playing the game once versus playing the game 1,000 times affect your decision?**

Solution: a) You can argue for either game, depending on whether you are willing to be a risk-taker or if you want to play it safe. The expected winnings of the two games are the same, but their standard deviations are different.   If you are only going to play once, Game 1 is considered the "safer" game because it has a smaller standard deviation than Game 2. This suggests that it is more likely that your winnings will be close to the mean in Game 1. So even though you may not win much more than $22.50, you are also not going to win much less. Game 2 is a riskier game. While there is a greater chance that you will win much more than $22.50, there is also a greater chance that you will win much less than $22.50.

Solution: b) If you are going to play 1,000 times, it does not matter which game you choose because both games have the same expected winnings. (The expected winnings is the amount you win per game if you average out your winnings over many, many games.)

■

Example 7: You and your roommate each pay $550 for rent each month. Your roommate is not very good with managing her money, and you know that there is a 40% chance she will have the money to pay her share each month, but if she does not, you will have to pay all of it for her. How much money do you expect to pay each month for rent?

┌───┐

STOP AND THINK!

How much will you have to pay if your roommate comes up with her share?

How much will you have to pay if your roommate does NOT come up with her share?

How likely are each of these possible outcomes?

How will you use this information to figure out how much you expect to pay?

└───┘

Solution: We are interested in how much you expect to pay each month rent, so we can define the random variable of interest:

$$X = \text{How much you pay each month for rent.}$$

If your roommate comes up with her share of the money, then you only have to pay your share, which is $550. If your roommate cannot come up with her share of the money, then you have to pay both shares, which totals $1100. So we know the two possible values of X are $550 and $1100.

There is a 40% chance that your roommate comes up with her share of the money, so:

$$P(X = 550) = 0.4$$

There is a 60% chance she will not come up with the money, so:

$$P(X = 1100) = 0.6$$

We can use these values to construct a *pdf*:

x	550	1100
P($X = x$)	0.4	0.6

The amount you expect to pay, in other words, the mean of X, is found as follows:

$$\mu = \sum_{\text{for all x}} xp$$

$$= 550(0.40) + 1100(0.60)$$

$$= 880$$

So on average, you can expect to pay $880.

■

Example 8: Below is the *pdf* for the random variable

$$X = \text{Number of dogs in a home in Isla Vista.}$$

x	0	1	2	3
P($X = x$)	0.67	0.21	0.09	0.03

a) What is the average number of dogs in a home in Isla Vista?
b) What is the standard deviation of the number of dogs in a home in Isla Vista?

STOP AND THINK!

How do you find the average of a discrete random variable?

How do you find the standard deviation of a discrete random variable?

Solution: a) We can find the mean of a discrete random variable in the following way:

$$\mu = \sum_{\text{for all x}} xp$$

$$= 0(0.67) + 1(0.21) + 2(0.09) + 3(0.03)$$

$$= 0.48$$

b) To find the standard deviation of a discrete random variable we first find the variance:

$$\sigma^2 = \left(\sum_{\text{for all x}} x^2 p \right) - \mu^2$$

$$= 0^2(0.67) + 1^2(0.21) + 2^2(0.09) + 3^2(0.03) - 0.48^2$$

$$= 0.6096$$

Then the standard deviation is found by taking the square-root of the variance:

$$\sigma = \sqrt{\sigma^2}$$
$$= \sqrt{0.6096}$$
$$= 0.7808$$

Example 9:   Rabbits are known to give birth to a lot of bunnies at once. Below is the *cdf* for the random variable:

X = Number of bunnies a rabbit will give birth to per litter

x	5	6	7
$P(X \le x)$	0.64	0.87	1

If your rabbit Windy is pregnant, what is the average number of bunnies she will give birth to?

STOP AND THINK!

You have been given the *cdf*. Is this what you need to find the mean of a discrete random variable?

Solution: We are given the *cdf*, but you cannot use the *cdf* when calculating the mean of a random variable. You need the *pdf*, which you can get from the *cdf*.

From the *cdf* we see that $P(X \le 5) = 0.64$. Since there are no values of X less than 5, this indicates:
$$P(X \le 5) = P(X = 5) = 0.64.$$

From the *cdf* we see that $P(X \le 6) = 0.87$. The values of X that are less than or equal to 6 are 5 and 6. This indicates:

$$P(X \le 6) = P(X = 5) + P(X = 6) = 0.87.$$

We know $P(X = 5) = 0.64$, so we can find $P(X = 6)$:

$$0.64 + P(X = 6) = 0.87$$
$$P(X = 6) = 0.23$$

Lastly, from the *cdf* we see that $P(X \le 7) = 1$. The values of X that are less than or equal to 7 are 5, 6, and 7. So:

Lesson 2.3: More Practice in Solving Discrete Probability Distribution
                    Problems

$$P(X \le 7) = P(X = 5) + P(X = 6) + P(X = 7) = 1$$

We know $P(X = 5) = 0.64$ and $P(X = 6) = 0.23$, so we can find $P(X = 7)$:

$$0.64 + 0.23 + P(X = 7) = 1$$
$$P(X = 7) = 0.13$$

We can now construct the *pdf* and use it to find the mean:

x	5	6	7
$P(X = x)$	0.64	0.23	0.13

$$\mu = \sum_{\text{for all x}} xp$$
$$= 5(0.64) + 6(0.23) + 7(0.13)$$
$$= 5.49$$

So Windy will have an average of 5.49 bunnies per litter.

■

Example 10: It is well known that if you buy a lottery ticket for $1, you are unlikely to win anything. Why then, do people buy lottery tickets?

STOP AND THINK!

If the average winnings are low, that cannot be the reason people buy lottery tickets. What else should you consider?

Solution: Even though most people do not win anything when they play the lottery, they know it is possible, although highly improbable, that they can win large amounts of money. The risk is small if you only buy a few tickets, so it is worth it. It is rational to bet a small amount for the (very slight) chance of winning a lot.

■

LESSON 2.3 EXERCISES
MORE PRACTICE IN SOLVING DISCRETE PROBABILITY DISTRIBUTION PROBLEMS

1. Define the random variable of interest for each of the following situations:
   a) A professor wants to know on average how many students will show up to her lecture.
   b) A student wants to know how many midterms they will have in a quarter.
   c) A local shelter wants to know on average how many people will sleep there each night.

2. College students at UCSB were asked how many times they cook dinner a week. Below is the *cdf* for the random variable:

   X = Number of times a UCSB student cooks dinner in a week

x	0	1	2	3	4	5
$P(X \le x)$	0.42	0.75	0.86	0.95	0.99	1

   a) Based on this *cdf*, how likely is it that a UCSB student cooks dinner every night of the week?
   b) Construct the *pdf* for X.
   c) How many times a week would you expect a UCSB college student to cook dinner?

3. You have taken a midterm in your chemistry class and another in your psychology class. Each midterm was worth 100 points. Your chemistry professor tells the class that people either did very well or very poorly. Your psychology professor tells the class that most people scored around the average.
   a) In which class would the test scores have a higher standard deviation? Explain your answer.
   b) Have you been given sufficient information to decide which class had the higher test average? Explain your answer.

ANSWERS

LESSON 2.3 EXERCISES

MORE PRACTICE IN SOLVING DISCRETE PROBABILITY DISTRIBUTIONS PROBLEMS.

Below are the answers to the exercises for Unit 2, Lesson 2.3.
For full solutions, please refer to the CD included with this textbook.

1. a) X = Number of students that show up to her lecture.
    b) X = Number of midterms a student has in a quarter.
    c) X = Number of people that sleep at the local shelter each night.

2. a) $P(X = 7) = 0$
    b) The *pdf* is:

x	0	1	2	3	4	5
$P(X = x)$	0.42	0.33	0.11	0.09	0.04	0.01

    c) On average, a UCSB student will cook dinner 1.03 days a week.

3. a) The standard deviation would be higher in the chemistry class, because the scores are more spread out than the psychology scores.
    b) No. You have no indication of the scores on the psychology test, simply that they were close to the average. But the average may have been higher or lower than the chemistry test average.

AVOIDING COMMON MISTAKES

☺ When computing the mean, variance, or standard deviation of a discrete random variable, you should always use the *pdf*. Never use the *cdf* for these calculations.

☺ If you add together all the probabilities in a *pdf* you should get 1; if you do not, you have made a mistake.

☺ The symbol for *at most* is '$\leq$', which stands for 'less than or equal to'. So if you want to say that the value of a random variable is *at most* 5, you would write '$X \leq 5$'. This would indicate you want all values of X that are *less than or equal to* 5.

☺ The symbol for *at least* is '$\geq$', which stands for 'greater than or equal to'. So if you want to say that the value of a random variable is *at least* 5, you would write '$X \geq 5$'. This would indicate you want all values of X that are *greater than or equal to* 5.

☺ The symbol for *less than* is '$<$'. So if you want to say that the value of a random variable is *less than* 5, you would write '$X < 5$'.

☺ The symbol for *greater than* is '$>$'. So if you want to say that the value of a random variable is *greater than* 5, you would write '$X > 5$'.

UNIT 2 SUMMARY

- A *random variable* is a variable whose values are determined by chance.

- A random variable is *discrete* if all its possible outcomes can be counted.

- A random variable is *continuous* if all its possible outcomes can be measured.

- A *probability distribution function* (*pdf*) is a table listing all possible outcomes of a discrete random variable X, along with the probabilities of observing each value of X.

- The probabilities in a *pdf* must add to 1.

- A *cumulative distribution function* (*cdf*) is a table listing all possible outcomes of a discrete random variable X, along with the probabilities of observing a value less than or equal to X.

- The terms '*average*', '*mean*', and '*expected value*' are interchangeable, although they are represented by different symbols.

- The symbol representing the *average* or *mean* of a discrete random variable is μ, which is a lower-case Greek letter pronounced 'mu'.

- The symbol representing the *expected value* of a discrete random variable is E(X), which is read as the 'expected value of X'.

- The formula for the mean of a discrete random variable is

$$\mu = \sum_{\text{for all x}} xp$$

- The terms '*standard deviation*' and '*variance*' are *not* interchangeable, but they are related.

- The symbol representing the *variance* of a discrete random variable is σ^2, which is a lower-case Greek letter pronounced 'sigma-squared'.

- The symbol representing the *standard deviation* of a discrete random variable is σ, which is a lower-case Greek letter pronounced 'sigma'.

- The formula for the variance of a discrete random variable is

$$\sigma^2 = \left(\sum_{\text{for all x}} x^2 p \right) - \mu^2$$

- Standard deviation is obtained by taking the square-root of the variance.

SELF-ASSESSMENT QUIZ

1. What three properties does a *pdf* satisfy?

2. Define the random variable X for each situation.
   a) The Santa Barbara Police Department is interested in how many parking tickets are issued by their police officers each week.
   b) A pediatrician wants to record the heights for each of her patients.

3. Is the random variable discrete or continuous?
   a) $X =$ the number of shirts people own
   b) $X =$ the height of buildings in Los Angeles

4. Every day a student drives to school she takes the same route, which passes through 4 traffic lights. Over a period of time, she gathers information as to how often she is stopped by a red light. She summarizes this information in a *pdf* as follows:

x	0	1	2	3	4
$P(X = x)$	0.18	0.24	0.41	0.11	0.06

   a) What is the random variable for this *pdf*?
   b) Find the probability that she is stopped exactly once by a red traffic light on her drive to school.
   c) What is the probability that she is stopped by more than 2 red lights?
   d) Find the mean number of red traffic lights she is stopped by on her way to school.
   e) Find the standard deviation of X.
   f) There is an alternate route the student could take. The mean number of red traffic lights for this route is 1.63 and the standard deviation is 0.5. Which route should the student take? Explain.
   g) Construct the *cdf* X.
   h) Find the probability that the number of red lights she encounters on her drive to school is at most 3.

ANSWERS
SELF-ASSESSMENT QUIZ

Below are the answers to the exercises for Unit 2, Self-Assessment Quiz. For full solutions, please refer to the CD included with this textbook.

1. The three properties of a *pdf* are:
    - A *pdf* lists all the values of the discrete random variable *X*.
    - A *pdf* lists all the probabilities for each value of *X*.
    - The sum of the probabilities in a *pdf* must equal 1.

2. a) *X* = Number of parking tickets issued by police officers each week.
    b) *X* = Heights for each of her patients.

3. a) *X* is discrete because we can *count* the number of shirts people own.
    b) *X* is continuous because we can *measure* the height of buildings in Los Angeles.

4. a) *X* = Number of red lights student will stop at on the route to school
    b) $P(X = 1) = 0.24$
    c) $P(X > 2) = 0.17$
    d) $\mu = 1.63$
    e) $\sigma = 1.083$
    f) If the student wants to play it safe, she should take the alternate route because it has a smaller standard deviation, so she is less likely to have to stop for more than the mean number of red lights. The original route is more risky.
    g) The *cdf X*:

x	0	1	2	3	4
$P(X \leq x)$	0.18	0.42	0.83	0.94	1

    h) $P(X \leq 3) = 0.94$

UNIT 3
THE BINOMIAL
DISTRIBUTION

Lesson 3.1 Counting and Binomial Probabilities
Exercises for Lesson 3.1
Answers to Exercises for Lesson 3.1

Lesson 3.2 Finding the Mean and Standard Deviation of a Binomial Random Variable
Exercises for Lesson 3.2
Answers to Exercises for Lesson 3.2

Lesson 3.3 More Practice in Solving Binomial Distribution Problems
Exercises for Lesson 3.3
Answers to Exercises for Lesson 3.3

Avoiding Common Mistakes
Unit 3 Summary
Self-Assessment Quiz
Answers to Self-Assessment Quiz

LESSON 3.1
COUNTING AND BINOMIAL PROBABILITIES

3.1.1

INTRODUCTION

In Unit 2 we discussed some discrete random variables and their probability distributions. We looked at *pdf*'s where the random variable of interest had several possible outcomes. In Unit 3, we will look at a *particular* discrete probability distribution called the Binomial distribution. A Binomial experiment involves a series of trials. The outcome of each trial can be designated as a *success* or a *failure*. For example, consider rolling a fair six-sided die 20 times and being interested in how many 6's you roll. In this case, rolling a 6 is considered a *success* and rolling anything that is *not* a 6 (in other words, a 1, 2, 3, 4, or 5) is considered a *failure*. Before discussing how to find Binomial probabilities, we must learn more about counting.

3.1.2

COUNTING

Suppose your schedule has to consist of 3 courses this quarter. You can choose from 2 science, 3 arts and 2 sports courses. How many different schedules can be selected if you choose one from each discipline?

Figure 3.1

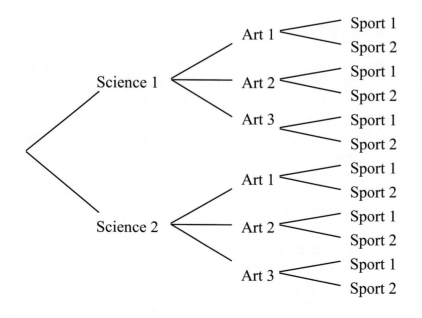

The tree diagram in Figure 3.1 shows there are 12 different schedules. Notice that this is the same result as multiplying $2(3)(2) = 12$.

When this result is generalized, it is called the Fundamental Counting Principle and is stated as follows:

Fundamental Counting Principle

If one event can occur x ways and a second event can occur y ways, the number of ways the two events can occur in sequence is xy. This rule can be extended for any number of events occurring in a sequence.

Now suppose you want to arrange three objects in *order*. For example, how many different *ordered* arrangements of the letters ABC are there? There are three choices for the first place, two for the second place and one for the third place. So there are $(3)(2)(1) = 6$ ways of arranging 3 objects in order. Check this by writing them all out:

$$ABC \quad ACB \quad BCA \quad BAC \quad CAB \quad CBA$$

Remember, this is an *ordered* arrangement, so ABC is NOT the same as BCA etc. Order matters. $(3)(2)(1)$ is also written 3! and read as '3 factorial'.

Factorials

To find $n!$, you multiply the whole numbers from n down to 1.
By definition, $0! = 1$.

For example, $5! = (5)(4)(3)(2)(1) = 120$.

Next, consider the situation where *order does not matter*. Suppose you have to take 3 courses next quarter and you can choose from: Statistics, Calculus, English Literature, French, and Dance. How many different *combinations* or choices are open to you? Remember, in each selection order does not matter, selecting English Literature, French and Dance gives you the same schedule as French, Dance and English Literature.

To find the number of ways you can choose 3 courses from a total of 5 courses you can make a list. Here is the complete list:

Statistics, Calculus, English Literature
Statistics, Calculus, French
Statistics, Calculus, Dance
Statistics, English Literature, French

Statistics, English Literature, Dance
Statistics, French, Dance
Calculus, English Literature, French
Calculus, English Literature, Dance
Calculus, French, Dance
English Literature, French, Dance.

Notice that this is a list of all possible *combinations* of choosing 3 courses from 5. An unordered arrangement is called a *combination*.

Now imagine you want to list all the ways of selecting 10 objects from 1000 objects. Listing all these would be tedious and you would very likely make a mistake. This is why we have a formula to help us figure out the possible combinations.

To generalize, when *order does not matter*, the number of ways to choose x objects from n objects is called the number of *combinations* of n objects taken x at a time, written as $_nC_x$. There is a formula you can use instead of having to write out the entire list:

Combinations

$$_nC_x = \frac{n!}{(n-x)!x!}$$

Let's check our solution to the courses problem; here it is again. Suppose you have to take 3 courses next quarter and you can choose from: Statistics, Calculus, English Literature, French and Dance. How many different *combinations* or choices are open to you? Here, $n = 5$ and $x = 3$, so we can compute:

$$_5C_3 = \frac{5!}{(5-3)!3!} = \frac{(5)(4)(3)(2)(1)}{(2)(1)(3)(2)(1)} = 10$$

This is the same number we got from our list.

Example: In the candy store there are 10 different Easter eggs to choose from. You have enough money to buy 4 Easter eggs.

Question
How many different ways are there of choosing your 4 Easter eggs if order does not matter?

Solution: We can solve this problem using combinations:

$$_{10}C_4 = \frac{10!}{(10-4)!4!} = \frac{10!}{6!4!} = \frac{(10)(9)(8)(7)(6)(5)(4)(3)(2)(1)}{(6)(5)(4)(3)(2)(1)(4)(3)(2)(1)} = 210$$

That's a lot of choices!

■

3.1.3   **BINOMIAL PROBABILITIES**

Now let's look in more detail at the idea of a Binomial experiment. A Binomial experiment is a probability experiment that has the following characteristics:

Binomial Criteria

1. There is a fixed number of trials, denoted by n.

2. These n trials are independent.

3. The outcome of each trial can be designated as a *success* or a *failure*.

4. For each trial, the probability of a *success* is the same and is denoted by p.

Since the outcome of each trial is either a *success* or a *failure*, these events are complements and their probabilities must add to 1. Since the probability of a *success* is denoted by p, the probability of a *failure* is denoted by $1-p$.

Example: Roll a fair six-sided die 20 times and count the number of times you got a six.

Question
Is this a Binomial experiment?

Solution: Check the four Binomial criteria:
1. There are 20 trials.
2. Each roll of the die is independent of the others.
3. Since we are interested in 'sixes', rolling a 6 is a *success* and rolling anything else is a *failure*.
4. For each trial, the probability of a *success* is 1/6.

So this is a Binomial experiment.

■

Having defined Binomial experiments, we now find probabilities associated with them. For example, in the Binomial experiment above, we might want to find the probability that we get exactly 2 sixes.

Generally, we are interested in the probability of x successes out of n trials. It is important to notice that X is a random variable that denotes the number of successes in n trials, and that we are interested in $P(X = x)$.

Example: Suppose you roll a fair die three times.

Question
What is the probability of getting exactly 2 sixes?

Solution: Check the four Binomial criteria:
1. There are 3 trials.
2. Each roll of the die is independent of the others.
3. Since we are interested in 'sixes', rolling a 6 is a *success* and rolling anything else is a *failure*.
4. For each trial, the probability of a *success* is 1/6.
So this is a Binomial experiment.

Let the random variable X = number of sixes scored in 3 tosses

Then let S represent a *success* and F represents a *failure*.
The probability of S is $p = 1/6$.
The probability of F is $1 - p = 5/6$.

We are looking for the probability that $X = 2$, which means we are looking for the probability of 2 *successes* and 1 *failure*. There are 3 different *combinations, SSF, SFS,* and *FSS.*

$$P(X = 2) = P(SSF) + P(SFS) + P(FSS)$$
$$= \left(\frac{1}{6}\right)\left(\frac{1}{6}\right)\left(\frac{5}{6}\right) + \left(\frac{1}{6}\right)\left(\frac{5}{6}\right)\left(\frac{1}{6}\right) + \left(\frac{1}{6}\right)\left(\frac{5}{6}\right)\left(\frac{1}{6}\right)$$

Notice that all three combinations have the same probability, and so we can rewrite the probability of $X = 2$ as:

$$P(X = 2) = 3\left(\frac{1}{6}\right)^2\left(\frac{5}{6}\right)^1$$

We want to generalize the above result. Notice that the '3' in the above formula represents the number of ways you can have 2 *successes* in 3 trials. We found

---

these combinations by listing them, but remember we have a formula to help us find the total number of combinations.

What are we interested in? We are interested in X, the number of sixes scored in 3 tosses. So when $X = 2$, we are interested in the number of ways we can score 2 sixes out of 3 tosses.

> **STOP AND THINK!**
>
> **How many ways are there of scoring 2 sixes out of 3 tosses?**

There are:

$$_3C_2 = \frac{3!}{(3-2)!2!} = \frac{(3)(2)(1)}{(1)(2)(1)} = 3$$

So we can write:

$$P(X = 2) = \; _3C_2 \left(\frac{1}{6}\right)^2 \left(\frac{5}{6}\right)^1$$

■

This expression is a case of the general formula for Binomial probabilities:

> **Binomial Probabilities**
>
> $$P(X = x) = \; _nC_x \, p^x \left(1-p\right)^{n-x}$$
>
> where:
> - n represents the number of trials
> - x represents the number of successes you want
> - p represents the probability of a success

When all the probabilities associated with a Binomial experiment have been found, we can construct a Binomial *pdf*.

Example: In Cabo San Lucas about 25% of the couples there at any one time are on their honeymoon. You choose 4 couples randomly and ask them if they are honeymooning.

> **Question 1**
> Is this a Binomial experiment? Explain.

Solution: Check the four Binomial criteria:
1. There are 4 trials.
2. The couples are chosen at random, so it is reasonable to assume they are independent.
3. A *success* is if the couple is on their honeymoon, and a *failure* is if the couple is not on their honeymoon.
4. For each trial, the probability of a *success* is 0.25.

So this is a Binomial experiment.

Question 2

Use the formula to find the probability that exactly one of the couples is honeymooning.

Solution: Let X = number of couples on their honeymoon out of the 4 chosen couples.

Then $x = 1$, $n = 4$, $p = 0.25$, $(1 - p) = 0.75$. So, using the formula we get:

$$P(X = 1) = \ _4C_1 \ (0.25)^1 (0.75)^{4-1}$$
$$= 4(0.25)(0.4219)$$
$$= 0.4219$$

The probability that exactly one of four couples in Cabo San Lucas is on their honeymoon is 0.4219.

Question 3

Construct the *pdf* for this experiment.

Solution: To find the *pdf* for this Binomial distribution, we need to find the probabilities for all values of X. In other words, we need to find:

$$P(X = 0), \ P(X = 1), \ P(X = 2), \ P(X = 3), \ P(X = 4)$$

Applying the formula, we obtain the following:

$$P(X = 0) = \ _4C_0 \ (0.25)^0 (0.75)^{4-0} = 0.3164$$
$$P(X = 1) = \ _4C_1 \ (0.25)^1 (0.75)^{4-1} = 0.4219$$
$$P(X = 2) = \ _4C_2 \ (0.25)^2 (0.75)^{4-2} = 0.2109$$
$$P(X = 3) = \ _4C_3 \ (0.25)^3 (0.75)^{4-3} = 0.0469$$
$$P(X = 4) = \ _4C_4 \ (0.25)^4 (0.75)^{4-4} = 0.0039$$

We can put these values in a *pdf*.

x	0	1	2	3	4
P($X = x$)	0.3164	0.4219	0.2109	0.0469	0.0039

These probabilities must add up to 1. If they do not, you have made a mistake!

We call this the Binomial distribution of *x* successes in *n* trials; it is denoted by Bin(*n, p*).

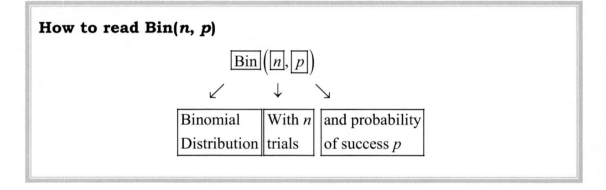

How to read Bin(*n, p*)

3.1.4

USING TABLES TO FIND BINOMIAL PROBABILITIES

Calculations with the formula can become quite long, so it is easy to make mistakes. To avoid these tedious calculations a table of Binomial probabilities for certain values of *n*, *x* and *p* has been constructed.   Sometimes we can use these tables instead of the formula but sometimes we cannot, so it is still important to know how to use the formula.

To see what the tables look like, turn to the Table of Binomial Probabilities at the back of the book. You can print out a copy from the CD. Here is a fragment of the table:

Figure 3.1

n	x	0.1	0.2	0.25	0.3	0.4	*p* 0.5	0.6	0.7	0.75	0.8	0.9
1	0	0.9000	0.8000	0.7500	0.7000	0.6000	0.5000	0.4000	0.3000	0.2500	0.2000	0.1000
	1	0.1000	0.2000	0.2500	0.3000	0.4000	0.5000	0.6000	0.7000	0.7500	0.8000	0.9000
2	0	0.8100	0.6400	0.5625	0.4900	0.3600	0.2500	0.1600	0.0900	0.0625	0.0400	0.0100
	1	0.1800	0.3200	0.3750	0.4200	0.4800	0.5000	0.4800	0.4200	0.3750	0.3200	0.1800
	2	0.0100	0.0400	0.0625	0.0900	0.1600	0.2500	0.3600	0.4900	0.5625	0.6400	0.8100
3	0	0.7290	0.5120	0.4219	0.3430	0.2160	0.1250	0.0640	0.0270	0.0156	0.0080	0.0010
	1	0.2430	0.3840	0.4219	0.4410	0.4320	0.3750	0.2880	0.1890	0.1406	0.0960	0.0270
	2	0.0270	0.0960	0.1406	0.1890	0.2880	0.3750	0.4320	0.4410	0.4219	0.3840	0.2430
	3	0.0010	0.0080	0.0156	0.0270	0.0640	0.1250	0.2160	0.3430	0.4219	0.5120	0.7290
4	0	0.6561	0.4096	0.3164	0.2401	0.1296	0.0625	0.0256	0.0081	0.0039	0.0016	0.0001
	1	0.2916	0.4096	0.4219	0.4116	0.3456	0.2500	0.1536	0.0756	0.0469	0.0256	0.0036
	2	0.0486	0.1536	0.2109	0.2646	0.3456	0.3750	0.3456	0.2646	0.2109	0.1536	0.0486
	3	0.0036	0.0256	0.0469	0.0756	0.1536	0.2500	0.3456	0.4116	0.4219	0.4096	0.2916
	4	0.0001	0.0016	0.0039	0.0081	0.0256	0.0625	0.1296	0.2401	0.3164	0.4096	0.6561

Along the top, we see that various values of p are given; for example, $p = 0.1$, $p = 0.2$, etc. Down the left side are the values for n and x. Let's look again at the example given in the previous section, but this time we will use tables to find probabilities:

Example: In Cabo San Lucas about 25% of the couples at any one time are on their honeymoon. You choose 4 couples randomly and ask them if they are honeymooning.

Question

Use the Binomial table to find the probability that exactly one of the couples is honeymooning.

Solution: As before, $x = 1$, $n = 4$, $p = 0.25$. To use the Binomial table, we can find the section where $n = 4$, within that section, we find the row where $x = 1$, and in that row, look in the column where $p = 0.25$. We find that the required probability is 0.4219, which is the same as the result given by the formula.

n	x	0.1	0.2	0.25	0.3	0.4	p 0.5	0.6	0.7	0.75	0.8	0.9
1	0	0.9000	0.8000	0.7500	0.7000	0.6000	0.5000	0.4000	0.3000	0.2500	0.2000	0.1000
	1	0.1000	0.2000	0.2500	0.3000	0.4000	0.5000	0.6000	0.7000	0.7500	0.8000	0.9000
2	0	0.8100	0.6400	0.5625	0.4900	0.3600	0.2500	0.1600	0.0900	0.0625	0.0400	0.0100
	1	0.1800	0.3200	0.3750	0.4200	0.4800	0.5000	0.4800	0.4200	0.3750	0.3200	0.1800
	2	0.0100	0.0400	0.0625	0.0900	0.1600	0.2500	0.3600	0.4900	0.5625	0.6400	0.8100
3	0	0.7290	0.5120	0.4219	0.3430	0.2160	0.1250	0.0640	0.0270	0.0156	0.0080	0.0010
	1	0.2430	0.3840	0.4219	0.4410	0.4320	0.3750	0.2880	0.1890	0.1406	0.0960	0.0270
	2	0.0270	0.0960	0.1406	0.1890	0.2880	0.3750	0.4320	0.4410	0.4219	0.3840	0.2430
	3	0.0010	0.0080	0.0156	0.0270	0.0640	0.1250	0.2160	0.3430	0.4219	0.5120	0.7290
4	0	0.6561	0.4096	0.3164	0.2401	0.1296	0.0625	0.0256	0.0081	0.0039	0.0016	0.0001
	1	0.2916	0.4096	0.4219	0.4116	0.3456	0.2500	0.1536	0.0756	0.0469	0.0256	0.0036
	2	0.0486	0.1536	0.2109	0.2646	0.3456	0.3750	0.3456	0.2646	0.2109	0.1536	0.0486
	3	0.0036	0.0256	0.0469	0.0756	0.1536	0.2500	0.3456	0.4116	0.4219	0.4096	0.2916
	4	0.0001	0.0016	0.0039	0.0081	0.0256	0.0625	0.1296	0.2401	0.3164	0.4096	0.6561

Notice that for any value of n, the value of x ranges from 0 to n. Each block of probabilities for given x, n and p, defines a Binomial distribution and hence adds up to 1.

It is not possible to construct tables for *all* values of x, n and p, so the formula is still useful. Where did the tables come from? They were constructed using the formula!

LESSON 3.1 EXERCISES
COUNTING AND BINOMIAL PROBABILITIES

1. How many different ways can you arrange the letters of the word 'GAUCHO'? (Do not try to write them all down, the question asks for: 'How many different ways?')

2. How many different arrangements of the letters of the word 'GAUCHO' start with a vowel?

3. Calculate the following:
    a) $_7C_4$
    b) $_{10}C_8$
    c) $_5C_0$
    Note: if you have a scientific or graphing calculator it most likely has a function that performs this calculation for you. Look for $_nC_r$.

4. Amy decides that, during exam week, she will eat a microwave dinner every evening, to save time cooking. A store sells 12 different microwave dinners. If Amy wants to choose 7 different dinners, one for each day of the week, how many different selections can she choose from?

5. Suppose the White House Internship Program is offering 5 positions next year. You apply and find that there are 10 qualified applicants. How many different groups of interns can be selected?

6. A fair coin is tossed 10 times. Find the probability that you get 3 heads.

7. A six-sided die is rolled 4 times. Find the probability of rolling:
    a) exactly one 4.
    b) at least one 2.
    c) more than 2 sixes.

8. In a statistics class about 22% of students get an 'A'. You poll 5 students randomly from last years' course and ask them if they got an 'A'.
    a) Is this a Binomial experiment? Explain.
    b) Specify n and p, and the random variable X.
    c) Use the formula to find the probability that exactly one of the students polled got an 'A'.
    d) Construct the Binomial *pdf* for this experiment.

9. A statistics professor decides to give a multiple-choice midterm examination. There are 10 questions on the test, each with 5 choices, only one of which is correct. You have not studied and decide to guess the answers to the questions. Find the probability that you will get:
   a) only one question correct.
   b) all 10 questions correct.

10. If you buy one Lotto ticket, then the probability that you will win a prize is 0.06. Suppose that you buy one ticket each month for six consecutive months. Find the probability that you will win:
   a) exactly one prize.
   b) at least one prize.
   c) more than 2 prizes

ANSWERS

LESSON 3.1 EXERCISES

COUNTING AND BINOMIAL PROBABILITIES

Below are the answers to the exercises for Unit 3, Lesson 3.1.
For full solutions, please refer to the CD included with this textbook.

1. There are 720 ways to arrange the letters in the word 'GAUCHO'.

2. There are 360 arrangements of the letters in the word 'GAUCHO' that start with a vowel.

3. a) $_7C_4 = 35$
   b) $_{10}C_8 = 45$
   c) $_5C_0 = 1$

4. Amy has 792 different selections.

5. There are 252 different groups of interns that can be selected.

6. $P(X = 3) = 0.1172$

7. a) $P(X = 1) = 0.3858$
   b) $P(X \geq 1) = 0.5177$
   c) $P(X > 2) = 0.0162$

8. a) Yes, because it satisfies the four Binomial criteria:
   1. There are 5 trials
   2. The students are chosen randomly so it is reasonable to assume they are independent.
   3. We are interested in whether a student got an 'A', so this is a *success* and a student who did not get an 'A' is a *failure*.
   4. We are told the probability a student got an 'A' is 0.22.
   b) $n = 5$ and $p = 0.22$
   X = Number of students in a statistics class who got an 'A' out of 5 randomly selected students.
   c) $P(X = 1) = 0.4072$
   d) The Binomial *pdf* is:

x	0	1	2	3	4	5
$P(X = x)$	0.2887	0.4072	0.2297	0.0648	0.0091	0.0005

9. a) $P(X = 1) = 0.2684$
    b) $P(X = 10) \approx 0$

10. a) $P(X = 1) = 0.2642$
    b) $P(X \geq 1) = 0.3101$
    c) $P(X > 2) = 0.0037$

LESSON 3.2
FINDING THE MEAN AND STANDARD DEVIATION OF A BINOMIAL RANDOM VARIABLE

3.2.1   INTRODUCTION

In Lesson 3.1 we discussed how to identify Binomial random variables and how to calculate Binomial probabilities. In this lesson we will show how to find the mean and standard deviation of Binomial random variables.

3.2.2   FINDING THE MEAN OF A BINOMIAL RANDOM VARIABLE

Consider tossing a fair coin 10 times. Suppose you are interested in the average number of tails. Since the probability that the coin shows tails is 0.5, we expect to observe tails on half of our flips. So, on average, we will see $10(0.5) = 5$ tails out of 10 flips.

This example describes a Binomial experiment because:
1. There are 10 trials.
2. The coin flips are considered to be independent from each other.
3. Since we are interested in observing tails, we can define *success* as 'coin shows tails' and *failure* as 'coin shows heads'.
4. The probability of a *success* is $p = 0.5$.

We then define a Binomial random variable:

$$X = \text{Number of tails observed in 10 flips}$$

and state its distribution:

$$X \text{ is Bin}(10, 0.5)$$

The mean of X was found by multiplying n by p. This is how the mean of a Binomial random variable is always calculated.

> ## The Mean of a Binomial Random Variable
> $$\mu = np$$

3.2.3

FINDING THE STANDARD DEVIATION OF A BINOMIAL RANDOM VARIABLE

Recall the coin example in Section 3.2.2. The mean number of tails in 10 flips was found to be 5. However, when we flip a coin 10 times, we are not always going to get 5 tails. This means that there is *variability* in the number of tails observed. As discussed in Lesson 2.2, the variability of a random variable is measured with the *standard deviation*, which is found by taking the square-root of the *variance*. Having identified a Binomial random variable, its variance is found with the following equation:

> ## The Variance of a Binomial Random Variable
> $$\sigma^2 = np(1-p)$$

Taking the square-root of the variance will give the standard deviation:

> ## The Standard Deviation of a Binomial Random Variable
> $$\sigma = \sqrt{np(1-p)}$$

Example:

Consider the coin example, where a fair coin was flipped 10 times. In Section 3.2.2, we showed that this was a Binomial experiment, and defined the Binomial random variable:

$$X = \text{Number of tails observed in 10 flips}$$

$$X \text{ is Bin(10, 0.5)}$$

> ## Question
> What is the standard deviation of X?

Solution:

Since X is a Binomial random variable, we find the standard deviation using the formula:

$$\sigma = \sqrt{np(1-p)}$$

Since $n = 10$ and $p = 0.5$, the standard deviation is:

$$\sigma = \sqrt{10(0.5)(1\text{-}0.5)}$$
$$= \sqrt{2.5}$$
$$= 1.5811$$

LESSON 3.2 EXERCISES
FINDING THE MEAN AND STANDARD DEVIATION OF A BINOMIAL RANDOM VARIABLE

1. The percentage of people reported to be living below the poverty level in the US in 1999 is 12.4% (Source: www.fedstats.gov). If you randomly sample 2000 people in the US, on average, how many were living below the poverty level in 1999?

2. The drawer in your desk has 6 red pens, 5 blue pens, and 8 black pens. Anytime you need a pen, you go to the drawer and blindly grab a pen. When you finish with the pen, you put it back in the drawer. You are interested in how many times you choose a red pen. If throughout the week you go to the drawer 15 times to get a pen:
   a) Define the Binomial random variable X.
   b) On average, how many times will you pick a red pen?
   c) What is the standard deviation for the number of red pens you pick?

3. In the year 2000, the percentage of people age 5 or older in Santa Barbara that spoke a language other than English at home was reported to be 36% (Source: www.fedstats.gov). If you sampled 700 people in Santa Barbara age 5 or older, on average, how many would report to speak a language other than English at home?

4. Suppose that when you go online to download driving directions, you receive correct directions 88% of the time. If 50 different people download directions:
   a) On average how many will receive *incorrect* directions?
   b) What is the standard deviation for the number of people that receive *incorrect* directions?

ANSWERS
LESSON 3.2 EXERCISES
FINDING THE MEAN AND STANDARD DEVIATION
OF A BINOMIAL RANDOM VARIABLE

Below are the answers to the exercises for Unit 3, Lesson 3.2.
For full solutions, please refer to the CD included with this textbook.

1. $\mu = 248$

2.   a) X = Number of red pens chosen out of 15 picks
     b) $\mu = 4.7368$
     c) $\sigma = 1.8003$

3. $\mu = 252$

4.   a) $\mu = 6$
     b) $\sigma = 2.2978$

LESSON 3.3
MORE PRACTICE IN SOLVING BINOMIAL DISTRIBUTION PROBLEMS

Translating word problems into math problems is difficult and requires practice. In this lesson we look at some more examples with full solutions. You are encouraged to work through these problems yourself if you need extra practice.

Example 1: Bob and Amy are arguing over what name to give their newborn son. Bob likes the names Andrew, David and James. Amy likes Sean and Colin. They are going to pick 2 names. How many different choices do they have if order does not matter?

> **STOP AND THINK!**
>
> **How can you compute the number of *unordered* choices?**

Solution: Since we are told that order does not matter, we can use combinations. We know there are 5 names, and they need to choose 2, so:

$$_5C_2 = \frac{5!}{(5-2)!2!} = \frac{5!}{3!2!} = \frac{(5)(4)(3)(2)(1)}{(3)(2)(1)(2)(1)} = 10$$

Please be aware that most scientific and graphing calculators will do this computation for you.

■

Example 2: It is estimated that 20% of the population between 65 and 80 years of age will suffer from a particular strain of influenza virus. In a random sample of 10 people aged between 65 and 80 find the probability that:

a) exactly one person will contract this strain of influenza.
b) no one will contract this strain of influenza.
c) at most one person will contract this strain of influenza.

> **STOP AND THINK!**
>
> **Check if the four Binomial criteria hold to determine whether you should use the Binomial distribution.**

Solution: a) This example describes a Binomial experiment because:
1. There are 10 trials.
2. The people are randomly selected, so it is reasonable to assume they are independent.
3. Since we are interested in a person contracting this strain of influenza, we can define *success* as 'person contracts this strain of influenza' and *failure* as 'person does not contract this strain of influenza'.
4. The probability of a *success* is $p = 0.2$.

Therefore, we can define the Binomial random variable and state its distribution:

X = Number of people between 65 and 80 years old out of 10 who contract this strain of influenza

X is Bin(10, 0.2)

To find the probability that exactly one person contracts this strain of influenza, we want to find $P(X = 1)$. We can use the formula for finding Binomial probabilities, knowing that $n = 10$, $p = 0.2$, and $x = 1$:

$$P(X = 1) = {}_{10}C_1 \ (0.2)^1 (1 - 0.2)^{10-1} = 0.2684$$

We could have also found $P(X = 1)$ by using the Binomial table, shown below:

n	x	0.1	0.2	0.25	0.3	0.4	0.5	0.6	0.7	0.75	0.8	0.9
10	0	0.3487	0.1074	0.0563	0.0282	0.0060	0.0010	0.0001				
	1	0.3874	0.2684	0.1877	0.1211	0.0403	0.0098	0.0016	0.0001			
	2	0.1937	0.3020	0.2816	0.2335	0.1209	0.0439	0.0106	0.0014	0.0004	0.0001	
	3	0.0574	0.2013	0.2503	0.2668	0.2150	0.1172	0.0425	0.0090	0.0031	0.0008	
	4	0.0112	0.0881	0.1460	0.2001	0.2508	0.2051	0.1115	0.0368	0.0162	0.0055	0.0001
	5	0.0015	0.0264	0.0584	0.1029	0.2007	0.2461	0.2007	0.1029	0.0584	0.0264	0.0015
	6	0.0001	0.0055	0.0162	0.0368	0.1115	0.2051	0.2508	0.2001	0.1460	0.0881	0.0112
	7		0.0008	0.0031	0.0090	0.0425	0.1172	0.2150	0.2668	0.2503	0.2013	0.0574
	8		0.0001	0.0004	0.0014	0.0106	0.0439	0.1209	0.2335	0.2816	0.3020	0.1937
	9				0.0001	0.0016	0.0098	0.0403	0.1211	0.1877	0.2684	0.3874
	10					0.0001	0.0010	0.0060	0.0282	0.0563	0.1074	0.3487

Solution: b) The four Binomial criteria, as well as the Binomial random variable and its distribution defined in part (a) still hold here.

To find the probability that no one contracts this strain of influenza, we can find $P(X = 0)$. We can use the formula for finding Binomial probabilities:

$$P(X=0) = {}_{10}C_0(0.2)^0(1-0.2)^{10-0} = 0.1074$$

We could have also found $P(X=0)$ by using the Binomial table to find, shown below:

n	x	0.1	0.2	0.25	0.3	0.4	p 0.5	0.6	0.7	0.75	0.8	0.9
10	0	0.3487	0.1074	0.0563	0.0282	0.0060	0.0010	0.0001				
	1	0.3874	0.2684	0.1877	0.1211	0.0403	0.0098	0.0016	0.0001			
	2	0.1937	0.3020	0.2816	0.2335	0.1209	0.0439	0.0106	0.0014	0.0004	0.0001	
	3	0.0574	0.2013	0.2503	0.2668	0.2150	0.1172	0.0425	0.0090	0.0031	0.0008	
	4	0.0112	0.0881	0.1460	0.2001	0.2508	0.2051	0.1115	0.0368	0.0162	0.0055	0.0001
	5	0.0015	0.0264	0.0584	0.1029	0.2007	0.2461	0.2007	0.1029	0.0584	0.0264	0.0015
	6	0.0001	0.0055	0.0162	0.0368	0.1115	0.2051	0.2508	0.2001	0.1460	0.0881	0.0112
	7		0.0008	0.0031	0.0090	0.0425	0.1172	0.2150	0.2668	0.2503	0.2013	0.0574
	8		0.0001	0.0004	0.0014	0.0106	0.0439	0.1209	0.2335	0.2816	0.3020	0.1937
	9				0.0001	0.0016	0.0098	0.0403	0.1211	0.1877	0.2684	0.3874
	10					0.0001	0.0010	0.0060	0.0282	0.0563	0.1074	0.3487

Solution:

c) The four Binomial criteria, as well as the Binomial random variable and its distribution defined in part (a) still hold here.

To find the probability that at most one person contracts this strain of influenza, we can find $P(X \leq 1)$. This means we are interested in values of X that are less than or equal to 1, which means we are interested in $X=0$ or $X=1$. We already found the probabilities for these values of X in parts (a) and (b), so we can simply add them together:

$$P(X \leq 1) = P(X=0) + P(X=1) = 0.1074 + 0.2684 = 0.3758$$

We could have also found $P(X \leq 1)$ by using the Binomial table to find $P(X=0)$ and $P(X=1)$, shown below, and adding them together:

n	x	0.1	0.2	0.25	0.3	0.4	p 0.5	0.6	0.7	0.75	0.8	0.9
10	0	0.3487	0.1074	0.0563	0.0282	0.0060	0.0010	0.0001				
	1	0.3874	0.2684	0.1877	0.1211	0.0403	0.0098	0.0016	0.0001			
	2	0.1937	0.3020	0.2816	0.2335	0.1209	0.0439	0.0106	0.0014	0.0004	0.0001	
	3	0.0574	0.2013	0.2503	0.2668	0.2150	0.1172	0.0425	0.0090	0.0031	0.0008	
	4	0.0112	0.0881	0.1460	0.2001	0.2508	0.2051	0.1115	0.0368	0.0162	0.0055	0.0001
	5	0.0015	0.0264	0.0584	0.1029	0.2007	0.2461	0.2007	0.1029	0.0584	0.0264	0.0015
	6	0.0001	0.0055	0.0162	0.0368	0.1115	0.2051	0.2508	0.2001	0.1460	0.0881	0.0112
	7		0.0008	0.0031	0.0090	0.0425	0.1172	0.2150	0.2668	0.2503	0.2013	0.0574
	8		0.0001	0.0004	0.0014	0.0106	0.0439	0.1209	0.2335	0.2816	0.3020	0.1937
	9				0.0001	0.0016	0.0098	0.0403	0.1211	0.1877	0.2684	0.3874
	10					0.0001	0.0010	0.0060	0.0282	0.0563	0.1074	0.3487

Example 3: According to a recent report, 30% of deaths in South Africa are caused by AIDS. (BBC News Report 18 May, 2005). If on a typical day there are 73 deaths, what is the probability that none of them were caused by AIDS? Assume the deaths are independent.

STOP AND THINK!

Check if the four Binomial criteria hold to determine whether you should use the Binomial distribution.

Solution: This example describes a Binomial experiment because:
1. There are 73 trials.
2. We are told to assume the deaths are independent.
3. Since we are interested in whether a death in South Africa was caused by AIDS, we can define *success* as 'death in South Africa was caused by AIDS' and *failure* as 'death in South Africa was not caused by AIDS'.
4. The probability of a *success* is $p = 0.3$.

Therefore, we can define the Binomial random variable and state its distribution:

X = Number of deaths in South Africa out of 73 due to AIDS

X is Bin(73, 0.3)

To find the probability that none of the deaths were caused by AIDS, we want to find $P(X = 0)$. We can use the formula for finding Binomial probabilities, knowing that $n = 73$, $p = 0.3$, and $x = 0$:

$$P(X = 0) = {}_{73}C_0 \, (0.3)^0 \, (1-0.3)^{73-0} \approx 0$$

The symbol '$\approx$' is read 'almost equals'. Therefore, we can say the probability that none of the 73 deaths are due to AIDS is almost 0. In other words, it is extremely unlikely, but still *possible*. When you compute this probability on your calculator, most calculators will show scientific notation.

We could not find this probability using the Binomial table because $n = 73$ is not found in the table.

■

Example 4:   68% of US women received a Valentine's Day gift of red roses this year. You ask 6 women at random if they received a Valentine's Day gift of red roses this year.
a) Is this a Binomial experiment? Explain.
b) Find the probability that 3 or more of the women asked received a Valentine's Day gift of red roses.
c) Write your answer as a sentence within the context of the problem.

STOP AND THINK!

Are the four Binomial criteria satisfied?

Solution: a) This example describes a Binomial experiment because:
1. There are 6 trials.
2. The women are randomly selected, so it is reasonable to assume they are independent.
3. Since we are interested in whether a woman received red roses for Valentine's Day this year, we can define *success* as 'woman received red roses for Valentine's Day this year' and *failure* as 'woman did not receive red roses for Valentine's Day this year'.
4. The probability of a *success* is $p = 0.68$.

Therefore, we can define the Binomial random variable and state its distribution:

X = Number of women out of 6 who received red roses for Valentine's Day this year

X is Bin(6, 0.68)

Solution: b) To find the probability that 3 or more women received red roses for Valentine's Day this year, we can find $P(X \geq 3)$. This means we are interested in $X = 3$, $X = 4$, $X = 5$, or $X = 6$. We can use the formula for finding Binomial probabilities for each value of X and add them together:

$$P(X = 3) = {}_6C_3(0.68)^3(1-0.68)^{6-3} = 0.2061$$

$$P(X = 4) = {}_6C_4(0.68)^4(1-0.68)^{6-4} = 0.3284$$

$$P(X = 5) = {}_6C_5(0.68)^5(1-0.68)^{6-5} = 0.2792$$

$$P(X = 6) = {}_6C_6(0.68)^6(1-0.68)^{6-6} = 0.0989$$

So,
$$P(X \geq 3) = P(X = 3) + P(X = 4) + P(X = 5) + P(X = 6)$$
$$= 0.2061 + 0.3284 + 0.2792 + 0.0989$$
$$= 0.9126$$

We cannot use the Binomial table for this problem because it does not display values for $p = 0.68$.

Solution: c) The probability that 3 or more women out of 6 received red roses for Valentine's Day this year is 0.9126.

Example 5:   According to the Humane Society of America, 65% of dog owners have one dog. You randomly select 5 dog owners. Find the probability that exactly four of them have just one dog.

> **STOP AND THINK!**
>
> **Are the four Binomial criteria satisfied?**

Solution: This example describes a Binomial experiment because:
1. There are 5 trials.
2. The dog owners are randomly selected, so it is reasonable to assume they are independent.
3. Since we are interested in whether a dog owner has one dog, we can define *success* as 'dog owner has one dog' and *failure* as 'dog owner does not have one dog'.
4. The probability of a *success* is $p = 0.65$.

Therefore, we can define the Binomial random variable and state its distribution:

X = Number of dog owners out of 5 that have just one dog

X is Bin(5, 0.65)

To find the probability that 4 of the dog owners have just one dog, we want to find $P(X = 4)$. We can use the formula for finding Binomial probabilities, knowing that $n = 5$, $p = 0.65$, and $x = 4$:

$$P(X = 4) = {_5C_4}\ (0.65)^4 (1 - 0.65)^{5-4} = 0.3124$$

Example 6:   I have a bag containing 20 chocolate eggs in a variety of colors. I want to make up a small basket of chocolate eggs and so I choose 5 eggs from the large bag, one at a time and place each one in the basket. Is this a Binomial experiment? Explain.

> **STOP AND THINK!**
>
> **Are all four Binomial criteria satisfied? Check each one.**

Solution: No, this is not a Binomial experiment. The trials are not independent because you do not replace the egg in the bag before choosing again. Therefore, the probability of choosing a red egg is not constant for each trial. In addition, there is no *success* specified.

Example 7:   A fair coin is tossed until you have 3 heads. Is this a binomial experiment? Explain.

> STOP AND THINK!
>
> Are all four Binomial criteria satisfied? Check each one.

Solution: No, this is not a Binomial experiment because there is no fixed number of trials, since you are flipping the coin *until* you have 3 heads.

■

Example 8:   There is a bag with 6 red candies, 4 yellow candies, and 8 purple candies. You select 3 candies one at a time without replacement, and you are interested in the number of red candies you get. Is this a Binomial experiment? Explain.

> STOP AND THINK!
>
> Are all four Binomial criteria satisfied? Check each one.

Solution: No, this is not a Binomial experiment because you are choosing the candies without replacement from a small sample. This means that what you pick the first time influences the probability of what color you pick the second time, which in turn influences the probability of what color you pick the third time. Therefore, the 3 trials are *not* independent.

■

Example 9:   A biology professor gave her class a midterm that 30% of her students failed. If you randomly talked to 15 of her students, on average how many of them failed the midterm?

> STOP AND THINK!
>
> Are all four Binomial criteria satisfied?
>
> What formula should you use to calculate the mean?

Solution: This example describes a Binomial experiment because:

1. There are 15 trials.
2. Since the students are chosen randomly, it is reasonable to assume they are independent.
3. Since we are interested in whether a student failed the midterm, we can define *success* as 'a student failed the midterm' and *failure* as 'a student did not fail the midterm'.
4. The probability of a *success* is $p = 0.3$

Therefore, we can define the Binomial random variable and state its distribution:

X = Number of students out of 15 that failed the midterm

X is Bin(15, 0.3)

We can then use the formulas for finding the mean of a Binomial random variable:

$$\mu = np = 15(0.3) = 4.5$$

∎

Example 10: You roll a fair six-sided die 50 times.
   a) What is the mean and standard deviation of the number of times an odd face is rolled?
   b) What is the mean and standard deviation of the number of times a 4 is rolled?

STOP AND THINK!

Are all four Binomial criteria satisfied?

What formulas should you use to calculate the mean and standard deviation?

Solution: a) This example describes a Binomial experiment because:
   1. There are 50 trials.
   2. Rolls of dice are independent.
   3. Since we are interested in whether we roll an odd face, we can define *success* as 'the face rolled is odd' and *failure* as 'the face rolled is not odd'.
   4. The probability of a success is $p = 0.5$

Therefore, we can define the Binomial random variable and state its distribution:

X = Number of rolls out of 50 that show an odd face

X is Bin(50, 0.5)

We can then use the formulas for finding the mean and standard deviation of a Binomial random variable:

$$\mu = np = 50(0.5) = 25$$

$$\sigma = \sqrt{np(1-p)} = \sqrt{50(0.5)(1-0.5)} = 3.5355$$

Solution:

b) This example describes a Binomial experiment because:
1. There are 50 trials.
2. Rolls of dice are independent.
3. Since we are interested in whether we roll a 4, we can define *success* as 'the face rolled is a 4' and *failure* as 'the face rolled is not a 4'.
4. The probability of a *success* is $p = 1/6$

Therefore, we can define the Binomial random variable and state its distribution:

X = Number of rolls out of 50 that show a 4

X is Bin(50, 1/6)

We can then use the formulas for finding the mean and standard deviation of a Binomial random variable:

$$\mu = np = 50(1/6) = 8.3333$$

$$\sigma = \sqrt{np(1-p)} = \sqrt{50(1/6)(1-1/6)} = 2.6352$$

$\mu = np$

$\sigma = \sqrt{np(1-p)}$

LESSON 3.3 EXERCISES
MORE PRACTICE IN SOLVING BINOMIAL DISTRIBUTION PROBLEMS

1. According to the US census 5,000,000 adults in California (approximately 22%) speak a language other than English in their home. You select 3 adults at random and ask them if speak a language other than English in their home.
   a) Identify X, the random variable of interest.
   b) Identify n and p.
   c) Construct a probability distribution for X.
   d) Find $P(X > 1)$.
   e) Write a sentence explaining the answer you found for (d).

2. According to ANRED (Anorexia and Related Eating Disorders, Inc.) one percent (1%) of female adolescents have anorexia. You randomly select 10 female adolescents. Find the probability that exactly one of these female adolescents suffers from anorexia. Write your answer as a sentence within the context of the question.

3. The Maryland Underage Drinking Prevention Coalition claims that 40% of youth under 18 years old in long-term, state-operated juvenile institutions in 1987 were under the influence of alcohol at the time of arrest. For a random sample of 20 such youth, find the probability that half of them were under the influence of alcohol at the time of their arrest.

4. There are 22 children in a kindergarten class. If the teacher wants to choose 3 children to do an art project, how many different combinations are possible?

ANSWERS

LESSON 3.3 EXERCISES

MORE PRACTICE IN SOLVING BINOMIAL DISTRIBUTION PROBLEMS

Below are the answers to the exercises for Unit 3, Lesson 3.3.
For full solutions, please refer to the CD included with this textbook.

1. a) X=Number of adults in California out of 3 that speak a language other than English in their home.
   b) $n = 3$
      $p = 0.22$
   c) The Binomial *pdf* for X is:

x	0	1	2	3
$P(X = x)$	0.4746	0.4015	0.1133	0.0106

   d) $P(X > 1) = 0.1239$
   e) The probability that more than 1 adult Californian out of 3 will speak a language other than English in their home is 0.1239.

2. The probability that exactly one out of 10 female adolescents suffers from anorexia is 0.0914.

3. $P(X = 10) = 0.1171$

4. There are 1540 possible combinations.

AVOIDING
COMMON MISTAKES

☺ Check the Binomial conditions before using any formulas or tables from this unit – the problem may not always be describing a Binomial experiment.

☺ Do not forget to take the square-root of the variance when finding the standard deviation.

UNIT 3 SUMMARY

- A *random variable* is a variable whose values are determined by chance.

- Fundamental Counting Principle: If one event can occur x ways and a second event can occur y ways, the number of ways the two events can occur in sequence is xy. This rule can be extended for any number of events occurring in a sequence.

- Factorials: To find $n!$, you multiply the numbers from n down to 1. By definition, $0! = 1$.

- Combinations: The formula for calculating the number of ways to choose x objects from n objects is:

$$_nC_x = \frac{n!}{(n-x)!x!}$$

- The four Binomial criteria are:
  1. There are a fixed number of trials
  2. The trials are independent
  3. Each trial results in a *success* or a *failure*
  4. The probability of a *success* remains constant from trial to trial

- The formula for calculating Binomial probabilities is:

$$P(X = x) = {_nC_x}\, p^x (1-p)^{n-x}$$

- The formula for calculating the mean of a Binomial random variable is:

$$\mu = np$$

- The formula for calculating the variance of a Binomial random variable is:

$$\sigma^2 = np(1-p)$$

- The formula for calculating the standard deviation of a Binomial random variable is:

$$\sigma = \sqrt{np(1-p)}$$

SELF-ASSESSMENT QUIZ

1. You have 8 different textbooks for your classes this quarter. How many different ways can they be arranged on your bookshelf?

2. There are 6 people in your study group for history. If your group wants to send 3 people to the library to do some research for an upcoming project, how many possible groups can be sent?

3. Every day, there is a 93% chance that the price of gas has gone up from the day before. You track the price of gas for a week. Assume the days are independent.
   a) Is this a Binomial experiment? Explain.
   b) Define the random variable X.
   c) What is the probability that the price of gas goes up every day that week?
   d) What is the mean number of days the price of gas will go up in a week?
   e) What is the standard deviation of the number of days the price of gas will go up in a week?

4. Suppose there are 8 men and 6 women on a recreational soccer team. Four people are to be selected to be in charge of bringing the soccer balls to practice. We are interested in seeing how many of the people chosen are women. Is this a Binomial experiment? Explain.

5. A candy company is holding a sweepstakes. To win, you must buy a candy that has a winning wrapper. If the company advertises that one in every 5 candies has a winning wrapper, how likely is it that if you bought 3 candies, they would all have a winning wrapper?

6. According to the Humane Society, 16% cats are adopted from an animal shelter. Out of a random sample of 42 cats:
   a) On average how many of them were adopted from an animal shelter?
   b) What is the standard deviation of the number of cats adopted from an animal shelter?

ANSWERS
SELF-ASSESSMENT QUIZ

Below are the answers to the exercises for Unit 3, Self-Assessment Quiz. For full solutions, please refer to the CD included with this textbook.

1. There are 40,320 different ways.

2. There are 20 different possibilities.

3. a) Yes, because it satisfies the four Binomial criteria:
   - There are 7 trials
   - We are told to assume the days are independent.
   - We are interested in whether the price of gas goes up. So we can define a *Success* as 'the price of gas goes up', and a *Failure* as 'the price of gas does not go up'.
   - We are told the probability the price of gas goes up is 0.93.

   b) X = Number of days in a week that the price of gas goes up

   c) $P(X = 7) = 0.6017$

   d) $\mu = 6.51$

   e) $\sigma = 0.6751$

4. No, this is not a Binomial experiment. The trials are not independent, since you are selecting without replacement from a small group, and therefore the probability of a *success* (choosing a woman) changes from trial to trial.

5. $P(X = 3) = 0.008$

6. a) $\mu = 6.72$

   b) $\sigma = 2.3759$

1. n!
2. indep?
3. success/failure?
4. p?

UNIT 4
CONTINUOUS DISTRIBUTIONS

Lesson 4.1   Continuous Random Variables and the Uniform Distribution
Exercises for Lesson 4.1
Answers to Exercises for Lesson 4.1

Lesson 4.2   The Normal Distribution
Exercises for Lesson 4.2
Answers to Exercises for Lesson 4.2

Lesson 4.3   More Practice in Solving Continuous Distribution Problems
Exercises for Lesson 4.3
Answers to Exercises for Lesson 4.3

Avoiding Common Mistakes
Unit 4 Summary
Self-Assessment Quiz
Answers to Self-Assessment Quiz

LESSON 4.1
CONTINUOUS RANDOM VARIABLES AND THE UNIFORM DISTRIBUTION

4.1.1   **INTRODUCTION**

In this unit, we look at two distributions that model continuous random variables; the Uniform distribution and the Normal distribution.

4.1.2   **CONTINUOUS RANDOM VARIABLES**

Random variables that are not discrete are continuous. Recall that random variables are discrete if we can *count* the number of outcomes. Random variables are continuous if we can *measure* the outcomes. For example:

- Height is continuous because we can measure it with a measuring tape.
- Weight is continuous because we can measure it with a scale.
- Time is continuous because we can measure it with a clock.

Continuous Random Variables

A random variable is *continuous* if all its possible outcomes can be measured.

Example: Use your understanding of discrete and continuous random variables to answer the following questions.

Question 1

Is the random variable 'X = Number of houses on a street' discrete or continuous?

Solution: The number of houses on a street can be counted. The key word here is 'count', so this is a *discrete random variable*.

Question 2
Is the random variable 'X = A person's body temperature' discrete or continuous?

Solution: A person's body temperature can be found using a thermometer to measure the temperature, so this is a *continuous random variable*.

■

Discrete random variables are represented by a *pdf*, whereas continuous random variables are more easily represented by a graph. Such a graph is called a density curve.

Density Curve

A curve that has the property that the area underneath it is equal to 1 is called a *density curve*.

If we have a density curve, then finding areas under the curve is equivalent to finding probabilities.

4.1.3   THE UNIFORM DISTRIBUTION
Suppose you go to a drive-thru to pick up some food. You do not know how long you will have to wait at the drive-thru, but you know from previous experience it can be anywhere from 1-10 minutes and that all waiting times are equally likely. What is the probability you will wait more than 7 minutes?

To answer this question, consider the continuous random variable:

X = The time you have to wait at the drive-thru.

Since all the waiting times are equally likely, X is called a *Uniform random variable*. The graph of X is shown in Figure 4.1.

Figure 4.1

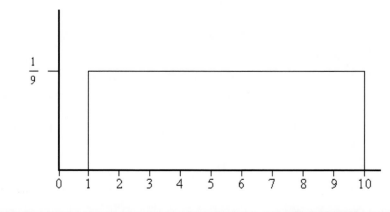

This is an example of the *Uniform distribution*. Since the Uniform distribution is a density curve, the area underneath the curve must equal 1. Furthermore, the Uniform distribution is a rectangle, so:

$$\text{Area of rectangle} = \text{base} \times \text{height}$$

In this example, the base of the rectangle is $10 - 1 = 9$ and so the height must be equal to 1/9 in order for the area to equal 1.

Once we have found the height of the rectangle, it is easy to calculate probabilities. We can shade the area that we are interested in, as shown in Figure 4.2.

Figure 4.2

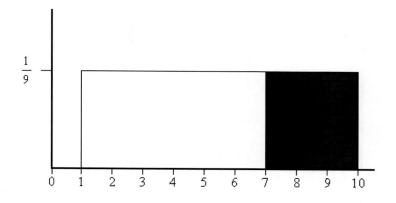

The area of the shaded region is equal to the probability that you will wait more than 7 minutes. The base of this shaded area equals $10 - 7 = 3$ and the height is 1/9, so this area can be calculated as follows:

$$\text{Area of rectangle} = \text{base} \times \text{height}$$
$$= 3\left(\frac{1}{9}\right)$$
$$= \frac{3}{9}$$

Therefore, the probability that you will wait at the drive-thru for more than 7 minutes is 3/9.

Now, what is the probability that you will wait less than 5 minutes?

STOP AND THINK!

Shade the area that you are interested in.

What is the base?

What is the height?

Figure 4.3

We can shade the area below $X = 5$, as shown in Figure 4.3.

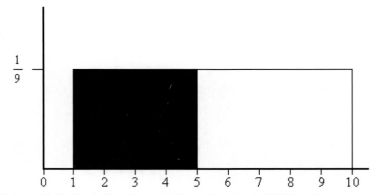

The area of the shaded region is equal to the probability that you will wait less than 5 minutes. The base of this shaded area equals $5 - 1 = 4$ and the height is still 1/9, so this area can be calculated as follows:

$$\text{Area of rectangle} = \text{base} \times \text{height}$$

$$= 4\left(\frac{1}{9}\right)$$

$$= \frac{4}{9}$$

Therefore, the probability that you will wait at the drive-thru for less than 5 minutes is 4/9.

Now consider the probability that you will wait exactly 2 minutes in the drive-thru.

STOP AND THINK!

What is the area you are interested in?

If we look at Figure 4.4, the probability that you will wait exactly 2 minutes is 0, because there is no area to be found.

Figure 4.4

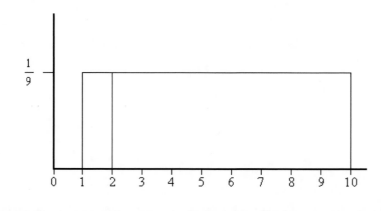

This illustrates an important fact about continuous distributions: the probability of observing a single value of a continuous random variable is always 0.

The general form of the Uniform distribution is depicted in Figure 4.5:

Figure 4.5

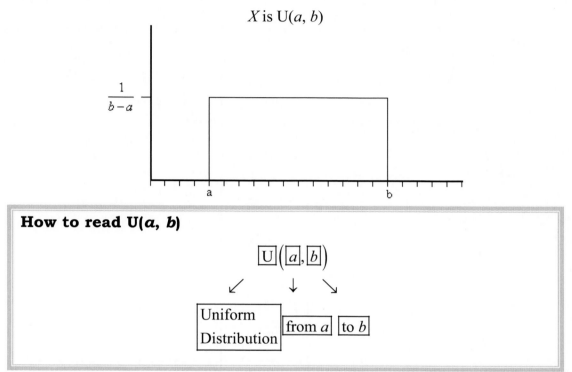

X is U(a, b)

$\dfrac{1}{b-a}$

a b

How to read U(a, b)

U$\left(\boxed{a},\boxed{b}\right)$

Uniform Distribution   from a to b

We can also compute the mean.

The mean of a Uniform Random Variable

$$\mu = \frac{b+a}{2}$$

As we can see in Figure 4.6, this places the mean halfway between a and b.

Figure 4.6

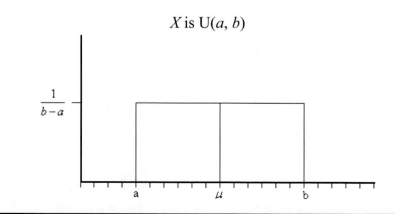

X is U(a, b)

$\dfrac{1}{b-a}$

a μ b

Lesson 4.1: Continuous Random Variables and the Uniform Distribution

Now consider the random variable

X = Calories burned during a one-hour kickboxing workout

and suppose that X is U(500, 800). What would the distribution of X look like?

STOP AND THINK!

How would you draw this Uniform distribution?
How do you determine the height?

Figure 4.7 shows the distribution of X.

Figure 4.7

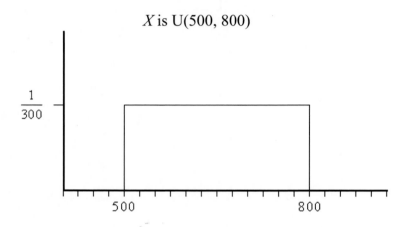

X is U(500, 800)

The base of the rectangle is 800 – 500 = 300. Therefore, the height of the rectangle must be 1/300.

What is the mean of the Uniform distribution shown in Figure 4.7?

STOP AND THINK!

What formula would you use to calculate the mean of a Uniform distribution?

To find the mean of a Uniform distribution, we apply the formula:

$$\mu = \frac{b+a}{2}$$
$$= \frac{800+500}{2}$$
$$= 650$$

LESSON 4.1 EXERCISES
CONTINUOUS RANDOM VARIABLES AND THE UNIFORM DISTRIBUTION

1. Are the following random variables discrete or continuous?
   a) X = 'The time it takes to travel to school'.
   b) X = 'The height of an adult American female'.
   c) X = 'the number of 4's scored when you roll a die 100 times'.

2. The price of a bar of chocolate ranges from \$3.50 to \$5.80. The prices are Uniformly distributed.
   a) What is the mean price of a bar of chocolate?
   b) If you go into any store and buy a bar of chocolate, what is the probability that it will cost more than \$4.00?   *0.7826*

3. The time it takes you to eat breakfast in the morning follows a Uniform distribution, and ranges from 5 – 12 minutes.
   a) Define the random variable X.
   b) Draw the distribution of X.
   c) What is the probability you will eat breakfast in less than 10 minutes?   *$\frac{5}{7} = 0.7143$*
   d) What is the probability it will take you between 6 and 7 minutes?   *0.1429*
   e) What is the probability it will take you exactly 9 minutes?   *0*

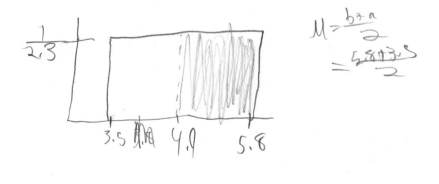

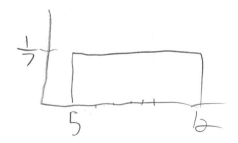

ANSWERS

LESSON 4.1 EXERCISES

CONTINUOUS RANDOM VARIABLES AND THE UNIFORM DISTRIBUTION

Below are the answers to the exercises for Unit 4, Lesson 4.1.
For full solutions, please refer to the CD included with this textbook.

1. a) X = 'The time it takes to travel to school' is continuous.
    b) X = 'The height of an adult American female' is continuous.
    c) X = 'the number of 4's scored when you roll a die 100 times' is discrete.

2. a) $\mu = \$4.65$
    b) $P(X > \$4.00) = 0.7826$

3. a) X = Time it takes you to eat breakfast in the morning
    b)

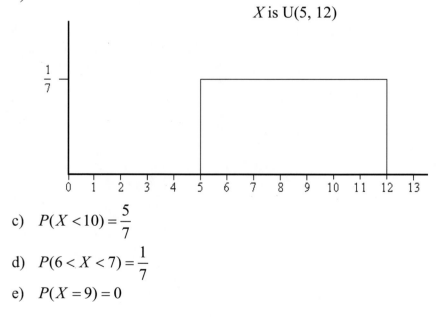

X is U(5, 12)

    c) $P(X < 10) = \dfrac{5}{7}$
    d) $P(6 < X < 7) = \dfrac{1}{7}$
    e) $P(X = 9) = 0$

LESSON 4.2
THE NORMAL DISTRIBUTION

4.2.1

INTRODUCTION
Another continuous distribution is the Normal distribution, sometimes called the 'bell curve'. In this lesson, we will discuss the properties of the Normal distribution, and how to find probabilities associated with it. Like the Uniform distribution, we can find probabilities for the Normal distribution by finding the area underneath the curve. The Normal distribution is central to the methods we will be learning in later units, therefore it is important that you have a sound understanding of the material in this lesson.

4.2.2

PROPERTIES OF THE NORMAL DISTRIBUTION
The Normal distribution is a bell-shaped, symmetric curve. Since it is a density function, like the Uniform distribution, the area under the Normal curve is 1.

The Normal distribution is described by its mean, denoted by μ, and its standard deviation, denoted by σ. When a continuous random variable X follows a Normal distribution, we write X is N(μ, σ).

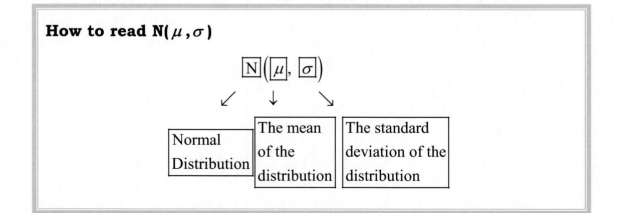

A typical Normal curve is shown in Figure 4.8.

Figure 4.8

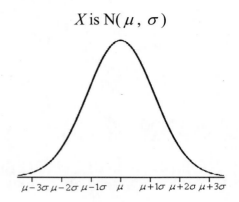

X is N(μ, σ)

Notice that the curve peaks at the mean. The Normal distribution extends forever in either direction. However, for practical reasons, we draw a Normal curve extending out three standard deviations from either side of the mean. An important property of the Normal distribution is that *almost all* (over 99%) of the data is within three standard deviations of the mean.

For example, consider the random variable:

$$X = \text{score on a math quiz}$$

where X is N(40, 5). If we wanted to draw the distribution of X, we would need to draw a Normal distribution that had a mean $\mu = 40$ and a standard deviation $\sigma = 5$.

STOP AND THINK!

Try drawing this curve.

How do you show that the mean of the curve is 40?

How do you show that the standard deviation of the curve is 5?

The distribution of X should look like Figure 4.9.

Figure 4.9

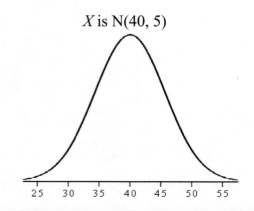

X is N(40, 5)

Notice the curve peaks at 40, which is the mean. Marking off three standard deviations above and below the mean gives us the scale shown on Figure 4.9. Every increment of one standard deviation is an increment of 5 units. This graph indicates that *most* of the scores on the math quiz were between 25 and 55. However, it is *possible*, though unlikely, that a few students scored below 25 or above 55.

Since the Normal distribution is described by its mean and standard deviation, we will look at how changing these values affects what the curve looks like. Figure 4.10 depicts three Normal curves that all have different means but the same standard deviation.

Figure 4.10

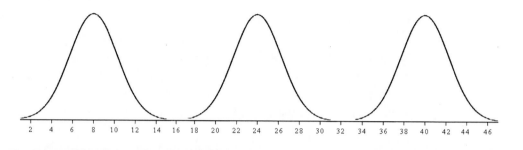

STOP AND THINK!

Can you figure out the means and standard deviation of all three curves?

All three curves have a standard deviation of 2, but the curve on the left has a mean of 8, the curve in the middle has a mean of 24, and the curve on the right has a mean of 40.

Figure 4.11 depicts three Normal curves that all have different means and different standard deviations.

Figure 4.11

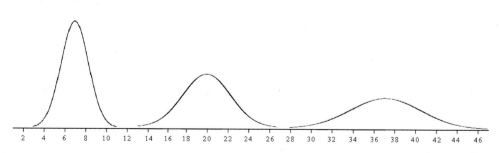

STOP AND THINK!

Can you figure out the means and standard deviations of all three curves?

Lesson 4.2: The Normal Distribution

The curve on the left has a mean of 7 and a standard deviation of 1. The curve in the middle has a mean of 20 and a standard deviation of 2. The curve on the right has a mean of 37 and a standard deviation of 3. Since all Normal curves have an area of 1 underneath them, the curves get taller and skinnier as the standard deviation decreases, and shorter and fatter as the standard deviation increases. So, we can see that a larger standard deviation indicates more spread from the mean, and a smaller standard deviation indicates less spread from the mean.

Next we will discuss how to find probabilities concerning a Normal random variable.

4.2.3   **FINDING PROBABILITIES**

Since the area under the Normal curve equals 1, we can find probabilities for Normal random variables by finding the appropriate area underneath the curve. For example, suppose grades on a psychology midterm vary according to a Normal distribution, with a mean of 81 and a standard deviation of 4. The random variable described in this situation is:

$$X = \text{grades on a psychology midterm}$$

So we can say X is N(81, 4), as shown in Figure 4.12.

Figure 4.12

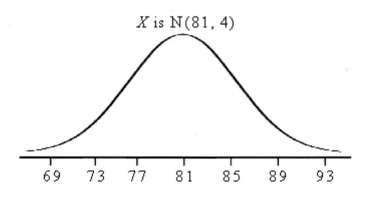

Suppose we want to find the probability that a student got less than 75 points on the psychology midterm, this means we are interested in

$$P(X < 75)$$

This probability is represented by shading the area under the curve below 75, as shown in Figure 4.13.

Figure 4.13

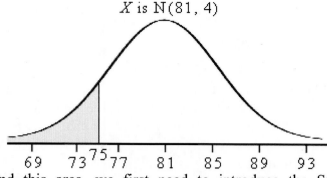

X is N(81, 4)

69   73 75 77   81   85   89   93

To help us find this area, we first need to introduce the Standard Normal distribution.

The Standard Normal Distribution

A Normal distribution that has a mean of 0 and a standard deviation of 1 is known as the Standard Normal distribution, denoted by the random variable Z.

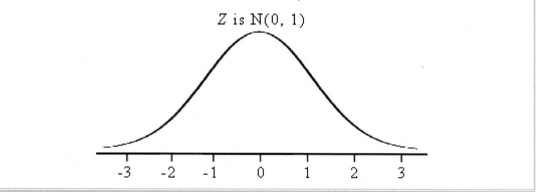

Z is N(0, 1)

-3   -2   -1   0   1   2   3

Tables have been constructed for finding probabilities associated with the Standard Normal distribution. So if we can convert *any* Normal distribution into the Standard Normal distribution, then we can use the table to find probabilities. The Standard Normal table can be found in the back of this textbook.

To convert any Normal distribution into the Standard Normal distribution, we need to introduce z-scores.

---

z-scores

If X is N(μ, σ), a z-score measures how many standard deviations a value of X is from the mean. A z-score is calculated as follows:

$$z = \frac{x - \mu}{\sigma}$$

In the example, we find the z-score for $x = 75$ by applying the formula:

$$z = \frac{x - \mu}{\sigma} = \frac{75 - 81}{4} = -1.50$$

The z-score is interpreted as follows: a grade of 75 points is 1.50 standard deviations to the left of the mean. This tells us that the area below 75 in the distribution of X is the same as the area below -1.50 in the Z distribution. Thus we have successfully converted the Normal distribution X to the Standard Normal distribution Z, as shown in Figure 4.14.

Figure 4.14

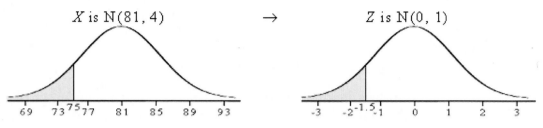

We can now use the Standard Normal table to find this area. Part of the table is shown below. It is important to understand that this table provides the areas *below* a given z-score. So, for example, the table shows that the area *below* $z = -1.50$ is 0.0668.

z	0.00	0.01	0.02	0.03	0.04	0.05	0.06	0.07	0.08	0.09
-2.0	0.0228	0.0222	0.0217	0.0212	0.0207	0.0202	0.0197	0.0192	0.0188	0.0183
-1.9	0.0287	0.0281	0.0274	0.0268	0.0262	0.0256	0.0250	0.0244	0.0239	0.0233
-1.8	0.0359	0.0351	0.0344	0.0336	0.0329	0.0322	0.0314	0.0307	0.0301	0.0294
-1.7	0.0446	0.0436	0.0427	0.0418	0.0409	0.0401	0.0392	0.0384	0.0375	0.0367
-1.6	0.0548	0.0537	0.0526	0.0516	0.0505	0.0495	0.0485	0.0475	0.0465	0.0455
-1.5	0.0668	0.0655	0.0643	0.0630	0.0618	0.0606	0.0594	0.0582	0.0571	0.0559
-1.4	0.0808	0.0793	0.0778	0.0764	0.0749	0.0735	0.0721	0.0708	0.0694	0.0681
-1.3	0.0968	0.0951	0.0934	0.0918	0.0901	0.0885	0.0869	0.0853	0.0838	0.0823

In other words,

$$P(Z < -1.50) = 0.0668$$

Since this is the area we are interested in, it corresponds to the probability that a student scores less than 75 on the psychology midterm, and hence,

$$P(X < 75) = 0.0668$$

Recall that we said that the Standard Normal table only provides the areas *below* the z-score. The area *above* the z-score can be found using the fact that the total area under the curve is equal to 1.

For example, what is be the probability a student scores *more* than 75 on the psychology midterm?

> **STOP AND THINK!**
>
> We know that the probability a student scores less than 75 is 0.0668. How does this help us?

We know that the area below 75 and the area above 75 must add to 1. Therefore, the probability that a student scores more than 75 on the psychology midterm can be found as follows:

$$P(X > 75) = 1 - 0.0668$$
$$= 0.9332$$

4.2.4   **FINDING PERCENTILES**

Suppose when Bob took the SAT, his score on the Math portion of the exam was at the 78th percentile. This means 78% of people scored lower than Bob on the Math-SAT. Although we know how Bob did in relation to other people, we do not know Bob's actual score. Similarly, if the doctor tells you that you are at the 60th percentile for your height, this means that 60% of people are *shorter* than you. In this section we discuss in general how to find the value of X that corresponds to a percentile.

> **Percentiles**
>
> If a value of X is the kth percentile, this means k% of the data is below X.

Now consider the Stanford-Binet IQ test, which is a common test for measuring IQ. Scores on this test are known to follow a Normal distribution with a mean of 100 and a standard deviation of 16. You take the test and are told you scored at the 87th percentile. How can we use this information to find your score?

The random variable of interest is:

X = Scores on the Stanford-Binet IQ test
X is N(100, 16)

> **STOP AND THINK!**
>
> What does it mean that your score is at the 87th percentile?

This means that 87% of people score *below* you. We can use this fact to find the z-score. Since 0.87 is the area *below z*, we can find the corresponding z-score by first finding the number closest to 0.8700 within the probabilities in the Standard

Normal table. Part of the table is shown below, and we can see that the closest probability to 0.8700 is 0.8708, which corresponds with $z = 1.13$.

z	0.00	0.01	0.02	0.03	0.04	0.05	0.06	0.07	0.08	0.09
0.7	0.7580	0.7611	0.7642	0.7673	0.7704	0.7734	0.7764	0.7794	0.7823	0.7852
0.8	0.7881	0.7910	0.7939	0.7967	0.7995	0.8023	0.8051	0.8078	0.8106	0.8133
0.9	0.8159	0.8186	0.8212	0.8238	0.8264	0.8289	0.8315	0.8340	0.8365	0.8389
1.0	0.8413	0.8438	0.8461	0.8485	0.8508	0.8531	0.8554	0.8577	0.8599	0.8621
1.1	0.8643	0.8665	0.8686	0.8708	0.8729	0.8749	0.8770	0.8790	0.8810	0.8830
1.2	0.8849	0.8869	0.8888	0.8907	0.8925	0.8944	0.8962	0.8980	0.8997	0.9015
1.3	0.9032	0.9049	0.9066	0.9082	0.9099	0.9115	0.9131	0.9147	0.9162	0.9177
1.4	0.9192	0.9207	0.9222	0.9236	0.9251	0.9265	0.9279	0.9292	0.9306	0.9319

So, $P(Z < 1.13) = 0.8708$, which is represented by the shaded area in Figure 4.15.

Figure 4.15

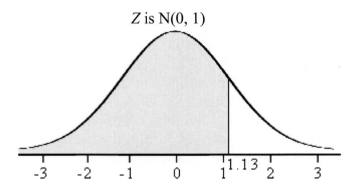

Z is N(0, 1)

Therefore, if you scored at the 87th percentile, this corresponds with a z-score of 1.13. To obtain your actual IQ score, use the formula for a z-score to solve for x.

$$z = \frac{x - \mu}{\sigma}$$

$$1.13 = \frac{x - 100}{16}$$

$$1.13(16) = x - 100$$

$$1.13(16) + 100 = x$$

$$118.08 = x$$

This means that you got a score of 118.08 on the Stanford-Binet IQ. Once again, we can see from Figure 4.16 that the value of X matches the z-score.

Figure 4.16

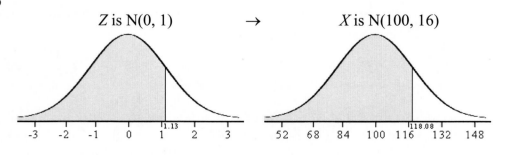

Z is N(0, 1)   → X is N(100, 16)

LESSON 4.2 EXERCISES
THE NORMAL DISTRIBUTION

For your convenience, you can print a copy of the Standard Normal table from the CD included with this textbook. The table is also available in the back of the textbook.

1. The fuel consumption (mpg) of a hybrid car follows a Normal distribution with a mean of 52 mpg and a standard deviation of 2.2 mpg.
   a) Define the random variable X.
   b) Draw the distribution of X.

2. Your dog Major always comes running to the kitchen whenever you open the refrigerator, in the hopes you will give him some cheese. Depending on where Major is in the house, the time it takes him to get to the kitchen once he hears the refrigerator open varies according to a Normal distribution with a mean of 4 seconds and a standard deviation of 1.2 seconds. What is the probability that it will take Major less than 2 seconds to get to the kitchen when you open the refrigerator door?

3. Reba and her husband Ray love taking their grandsons on camping trips. They always travel in their motor home, and the time it takes them to get to the campsite follows a Normal distribution, with a mean of 83 minutes and a standard deviation of 9 minutes. What percentage of their trips will take them over an hour?

4. The weight of newborn babies follows a Normal distribution with a mean of 7.5 pounds and a standard deviation of 0.6 pounds. When Noel was born, her weight was at the 69th percentile. How much did Noel weigh when she was born?

5. The amount of time college students spend sleeping per night varies according to a Normal distribution with a mean of 6.9 hours and a standard deviation of 0.8 hours. What percentage of college students sleep less than the recommended 8 hours each night?

6. Your chemistry final was very difficult. You earned 72% of the points on the test, and this score was the 94th percentile. Which of the following *has* to be true?
   A. You got 94 points on the test.
   B. Your score was higher than 94% of the other scores.
   C. You did better than 72% of people in the class.
   D. You got 72 points on the test.

ANSWERS
LESSON 4.2 EXERCISES
THE NORMAL DISTRIBUTION

Below are the answers to the exercises for Unit 4, Lesson 4.2.
For full solutions, please refer to the CD included with this textbook.

1. a) X = Fuel consumption (in mpg) of a hybrid car
    b)

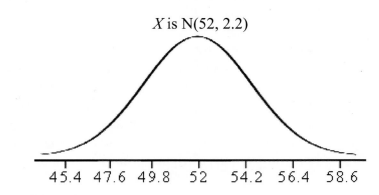

X is N(52, 2.2)

45.4 47.6 49.8 52 54.2 56.4 58.6

2. $P(X < 2) = 0.0475$

3. 99.48% of their trips will take them over an hour.

4. Noel weighed 7.8 pounds when she was born.

5. 91.62% of college students sleep less than the recommended 8 hours each night.

6. Choice B has to be true.

LESSON 4.3
MORE PRACTICE IN SOLVING CONTINUOUS DISTRIBUTION PROBLEMS

In this lesson we look at some more examples with full solutions. You are encouraged to work through these problems yourself if you need extra practice.

Example 1: Is the random variable discrete or continuous?
a) X = The time it takes for a mechanic to change the oil in your car
b) X = The annual rainfall in Santa Barbara
c) X = The number of penguins in Antarctica

> STOP AND THINK!
>
> **What is the difference between discrete and continuous random variables?**

Solution: a) If you wanted to know time it takes for a mechanic to change the oil in your car, you would use a clock to measure the time, so this is a *continuous random variable*.

Solution: b) If you wanted to know the annual rainfall in Santa Barbara you would use a range gauge to measure the amount of rain, so this is a *continuous random variable*.

Solution: c) You can count the number of penguins in Antarctica. The key word here is 'count', so this is a *discrete random variable*.

■

Example 2: Campbell Hall can be reserved for review classes for no more than 3 hours at a time. Some review classes are very short, (e.g. Advanced Human Sexuality) and some are very long (e.g. Statistics). From previous experience the bookings officer knows that X, the time of a review class, is Uniformly distributed and ranges from 0.5 hr to 3 hrs.

a) What is the probability that any review class lasts less than 1 hour?
b) What is the average length of a review class?

> **STOP AND THINK!**
>
> **Draw the distribution of X.**
>
> **Shade the area you are interested in.**
>
> **How can you find this area?**
>
> **How do you find the mean of X?**

Solution: a) We know the random variable X ranges from 0.5 to 3 and is Uniformly distributed. The base of the rectangle has a length of $3 - 0.5 = 2.5$, which means the height of the rectangle is $\frac{1}{2.5} = 0.4$. The distribution of X is shown below.

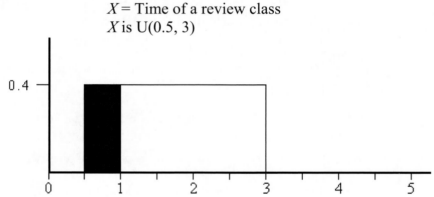

X = Time of a review class
X is U(0.5, 3)

The area of the shaded region is equal to the probability that the review class lasts less than 1 hour.

The base of this shaded area is $1 - 0.5 = 0.5$, so this area can be calculated as follows:

$$\text{Area of rectangle} = \text{base} \times \text{height}$$
$$= 0.5(0.4)$$
$$= 0.2$$

Therefore, the probability that any review class lasts less than 1 hour is 0.2.

Solution: b) To find the mean of a Uniform distribution, we can apply the formula:

$$\mu = \frac{b+a}{2} = \frac{3+0.5}{2} = 1.75$$

Example 3:   If X is Normally distributed with a mean of 20 and a standard deviation of 5, find:

   a) $P(X \le 10)$

   b) $P(X \ge 12)$

   c) $P(X \ge 22.5)$

> **STOP AND THINK!**
>
> **Draw the distribution of X.**
>
> **Shade the area you are interested in.**
>
> **How can you find this area?**

Solution: a) The graph below represents the distribution of X.   The shaded area is $P(X \le 10)$.

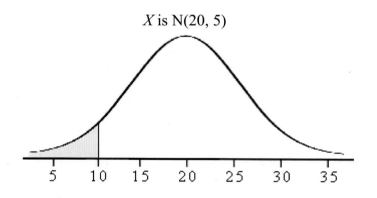

X is N(20, 5)

To find $P(X \le 10)$ we first need to convert the above Normal distribution into the Standard Normal distribution, then we can use the table to find the required probability. We do this by finding the z-score:

$$z = \frac{x - \mu}{\sigma} = \frac{10 - 20}{5} = -2$$

So asking for $P(X \le 10)$ is the same as asking for $P(Z \le -2)$, as shown in the figure below:

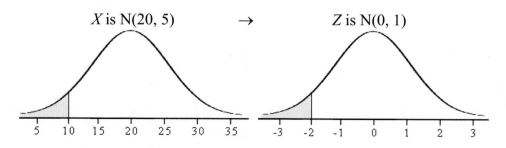

X is N(20, 5)   →   *Z is N(0, 1)*

Lesson 4.3: More Practice in Solving Continuous Distribution Problems

Using the Standard Normal table, we see that $P(Z \leq -2) = 0.0228$.

Therefore, $P(X \leq 10) = 0.0228$.

Solution: b) The distribution of X is shown below, with the shaded area representing $P(X \geq 12)$.

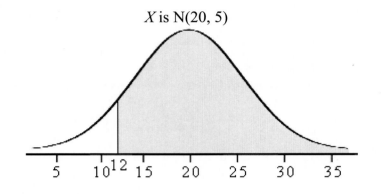

X is N(20, 5)

To find $P(X \geq 12)$, we find the z-score, then use the Standard Normal table.

$$z = \frac{x - \mu}{\sigma} = \frac{12 - 20}{5} = -1.6$$

So asking for $P(X \geq 12)$ is the same as asking for $P(Z \geq -1.6)$, as shown in the figure below:

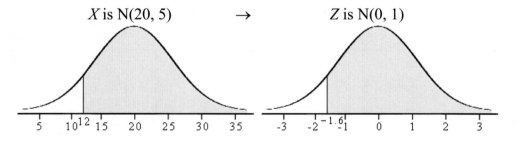

X is N(20, 5) $\rightarrow$ Z is N(0, 1)

Using the Standard Normal table gives $P(Z < -1.6) = 0.0548$. This is the area that is *not* shaded. The shaded area is:

$$P(Z \geq -1.6) = 1 - P(Z < -1.6) = 1 - 0.0548 = 0.9452$$

So, $P(X \geq 12) = 0.9452$

Solution: c) The distribution of X is shown below, with the shaded area representing $P(X \geq 22.5)$.

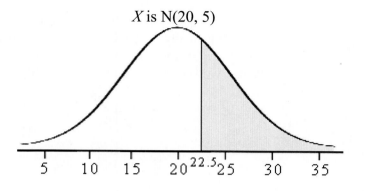

X is N(20, 5)

To find $P(X \geq 22.5)$, we find the z-score, then use the Standard Normal table.

$$z = \frac{x - \mu}{\sigma} = \frac{22.5 - 20}{5} = 0.5$$

So asking for $P(X \geq 22.5)$ is the same as asking for $P(Z \geq 0.5)$, as shown in the figure below:

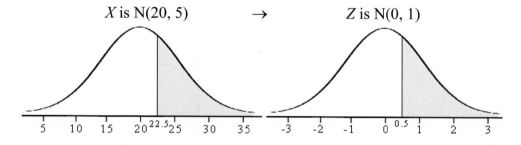

Using the Standard Normal table gives $P(Z < 0.5) = 0.6915$. This is the area that is *not* shaded. The shaded area is:

$$P(Z \geq 0.5) = 1 - P(Z < 0.5) = 1 - 0.6915 = 0.3085$$

So, $P(X \geq 22.5) = 0.3085$

Example 4: If X is Normally distributed with a mean of 20 and a standard deviation of 5, find x such that:
a) $P(X \leq x) = 0.5793$
b) $P(X \geq x) = 0.0409$
c) $P(X \geq x) = 0.5$

STOP AND THINK!

You have been given an area and are asked to find x. How can you use this information to find x?

Solution: a) *X* is N(20, 5). We are told that there is some value *x* such that the area *below* *x* is 0.5793. So the area *below z* is 0.5793, and we look this up in the Standard Normal table.   Looking for the number closest to 0.5793 within the probabilities, we see that it corresponds with $z = 0.20$, as shown below.

z	0.00	0.01	0.02	0.03	0.04	0.05	0.06	0.07	0.08	0.09
0.0	0.5000	0.5040	0.5080	0.5120	0.5160	0.5199	0.5239	0.5279	0.5319	0.5359
0.1	0.5398	0.5438	0.5478	0.5517	0.5557	0.5596	0.5636	0.5675	0.5714	0.5753
0.2	0.5793	0.5832	0.5871	0.5910	0.5948	0.5987	0.6026	0.6064	0.6103	0.6141
0.3	0.6179	0.6217	0.6255	0.6293	0.6331	0.6368	0.6406	0.6443	0.6480	0.6517
0.4	0.6554	0.6591	0.6628	0.6664	0.6700	0.6736	0.6772	0.6808	0.6844	0.6879

This tells us that $P(Z \le 0.20) = 0.5793$, which is represented by the shaded area below.

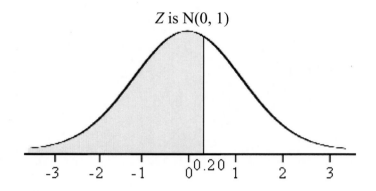

To obtain the value of *x*, use the formula for a *z*-score to solve for *x*.

$$z = \frac{x - \mu}{\sigma}$$

$$0.20 = \frac{x - 20}{5}$$

$$0.20(5) = x - 20$$

$$0.20(5) + 20 = x$$

$$21 = x$$

We can see that this value of *x* does match the *z*-score of 0.20.

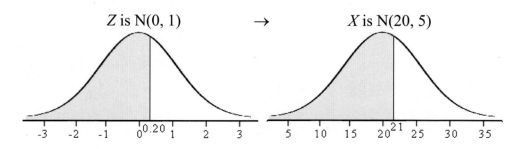

b) X is N(20, 5). We are told that there is some value x such that the area *above* x is 0.0409. This means that the area *above z* is 0.0409. To use the Standard Normal table, we must look up the area *below z*, so the area we should look up is $z = 1 - 0.0409 = 0.9591$. Looking for the number closest to 0.9591 within the probabilities, we see that the it corresponds with $z = 1.74$, as shown below.

z	0.00	0.01	0.02	0.03	0.04	0.05	0.06	0.07	0.08	0.09
1.5	0.9332	0.9345	0.9357	0.9370	0.9382	0.9394	0.9406	0.9418	0.9429	0.9441
1.6	0.9452	0.9463	0.9474	0.9484	0.9495	0.9505	0.9515	0.9525	0.9535	0.9545
1.7	0.9554	0.9564	0.9573	0.9582	0.9591	0.9599	0.9608	0.9616	0.9625	0.9633
1.8	0.9641	0.9649	0.9656	0.9664	0.9671	0.9678	0.9686	0.9693	0.9699	0.9706
1.9	0.9713	0.9719	0.9726	0.9732	0.9738	0.9744	0.9750	0.9756	0.9761	0.9767

So $P(Z \geq 1.74) = 0.9591$, which is represented by the shaded area shown below.

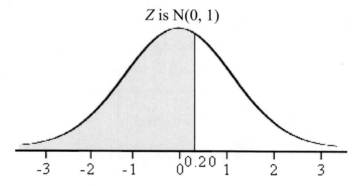

To obtain the value of x, use the formula for a z-score to solve for x.

$$z = \frac{x - \mu}{\sigma}$$

$$1.74 = \frac{x - 20}{5}$$

$$1.74(5) = x - 20$$

$$1.74(5) + 20 = x$$

$$28.7 = x$$

We see that this value of x does match the z-score of 1.74.

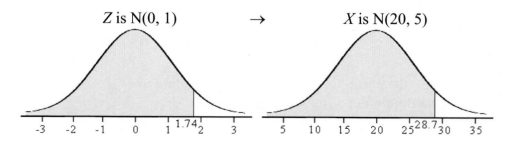

c) We are told that P($X \geq x$) = 0.5, the area *above* x is 0.5, and therefore, the area *below* x must also be 0.5. One of the properties of the Normal distribution is that half the area is above the mean and half is below the mean. Therefore, we can deduce that the required value is the mean, so $x = 20$.

◼

Example 5: The time it takes you to ride your bike to school varies according to a Normal distribution with a mean of 8 minutes and a standard deviation of 1.2 minutes. What is the probability that the time it takes you to ride your bike to school is between 5 and 10 minutes?

> **STOP AND THINK!**
>
> **Define the random variable X.**
>
> **Draw the distribution of X.**
>
> **Shade the area you are interested in.**
>
> **How can you find this area?**

Solution: The random variable of interest is:

$$X = \text{Time it takes you to ride your bike to school}$$

The distribution of X is:

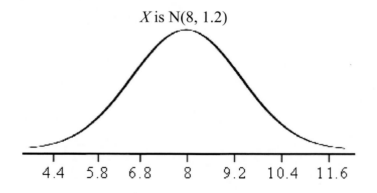

X is N(8, 1.2)

4.4   5.8   6.8   8   9.2   10.4   11.6

We want to find the probability that it takes you between 5 and 10 minutes to ride your bike to school. In other words, we are looking for:

$$P(5 < X < 10)$$

We represent this probability by shading the area between 5 and 10 in the distribution of X, as shown below:

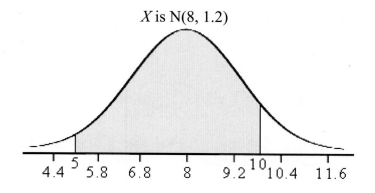

X is N(8, 1.2)

We will need to compute a z-score for both $X = 5$ and $X = 10$.

$$z = \frac{x - \mu}{\sigma} = \frac{5 - 8}{1.2} = -2.50$$

$$z = \frac{x - \mu}{\sigma} = \frac{10 - 8}{1.2} = 1.67$$

So, the area between 5 and 10 in the distribution of X is the same as the area between -2.50 and 1.67 in the Z distribution, as shown below:

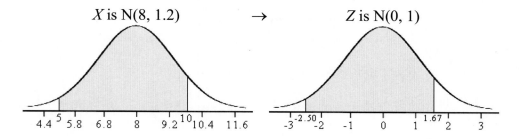

X is N(8, 1.2) $\rightarrow$ Z is N(0, 1)

Once we have computed the z-scores, we can look them up in the Standard Normal table. Remember, the Standard Normal table gives the area *below* the z-score. So when we look up $z = 1.67$, the table indicates that the area *below* 1.67 is 0.9525. Likewise, when we look up $z = -2.50$, the table indicates that the area *below* -2.50 is 0.0062.

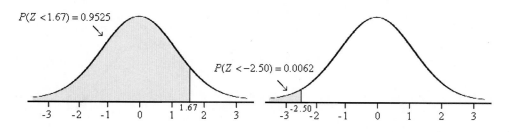

$P(Z < 1.67) = 0.9525$

$P(Z < -2.50) = 0.0062$

We can get the area in between -2.50 and 1.67 by subtracting the two areas from each other:

$$P(-2.50 < Z < 1.67) = P(Z < 1.67) - P(Z < -2.50)$$
$$= 0.9525 - 0.0062$$
$$= 0.9463$$

Therefore, $P(5 < X < 10) = 0.9463$.

So, the probability is 0.9463 that it takes you between 5 and 10 minutes to ride your bike to school.

■

Example 6:   The amount of gas people purchase when they fill up at a gas station varies according to a Normal distribution, with a mean of 14.6 gallons and a variance of 2.25 gallons. What percent of people purchase more than 15 gallons when they fill up?

> **STOP AND THINK!**
>
> **Define the random variable X.**
>
> **Draw the distribution of X.**
>
> **Shade the area you are interested in.**
>
> **How can you find this area?**

Solution: The random variable of interest is:

X = Amount of gas people purchase when they fill up at a gas station

X is Normal, with a mean of 14.6 and a *variance* of 2.25. To find probabilities about X, we need the mean and the *standard deviation*. Recall that we compute the standard deviation by taking the square-root of the variance. Thus, the standard deviation is:

$$\sigma = \sqrt{2.25} = 1.5$$

So, the distribution of X is:

X is N(14.6, 1.5)

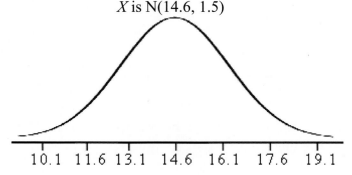

10.1   11.6   13.1   14.6   16.1   17.6   19.1

We want to know what percent of people purchase more than 15 gallons when they fill up. First we find the probability:

$$P(X > 15)$$

This probability is represented by shading the area *above* 15, as shown below:

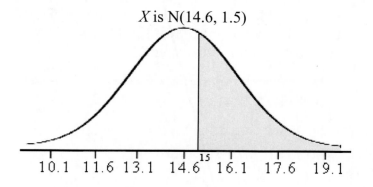

We will need to compute a *z*-score for *x* = 15.

$$z = \frac{x - \mu}{\sigma} = \frac{15 - 14.6}{1.5} = 0.27$$

So the area above 15 in the distribution of *X* is the same as the area above 0.27 in the *Z* distribution, as shown below:

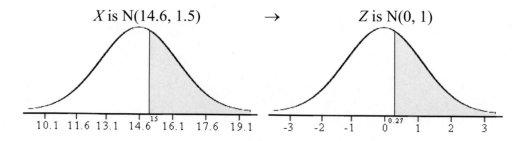

Once we have computed the *z*-score, we can look it up in the Standard Normal table. Remember that the Standard Normal table gives the area *below* the *z*-score. So when we look up *z* = 0.27, the table indicates that the area *below* 0.27 is 0.6064. This is the area that is *not* shaded. We find the shaded area using the idea of complements:

$$P(Z > 0.27) = 1 - P(Z < 0.27)$$
$$= 1 - 0.6064$$
$$= 0.3936$$

Therefore, $P(X > 15) = 0.3936$

This tells us that the probability is 0.3936 that someone will purchase more than 15 gallons of gas when they fill up. Hence, 39.36% of people will purchase more than 15 gallons when they fill up.

■

Example 7:   Lauren and Joe are looking for a one-bedroom apartment to rent in the Bay area. Suppose rents for such apartments in the area follow a Normal distribution with a mean of $1050 and a standard deviation of $90. If Lauren and Joe are hoping to find a place with rent between $1000 and $1100, what percentage of one-bedroom apartments fit this price range?

STOP AND THINK!

Define the random variable X.

Draw the distribution of X.

Shade the area you are interested in.

How can you find this area?

Solution: The random variable of interest is:

$$X = \text{Rent of a one-bedroom apartment in the Bay area}$$

The distribution of X is:

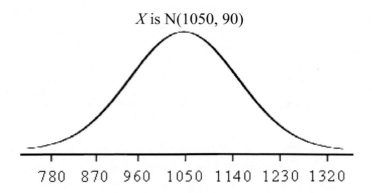

X is N(1050, 90)

780   870   960   1050   1140   1230   1320

We want to find the percent of one-bedroom apartments that Lauren and Joe can find that cost between $1000 and $1100. We can find the percent by first finding the probability:

$$P(1000 < X < 1100)$$

We can represent this probability by shading the area between 1000 and 1100 in the distribution of X, as shown below:

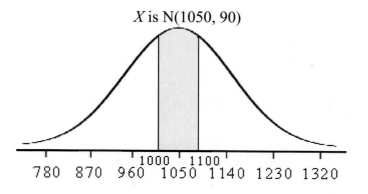

We will need to compute a z-score for both $X = 1000$ and $X = 1100$.

$$z = \frac{x - \mu}{\sigma} = \frac{1000 - 1050}{90} = -0.56$$

$$z = \frac{x - \mu}{\sigma} = \frac{1100 - 1050}{90} = 0.56$$

The area between 1000 and 1100 in the distribution of X is the same as the area between -0.56 and 0.56 in the Z distribution, as shown below:

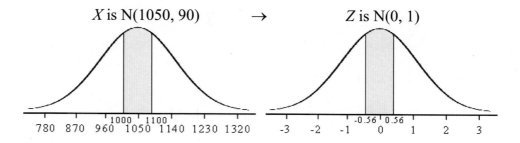

Once we have computed the z-scores, we can look them up in the Standard Normal table. Remember that the Standard Normal table gives the area *below* the z-score. So when we look up $z = 0.56$, the table indicates that the area *below* 0.56 is 0.7123. Likewise, when we look up $z = -0.56$, the table indicates that the area *below* -0.56 is 0.2877.

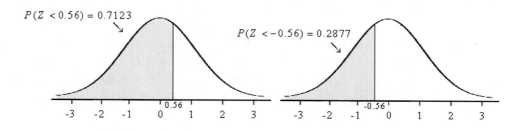

We can get the area in between -0.56 and 0.56 by subtracting the two areas from each other:

$$P(-0.56 < Z < 0.56) = P(Z < 0.56) - P(Z < -0.56)$$
$$= 0.7123 - 0.2877$$
$$= 0.4246$$

Therefore, $P(1000 < X < 1100) = 0.4246$

So the probability that Lauren and Joe find a one-bedroom apartment between $1000 and $1100 is 0.4246. Hence, 42.46% of the one-bedroom apartments in the Bay area cost between $1000 and $1100.

◾

Example 8:   Your biology professor announces to the class that if you want an A in the class, your final grade must be at the 80th percentile or higher. If the grades in this biology class follow a Normal distribution with a mean of 62 and a standard deviation of 7, what is the lowest grade you can earn if you want an A in the class?

STOP AND THINK!

Define the random variable X.

You have been given an area and are asked to find x. How can you use this information to find x?

Solution: The random variable of interest is:

$$X = \text{Grades in your biology class}$$

The distribution of X is N(62, 7)

We want to find the lowest grade you can earn if you want an A in the class, and we are told that you need to be at the 80th percentile or higher if you want an A. This means that the lowest A is the 80th percentile, and that 80% of the class will earn *less* than an A. We can use this probability to find the z-score that corresponds, and use that z-score to find x.

Since 0.8 is the area *below z*, when you go to the Standard Normal table, you will look for the number closest to 0.8000 within the probabilities, and then see the z-score that corresponds. Part of the table is shown below, and we can see that the closest probability to 0.8000 is 0.7995. This corresponds with $z = 0.84$.

z	0.00	0.01	0.02	0.03	0.04	0.05	0.06	0.07	0.08	0.09
0.6	0.7257	0.7291	0.7324	0.7357	0.7389	0.7422	0.7454	0.7486	0.7517	0.7549
0.7	0.7580	0.7611	0.7642	0.7673	0.7704	0.7734	0.7764	0.7794	0.7823	0.7852
0.8	0.7881	0.7910	0.7939	0.7967	0.7995	0.8023	0.8051	0.8078	0.8106	0.8133
0.9	0.8159	0.8186	0.8212	0.8238	0.8264	0.8289	0.8315	0.8340	0.8365	0.8389

This tells us that $P(Z < 0.84) = 0.7995$, which is represented by the shaded area below.

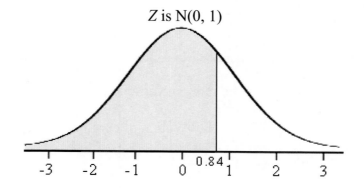

Z is N(0, 1)

In other words, if you scored at the 80th percentile, this corresponds with a z-score of 0.84. To obtain the grade you need for an A, you can use the formula for a z-score to solve for x.

$$z = \frac{x - \mu}{\sigma}$$

$$0.84 = \frac{x - 62}{7}$$

$$0.84(7) = x - 62$$

$$0.84(7) + 62 = x$$

$$67.88 = x$$

This tells us that if you scored at the 80th percentile, you got a score of 67.88 in your Biology class. We can see that this value of x does match the z-score of 0.84.

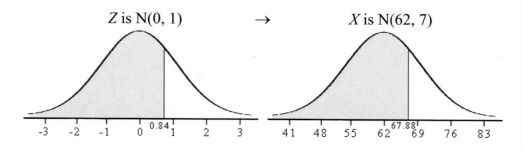

Z is N(0, 1)   →   X is N(62, 7)

This means that to get an A, you need to get at least a 67.88 in the class.

Example 9: Suppose for a certain breed of dwarf rabbits, their weights vary according to a Normal distribution with a mean of 4.2 pounds and a standard deviation of 0.3 pounds. Nibbles is a dwarf rabbit of this particular breed. If 91% of this breed weigh more than Nibbles, how much does Nibbles weigh?

Solution: We can define the random variable:

$$X = \text{Weight of certain breed of dwarf rabbits}$$

The distribution of X is N(4.2, 0.3)

We want to find out how much Nibbles weighs if 91% of dwarf rabbits of her breed weigh *more* than her. This means that 9% of her breed of dwarf rabbits weigh *less* than her. Since the Standard Normal table provides the area *below z*, the probability we want to look up is 0.09 rather than 0.91. So, we must find the probability closest to 0.0900 in the table and see what z-score corresponds.

An excerpt from the table is shown below, and we can see that the closest probability to 0.0900 is 0.0901. This corresponds with $z = -1.34$.

z	0.00	0.01	0.02	0.03	0.04	0.05	0.06	0.07	0.08	0.09
-1.6	0.0548	0.0537	0.0526	0.0516	0.0505	0.0495	0.0485	0.0475	0.0465	0.0455
-1.5	0.0668	0.0655	0.0643	0.0630	0.0618	0.0606	0.0594	0.0582	0.0571	0.0559
-1.4	0.0808	0.0793	0.0778	0.0764	0.0749	0.0735	0.0721	0.0708	0.0694	0.0681
-1.3	0.0968	0.0951	0.0934	0.0918	0.0901	0.0885	0.0869	0.0853	0.0838	0.0823
-1.2	0.1151	0.1131	0.1112	0.1093	0.1075	0.1056	0.1038	0.1020	0.1003	0.0985
-1.1	0.1357	0.1335	0.1314	0.1292	0.1271	0.1251	0.1230	0.1210	0.1190	0.1170

So $P(Z < -1.34) = 0.0901$, which is represented by the shaded area below.

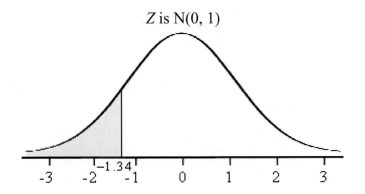

Z is N(0, 1)

In other words, 9% of the area in the z distribution is below -1.34, which means that 91% of the area lies above this point. To find out how much Nibbles weighs, you can use the formula for a z-score to solve for x.

$$z = \frac{x - \mu}{\sigma}$$

$$-1.34 = \frac{x - 4.2}{0.3}$$

$$-1.34(0.3) = x - 4.2$$

$$-1.34(0.3) + 4.2 = x$$

$$3.798 = x$$

This means 9% of this breed of dwarf rabbits weigh *less* than 3.798 pounds. Therefore, 91% weigh *more* than 3.798 pounds. We can see that this value of x does match the z-score of -1.34.

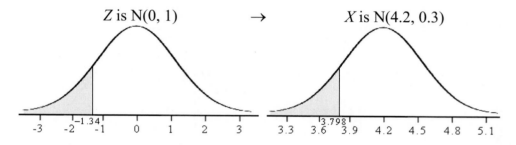

Therefore, Nibbles weighs 3.798 pounds.

![black square]

Example 10: Daily high temperatures in Santa Barbara follow a Normal distribution with a mean of $70°$ and a standard deviation of $3°$. If today's daily high temperature in Santa Barbara was at the 43rd percentile, what was the temperature?

STOP AND THINK!

Define the random variable X.

You have been given an area and are asked to find x. How can you use this information to find x?

Solution: The random variable of interest is:

$$X = \text{Daily high temperature in Santa Barbara}$$

The distribution of X is N(70, 3)

We want to know what today's daily high temperature was if we know it was at the 43rd percentile. This means 43% of the daily high temperatures in Santa Barbara are *lower* than today's. We can use this probability to find the z-score that corresponds, and use that z-score to find x.

Since 0.43 is the area *below z,* when you go to the Standard Normal table, you will look for the number closest to 0.4300 within the probabilities, and then see the *z*-score that corresponds. Part of the table is shown below, and we can see that the closest probability to 0.4300 is 0.4286. This corresponds with $z = -0.18$.

z	0.00	0.01	0.02	0.03	0.04	0.05	0.06	0.07	0.08	0.09
-0.4	0.3446	0.3409	0.3372	0.3336	0.3300	0.3264	0.3228	0.3192	0.3156	0.3121
-0.3	0.3821	0.3783	0.3745	0.3707	0.3669	0.3632	0.3594	0.3557	0.3520	0.3483
-0.2	0.4207	0.4168	0.4129	0.4090	0.4052	0.4013	0.3974	0.3936	0.3897	0.3859
-0.1	0.4602	0.4562	0.4522	0.4483	0.4443	0.4404	0.4364	0.4325	0.4286	0.4247
-0.0	0.5000	0.4960	0.4920	0.4880	0.4840	0.4801	0.4761	0.4721	0.4681	0.4641

This tells us that $P(Z < -0.18) = 0.4286$, which is represented by the shaded area below.

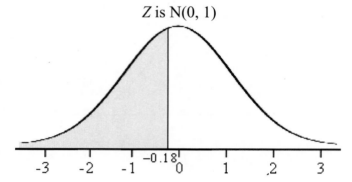

In other words, if today's high temperature is at the 43rd percentile, this corresponds with a *z*-score of –0.18. To obtain today's high temperature, you can use the formula for a *z*-score to solve for *x.*

$$z = \frac{x - \mu}{\sigma}$$

$$-0.18 = \frac{x - 70}{3}$$

$$-0.18(3) = x - 70$$

$$-0.18(3) + 70 = x$$

$$69.46 = x$$

So, if today's high temperature is at the 43rd percentile, then today's high temperature was 69.46. We can see that this value of *x* does match the *z*-score of –0.18.

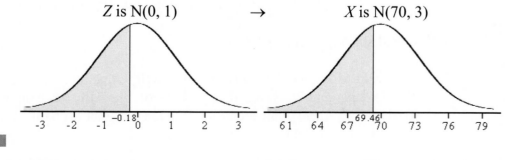

LESSON 4.3 EXERCISES
MORE PRACTICE IN SOLVING CONTINUOUS DISTRIBUTION PROBLEMS

1. In which of the following experiments will the random variable of interest be discrete and which continuous?
   a) Measuring the time it takes to see patients at a dental surgery.
   b) Weighing the freight carried by a train.
   c) Conducting a survey on the weight of newborns.
   d) Conducting a survey to find out how many donuts each American eats each day.

2. You are interviewing for a job at a company where interviews can be scheduled anytime between 9am and 12 noon. The times are Uniformly distributed. What is the probability that you will be interviewed:
   a) between 10am and 11 am?
   b) between 9 am and 9:30 am?
   c) later than 11am?

3. After the statistics lecture, students usually come up and ask questions. This takes between 0 minutes (if there are no questions) and 10 minutes. The times are Uniformly distributed. What is the probability that the time it takes answering questions is:
   a) between 0 and 3 minutes?
   b) more than 5 minutes?
   c) fewer than 4 minutes?

4. The height of adult males varies according to a Normal distribution with a mean of 69 inches and a standard deviation of 2.5 inches. Lindsay is 70 inches tall and will only date men who are taller than she is. What percentage of men are too short for Lindsay?

5. Al and Mona love to watch the Angels, a professional baseball team. Suppose the duration of an Angels game follows a Normal distribution with a mean of 168 minutes and a standard deviation of 4 minutes. When a game is televised, the television network allows 3 hours (180 minutes) for the game. What is the probability that Al and Mona watch an Angels game that runs over the allotted time?

ANSWERS
LESSON 4.3 EXERCISES
MORE PRACTICE IN SOLVING CONTINUOUS DISTRIBUTION PROBLEMS

Below are the answers to the exercises for Unit 4, Lesson 4.3.
For full solutions, please refer to the CD included with this textbook.

1. a) 'X = The time it takes to see patients at a dental surgery' is continuous.
    b) 'X = The weight of the freight carried by a train' is continuous.
    c) 'X = The weight of newborns' is continuous.
    d) 'X = How many donuts each American eats each day' is discrete.

2. a) $P(10 < X < 11) = \dfrac{1}{3}$

    b) $P(9 < X < 9.5) = \dfrac{1}{6}$

    c) $P(X > 11) = \dfrac{1}{3}$

3. a) $P(0 < X < 3) = 0.3$
    b) $P(X > 5) = 0.5$
    c) $P(X < 4) = 0.4$

4. 65.54% of men are too short for Lindsay

5. $P(X > 180) = 0.0013$

AVOIDING COMMON MISTAKES

☺ Remember that all probabilities are between 0 and 1.

☺ For a Uniform distribution ranging from *a* to *b*, remember that the height of the rectangle is:

$$\frac{1}{b-a}$$

☺ Remember that the Standard Normal table *only* provides the areas *below z-scores*.

☺ To find the area *between* two *z*-scores, look up both *z*-scores in the Standard Normal table and subtract the smaller area from the larger.

☺ To compute *z*-scores you need the standard deviation, not the variance. If you are given the variance, take the square-root of it to get the standard deviation.

☺ For a Normal distribution a percentile is the area *below z* and so this is the area you should look up in the Standard Normal table.

☺ For the Normal distribution, if you are given a percentage, you must determine whether it is the area *above* or *below z*. Then look up the area *below* in the Standard Normal table.

UNIT 4 SUMMARY

- The area under any density curve must equal 1. The Uniform distribution and the Normal distribution are both examples of density curves.

- X is U(a, b) means that X is a Uniform random variable whose values range from a to b.

- If X is U(a, b), then the distribution of X looks like this:

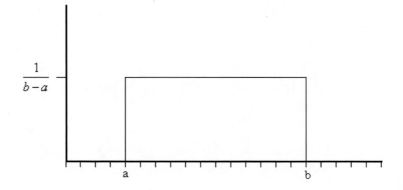

- If X is U(a, b), the mean of X is:

$$\mu = \frac{b+a}{2}$$

- X is N(μ, σ) means that X is a Normal random variable with a mean of μ and a standard deviation of σ.

- If X is N(μ, σ), the distribution of X looks like this:

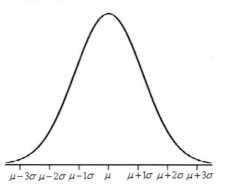

The mean is at the peak and most of the data (over 99%) is within three standard deviations from the mean.

- If X is N(μ, σ), you can find probabilities by computing a z-score:

$$z = \frac{x - \mu}{\sigma}$$

- You can also use the Normal distribution to find percentiles.

SELF-ASSESSMENT QUIZ

1. In which of the following experiments will the random variable of interest be discrete and which continuous?
   a) Counting the number of ice plants in a square meter of Ellwood Bluffs
   b) Recording the annual depth of snow on the summit of Mammoth Mountain.
   c) Conducting a survey to find out how many dogs are adopted in California each year.
   d) A balloon seller measures the volume of helium required to fill their standard sized balloons.

2. A continuous random variable X is Uniformly distributed from 30 to 70.
   a) What is the probability that X is greater than 60?
   b) What is the probability that X is less than 45?
   c) What is the mean of X?

3. The height of tides at a certain beach are Normally distributed with a mean of 2.5 meters and a standard deviation of 0.5 meter. Find the probability that the height of a chosen tide will be:
   a) greater than 2.8 meters?
   b) less than 1.3 meters?
   c) between 1.5 meters and 2.1 meters?

4. If X is Normally distributed with a mean of 130 and a standard deviation of 45 find:
   a) $P(X \leq 100)$
   b) $P(X \geq 220)$
   c) $P(150 \leq X \leq 205)$

5. The heights of adult Weimaraner dogs are Normally distributed with a mean of 65 cm and a standard deviation of 1.3 cm.
   a) What percentage of Weimaraner dogs are taller than 66 cm?
   b) Lucky is a Weimaraner dog whose at the 10th percentile in heights. How tall is Lucky?

ANSWERS

SELF-ASSESSMENT QUIZ

Below are the answers to the exercises for Unit 4, Self-Assessment Quiz. For full solutions, please refer to the CD included with this textbook.

1. a) 'X = The number of ice plants in a square meter of Ellwood Bluffs' is discrete.
   b) 'X = The annual depth of snow on the summit of Mammoth Mountain' is continuous.
   c) 'X = How many dogs are adopted in California each year' is discrete.
   d) 'X = The volume of helium required to fill their standard sized balloons' is continuous.

2. a) $P(X > 60) = 0.25$
   b) $P(X < 45) = 0.375$
   c) $\mu = 50$

3. a) $P(X > 2.8) = 0.2743$
   b) $P(X < 1.3) = 0.0082$
   c) $P(1.5 < X < 2.1) = 0.1891$

4. a) $P(X \leq 100) = 0.2514$
   b) $P(X \geq 220) = 0.0228$
   c) $P(150 \leq X \leq 205) = 0.2825$

5. a) 22.06% of Weimaraner dogs are taller than 66 cm.
   b) Lucky is 63.336 cm tall.

UNIT 5
SAMPLE STATISTICS

Lesson 5.1   Descriptive Statistics
Exercises for Lesson 5.1
Answers to Exercises for Lesson 5.1

Lesson 5.2   Sample Statistics as Random Variables
Exercises for Lesson 5.2
Answers to Exercises for Lesson 5.2

Lesson 5.3   More Practice in Solving Sample
Statistics Problems
Exercises for Lesson 5.3
Answers to Exercises for Lesson 5.3

Avoiding Common Mistakes
Unit 5 Summary
Self-Assessment Quiz
Answers to Self-Assessment Quiz

LESSON 5.1
DESCRIPTIVE STATISTICS

5.1.1   **INTRODUCTION**
In Units 1-4 we studied probability; we now turn our attention to statistics. There are two main branches of statistics; descriptive statistics and inferential statistics and we will consider each in turn. In the study of descriptive statistics we learn how to produce useful and informative numerical summaries of data. Additionally, we learn to interpret graphical summaries of data. By gathering data and analyzing it using the techniques of inferential statistics, we are able to draw interesting conclusions about entire populations.

5.1.2   **POPULATION AND SAMPLE**
The terms 'population' and 'sample' have a very specific meaning in statistics. The population is the entire group that you are interested in studying. It does not have to be a population of people. For example, suppose you are interested in studying the incidence of bubonic plague in squirrels in California. The population of interest is 'all squirrels in California'. Since it is not possible to test *all* the squirrels in California for bubonic plague, you test a sample or small group of them. A sample is simply a subset of the population.

Population versus Sample

A *population* is the entire group you are interested in studying.
A *sample* is the subset of the population that you actually study.

Example: You work for a wildlife tour operator on Kodiak Island in Alaska. You are interested in the percentage of visitors to the island who go on bear watching trips. You conduct a survey in which you ask 3000 visitors to Kodiak Island whether they went on a bear watching trip. Eight hundred of them said yes.

Question 1
Identify the population.

Solution: The population is *everyone* we are interested in studying. We are interested in *all* visitors to Kodiak Island. Therefore, the population of interest is *all* the visitors to Kodiak Island.

> **Question 2**
> Identify the sample.

Solution: The sample is the subset of the population we actually studied. In this case, the sample consists of the 3000 visitors to Kodiak Island who were asked whether they went on a bear watching trip.

■

Now suppose we are interested in the mean GPA of all UCSB undergraduates. To study this, we interview 500 UCSB undergraduates and ask them their GPA.

> **STOP AND THINK!**
>
> **What is the population?**
>
> **What is the sample?**

The population is 'all UCSB undergraduates', and the sample is 'the 500 UCSB undergraduates that were interviewed'.

Consider another example in which we are interested in the percentage of UCSB undergraduates that are female. We survey 100 UCSB undergraduates and inquire about their gender.

> **STOP AND THINK!**
>
> **What is the population?**
>
> **What is the sample?**

The population is 'all UCSB undergraduates', and the sample is ' the 100 UCSB undergraduates that were surveyed'.

5.1.3   SAMPLE STATISTICS

We have been discussing sample data. From sample data we calculate statistics, which measure some characteristic of the sample. Before turning our attention to these calculations, we need to distinguish between two different kinds of data; qualitative and quantitative. It is important to draw this distinction because different statistical procedures apply to each.

Qualitative versus Quantitative

Qualitative data are non-numerical.

Quantitative data are numerical.

Example: Consider a study in which information is collected on people's gender.

Question

Is gender a qualitative or quantitative variable?

Solution: If people are asked their gender, they will say 'male' or 'female'. This means that gender is *qualitative* because the data are non-numerical.

■

Example: Consider a study in which information is collected on how many DVD's people own.

Question

Is how many DVD's people own a qualitative or quantitative variable?

Solution: If we ask people how many DVD's they own, they will tell us a number. This means that how many DVD's people own is *quantitative* because the data are numerical.

■

If data is qualitative, a useful statistic that we can calculate is the sample proportion. In Unit 3, we discussed the Binomial distribution, which is defined by the number of trials and the probability of a success *p*. Recall from Unit 1 that probabilities are proportions, so *p* is a population proportion. We now turn our attention to the proportion we observe in a sample; this is denoted $\hat{p}$.

Sample Proportion

The symbol for a sample proportion is $\hat{p}$, read 'p-hat'.

A sample proportion is computed by dividing the number of successes *x* by the number of trials *n*.

$$\hat{p} = \frac{x}{n}$$

Example: In a survey of 1000 climbers reaching Everest base camp, 300 said they had suffered from some degree of high-altitude sickness.

> ## Question 1
> What is the proportion of those who suffered from some degree of high-altitude sickness?

Solution: We wish to calculate the sample proportion, which is denoted by $\hat{p}$:

$$\hat{p} = \frac{x}{n} = \frac{300}{1000} = 0.3$$

> ## Question 2
> If a climber is selected at random, what is the probability that she suffered from some degree of high-altitude sickness?

Solution: Since the proportion of those who suffer from some degree of high-altitude sickness is 0.3, this means the probability is 0.3.

■

If the data are quantitative, several different statistics can be calculated that will describe or summarize the sample data. We may wish to describe the center of the data and the spread of the data. We will first discuss the three measures of center.

> ## Measures of Center
> There are three measures of center: the *sample mean*, the *median*, and the *mode*.

We now discuss each of these three measures of center in turn, starting with the sample mean.

> ## Sample Mean
> The symbol for the sample mean is $\overline{x}$, read 'x-bar'.
>
> The sample mean is computed by adding up all the data and dividing by the sample size *n*.
>
> $$\overline{x} = \frac{\displaystyle\sum_{\text{for all x}} x}{n}$$

Example: You ask 5 men how tall they are and you get the following data, in inches:

$$68 \quad 72 \quad 69 \quad 73 \quad 66$$

> **Question**
> What is the sample mean height of the men?

Solution: The sample mean is found by adding the five heights together and dividing by 5:

$$\bar{x} = \frac{\sum\limits_{\text{for all x}} x}{n} = \frac{68 + 72 + 69 + 73 + 66}{5} = 69.6$$

So the average height of the 5 men sampled is 69.6 inches.

The second measure of center we will discuss is the median.

> **Median**
> The median is the middle number of an ordered data set.
> To find the median, first put the data in increasing order.
> If the sample size is odd, the median is the exact middle number.
> If the sample size is even, there will be 2 middle numbers, and the median is the average of these two middle numbers.

The median is always a good measure of center because it is not influenced by *outliers* – values that are much smaller or larger than the majority of the data. Since the median is in the middle of the data, it is not affected by extreme values. The sample mean, on the other hand, is calculated using all the values in the data, so it is easily affected by outliers.

Example: You ask 7 college students how old they are and get the following data:

$$18 \quad 19 \quad 21 \quad 39 \quad 18 \quad 20 \quad 19$$

> **Question 1**
> What is the mean age of the sample?

Solution: The sample mean is:

$$\bar{x} = \frac{\displaystyle\sum_{\text{for all } x} x}{n} = \frac{18+19+21+39+18+20+19}{7} = 22$$

Question 2
What is the median age of the sample?

Solution: The median is found by first putting the data in order, then finding the middle number:

18   18   19 $\boxed{19}$ 20   21   39

Since we have an odd number of data points, the median is the middle number:

Median = 19

Notice that the mean and median differ in value. Even though there are 'returning' students in college who are older than the norm, the majority of students are between 18 and 21, and so a good measure of center should indicate that. When we include the 39 year old, the mean of the data is 22, which is 3 years older than the median age. This is because the outlying value of 39 influences the mean, making it bigger than the median. The median is not influenced by the outlying value of 39, and remains in within the range of the majority of the data.

Suppose we remove the outlying value, so that we only have 6 data points as follows:

18   18   19   19   20   21

STOP AND THINK!

Does removing the outlier affect the sample mean?

Does removing the outlier affect the median?

The sample mean of this data set is:

$$\bar{x} = \frac{\displaystyle\sum_{\text{for all } x} x}{n} = \frac{18+18+19+19+20+21}{6} = 19.167$$

The median of this data set is the average of the two middle numbers:

$$18 \quad 18 \quad \boxed{19 \quad 19} \quad 20 \quad 21$$

$$Median = \frac{19+19}{2} = 19$$

Now that we have removed the extreme value, the mean and median are nearly identical. Notice that the median stayed the same with and without the outlier, whereas the mean changed.

The third measure of center we will discuss is the mode.

Mode

The mode is the most frequently occurring value.

There may be no mode if all values occur with equal frequency.

There may be one mode if one value occurs more than any other.

There may be several modes if several values occur with equal frequency and more than other value.

The mode, when it exists, is a good measure of center because like the median, it is not affected by outliers.

Example: Consider the following data:

$$5 \quad 10 \quad 6 \quad 7 \quad 7 \quad 9 \quad 7$$

Question
What is the mode of the sample?

Solution: The mode is the most frequently occurring value, so the mode of this sample is 7.

Quartiles are another useful measure for summarizing data.

Quartiles

Quartiles divide the data into fourths.

Q_1 is the first quartile, also known as the lower quartile.

Q_2 is the second quartile, also known as the median.

Q_3 is the third quartile, also known as the upper quartile.

Example: Consider the following data:

$$2 \quad 9 \quad 7 \quad 4 \quad 8 \quad 9 \quad 8 \quad 1 \quad 3$$

Question
What are the quartiles of this sample?

Solution: The first thing we must do when finding quartiles is to put the data in order.

$$1 \quad 2 \quad 3 \quad 4 \quad 7 \quad 8 \quad 8 \quad 9 \quad 9$$

If you are dividing the data into fourths, first divide it in half, and then divide each half in half. So we first find the median, also known as the second quartile. The median is the middle number, so we see that the median is 7.

$$1 \quad 2 \quad 3 \quad 4 \quad \boxed{7} \quad 8 \quad 8 \quad 9 \quad 9$$

Next, we find the first quartile by dividing the first half of the data in half. The first half of the data is everything from the minimum up to, but not including, the median:

$$1 \quad \boxed{2 \quad 3} \quad 4$$

As we see, there are two middle numbers, 2 and 3, so the first quartile is the average of these numbers:

$$Q_1 = \frac{2+3}{2} = 2.5$$

Finally, we find the third quartile by dividing the second half of the data in half. The second half of the data is everything from, but not including, the median, up to the maximum value:

$$8 \quad \boxed{8 \quad 9} \quad 9$$

As we see, there are two middle numbers, 8 and 9, so the third quartile is the average of these numbers:

$$Q_3 = \frac{8+9}{2} = 8.5$$

A useful summary of the data is the five-number summary.

Five-Number Summary

The five-number summary is a list which includes the minimum value, the first quartile, the median, the third quartile and the maximum value.

The five-number summary is written:

$$(Min, Q_1, Median, Q_3, Max)$$

Example: Consider the following data:

$$10 \quad 5 \quad 18 \quad 3 \quad 19 \quad 14 \quad 13 \quad 7 \quad 8 \quad 29$$

Question
Find the five-number summary.

Solution: First put the data in order:

$$3 \quad 5 \quad 7 \quad 8 \quad 10 \quad 13 \quad 14 \quad 18 \quad 19 \quad 29$$

The easiest values to identify first are the minimum and the maximum.

The minimum value is 3, so we know that

$$Min = 3$$

The maximum value is 29, so we know that

$$Max = 29$$

The next value you should find is the median. There are two middle values, 10 and 13, so we average these to get the median.

$$3 \quad 5 \quad 7 \quad 8 \quad \boxed{10 \quad 13} \quad 14 \quad 18 \quad 19 \quad 29$$

$$Median = \frac{10+13}{2} = 11.5$$

To find the first quartile, find the median of the first half of the data. The first half of the data is everything from the minimum value up to, but not including, the median.

---

3   5   7   8   10

We see that the middle number is 7, so $Q_1 = 7$.

Note that we include the value 10 because even though it is used to *find* the median, it is not the median.

To find the third quartile, find the median of the second half of the data. The second half of the data is everything from, but not including, the median up to the maximum value.

13   14   18   19   29

We see that the middle number is 18, so $Q_3 = 18$.

Note that we include the value 13 in the second half of the data because even though it is used to *find* the median, it is not the median.

So the five-number summary is: (3, 7, 11.5, 18, 29)

■

We will now discuss the three measures of spread.

Measures of Spread

There are three measures of spread: the *range*, the *inter-quartile range* (*IQR*), and the *sample standard deviation*.

The range measures the overall spread from the smallest to the largest value in the data set.

Range

The range is the difference between the maximum value and minimum value.

Range = Max – Min

Example: Recall from the previous example, we found the five-number summary for the data to be:

(3, 7, 11.5, 18, 29)

Question
Find the range of the data.

Solution: The range is the difference between the maximum value and minimum value. From the five-number summary, we know that

$$Min = 3 \text{ and } Max = 29$$

The range is:

$$Range = Max - Min = 29 - 3 = 26$$

■

The range is influenced by outliers, because it only compares the end points. So, when there are outliers, it may be preferable to give the inter-quartile range.

Inter-Quartile Range (IQR)

The IQR is the difference between the third and the first quartiles.

$$IQR = Q_3 - Q_1$$

Since the IQR measures the spread from the first to the third quartiles, it is not influenced by any extreme values that may be in the data.

Example: The five-number summary given in the previous example is:

$$(3, 7, 11.5, 18, 29)$$

Question

Find the IQR of the data.

Solution: The IQR is the difference between the third and first quartiles. From the five-number summary, we know that:

$$Q_1 = 7 \text{ and } Q_3 = 18$$

and so the IQR is:

$$IQR = Q_3 - Q_1 = 18 - 7 = 11$$

■

The third measure of spread that we will consider is the sample standard deviation, which measures how spread out the data is from the sample mean. As we have seen in previous units, the standard deviation is the square-root of the variance.

Sample Standard Deviation

To obtain the sample standard deviation, first compute the sample variance.

$$s^2 = \frac{\displaystyle\sum_{\text{for all x}} (x-\bar{x})^2}{n-1}$$

The sample standard deviation s is the square-root of the variance.

Example: You have the following data:

$$3 \quad 6 \quad 8 \quad 3$$

Question
Find the sample standard deviation of the data.

Solution: First we need to find the sample variance. In order to do so, we need to find the sample mean.

$$\bar{x} = \frac{\displaystyle\sum_{\text{for all x}} x}{n} = \frac{3+6+8+3}{4} = 5$$

We now use this to find the sample variance.

$$s^2 = \frac{\displaystyle\sum_{\text{for all x}} (x-\bar{x})^2}{n-1}$$

First calculate the numerator. We take the difference between each value of x and the sample mean, square that difference, then add them all up.

$$\sum_{\text{for all x}} (x-\bar{x})^2 = (3-5)^2 + (6-5)^2 + (8-5)^2 + (3-5)^2$$

$$= 18$$

We can now find the sample variance:

$$s^2 = \frac{\displaystyle\sum_{\text{for all x}} (x-\bar{x})^2}{n-1} = \frac{18}{4-1} = 6$$

The sample standard deviation is the square-root of the sample variance:

$$s = \sqrt{s^2} = \sqrt{6} = 2.4495$$

5.1.4   **INTERPRETING GRAPHS**

To represent qualitative data graphically, we use a bar chart or pie chart. You will not be required to learn how to draw these graphs by hand, since they can be drawn very easily by computers, but you should know how to read them.

The basic idea of bar charts and pie charts is that the bigger the area, the more individuals were in that particular category. Bar charts have one rectangle for each category. Provided the rectangles are equal in width, the rectangle with the bigger area will be the one that is the longest. Since the categories are mutually exclusive (no individual can belong to more than one category), there is always a space between the bars to represent the separate categories.

For example, in Summer 2002, there were 15 Males and 58 Females enrolled in UCSB's introductory statistics course, PSTAT 5A. Gender is a qualitative variable, so we can make a bar chart to represent the data, as shown in Figure 5.1.

Figure 5.1

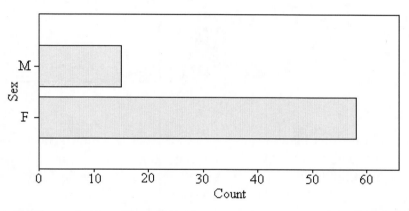

We can see from the bar chart that there are many more females than males in the class.

This information can also be shown in a pie chart, as shown in Figure 5.2.

Figure 5.2

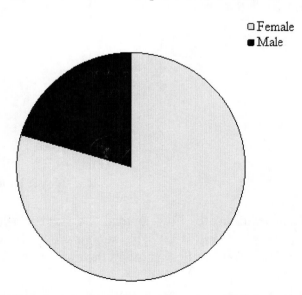

As we see, the bigger the piece of the pie, the more individuals are in that category.

There are many ways to graph quantitative data, but we will restrict ourselves to the most popular: histograms, boxplots, and stem-and-leaf plots.

Histograms compare frequencies, or counts, between two or more numerical intervals. The frequency for each interval is represented by a bar. There are no spaces between bars and all bars have the same width. The taller the bar, the higher the count in that interval.

For example, in Summer 2002, students in PSTAT 5A reported how much rent they paid each month. The data is represented in the histogram in Figure 5.3.

Figure 5.3

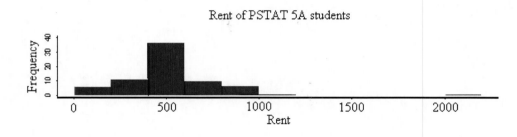

From this histogram, we can see that the rent is fairly symmetrically distributed around $500, with the notable exception of someone who pays between $2000 and $2200 a month. Odd values like this are easier to spot in a histogram rather than just by looking at the raw data.

Another plot that is useful for quantitative data is a stem-and-leaf plot. Stem-and-leaf plots give you the same information as a histogram in regards to shape, but have the added benefit of retaining the data values. A stem-and-leaf plot is shown in Figure 5.4.

Figure 5.4

```
1 | 6 9
2 | 4 4 9 9
3 | 1 2 4
4 | 2 3
5 | 9
6 | 7
7 |
8 | 4
```
                                        Key: 1 | 6 is read "16"

The key indicates how to read the stem-and-leaf plot. The first row shows the numbers 16 and 19. The second row shows the numbers 24 and 29, each repeated. The highest value in the data is 84, and there are no values in the 70's.

A third way to graph quantitative data is with a boxplot. A boxplot represents the five-number summary. Two or more boxplots are useful for comparing the five-number summary of two or more groups.

For example, students in PSTAT 5A during Summer 2002 were asked how many hours they spend sleeping each week. You can use boxplots to decide who spends more time sleeping each week, males or females. The boxplots of the data for males and females are shown in Figure 5.5.

Figure 5.5

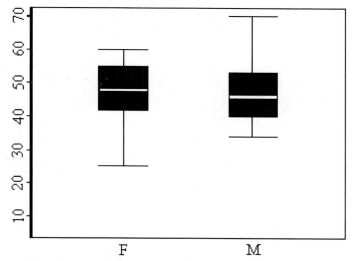

In both cases, the bottom line represents the minimum value in the data. As we see, the minimum value for females is about 25, and the minimum value for males is about 35. The bottom of the box represents the first quartile. The white line inside the box represents the median. The top of the box represents the third quartile. The top line represents the maximum value.

When you are comparing groups with box-plots, you need to see where the medians are in relation to each other, as well as where the quartiles are in relation to each other. DO NOT just compare minimums and maximums, as these can be extreme due to outliers. We can see from Figure 5.5 that the boxes representing the male and female data are fairly in line, which tells us that in general, males and females sleep about the same number of hours per week.

LESSON 5.1 EXERCISES
DESCRIPTIVE STATISTICS

1. MegaBurger USA wants to estimate the proportion of adults who regularly eat junk food. They found that, out of 1065 adults surveyed, 373 said they regularly eat junk food.
   a) Identify the population of interest. ~~not~~ All USA adults
   b) Identify the sample. 1065 adults
   c) What is the proportion of adults surveyed that said they regularly eat junk food? $\frac{373}{1065} = 35.02\% = 0.3502$
   d) What is the probability that an adult chosen randomly will report that they regularly eat junk food?
   35.02%

2. Which of the following variables are qualitative and which are quantitative?
   a) Number of colors offered by Hair Stylists Inc. quantitative
   b) Colors offered by Hair Stylists Inc. quantitative
   c) Height of US males age 14-16. quantitative

3. Cookiewich's, ice cream sandwiched between two cookies, are the latest food craze to hit Isla Vista. The prices (in dollars) of seven Cookiewich's sold in Isla Vista were as follows:

   1.50, 1.25, 1.30, 1.25, 1.60, 1.80, 1.10

   1.10, 1.25, 1.25, 1.30 1.50, 1.60, 1.80
   For this sample of Cookiewich's sold in Isla Vista, find:
   a) the mean price. 1.4
   b) the median price. 1.30
   c) the mode. ~~1.3~~ 1.25
   d) the lower quartile. 1.25
   e) the upper quartile. 1.60
   f) Construct the 5-number summary.
   1.10, 1.25, 1.30, 1.60, 1.80

4. Here are four scores on a quiz:

7	9	11	3
3	7	9	11

   Find the standard deviation.

   $\frac{3+7+9+11}{4} = 7.66 \quad \frac{35}{(4-1)} = \sqrt{11.66}$
   $= 3.42$

5. Babe Ruth and Roger Maris, both famous baseball players, are remembered for hitting a lot of home runs. Until recently, Roger Maris held the record for the most home runs (61) in a single year. Use the chart below to discuss whether there is a difference between Babe Ruth and Roger Maris as home run hitters. Who would you conclude is the better overall home run hitter? Support your conclusion with the information the chart provides.

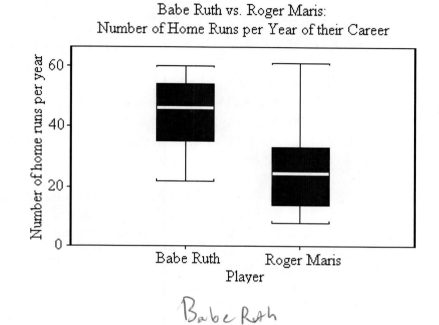

Babe Ruth

ANSWERS
LESSON 5.1 EXERCISES
DESCRIPTIVE STATISTICS

Below are the answers to the exercises for Unit 5, Lesson 5.1.
For full solutions, please refer to the CD included with this textbook.

1. a) The population is all adults.
    b) The sample is the 1065 adults surveyed.
    c) $\hat{p} = 0.3502$
    d) The probability that an adult chosen randomly will report that they regularly eat junk food is 0.3502.

2. a) Number of colors offered by Hair Stylists Inc. is *quantitative.*
    b) Colors offered by Hair Stylists Inc. is *qualitative.*
    c) Height of US males age 14-16 is *quantitative.*

3. a) $\bar{x} = \$1.40$
    b) Median = $\$1.30$
    c) Mode = $\$1.25$
    d) $Q_1 = \$1.25$
    e) $Q_3 = \$1.60$
    f) Five-number summary:
        ($1.10, $1.25, $1.30, $1.60, $1.80)

4. $s = 3.4157$

5. Babe Ruth is the better home-run hitter. We can see from the boxplot that Babe Ruth has a higher median than Roger Maris. Moreover, Babe Ruth's minimum is at Roger Maris's median.

LESSON 5.2
SAMPLE STATISTICS AS RANDOM VARIABLES

5.2.1   **INTRODUCTION**

In Lesson 5.1 we discussed many sample statistics that are helpful for summarizing data. Two such statistics that are particularly useful are the sample mean and the sample proportion. In this lesson, we will focus on understanding these two sample statistics.

5.2.2   **PARAMETERS VERSUS STATISTICS**

One of the main objectives in statistics is to learn about populations by studying representative samples. Specifically, we can use sample *statistics* to help us learn about population *parameters*.

Numerical summaries of sample data, such as the sample proportion or the sample mean, are called *statistics*. In contrast, numerical summaries of population data, such as the population proportion or the population mean, are called *parameters*.

Parameters versus Statistics

A *parameter* is a value that describes a population.

A *statistic* is a value that describes a sample.

We use different symbols to denote statistics and parameters. These symbols are shown in Table 5.1.

Table 5.1

	Sample Statistic	Population Parameter
Mean	$\overline{x}$	μ
Variance	s^2	σ^2
Standard Deviation	s	σ
Proportion	$\hat{p}$	p

Example: Five Kodiak bears were tranquillized with a dart gun. A biologist found that one of the five bears (20%) had suffered oil-spill damage to its coat.

Question

State whether the given percentage is a statistic or a parameter.

20% of the *sample* of 5 bears had suffered oil-spill damage to its coat. So this is a statistic.

■

Consider the following example. The mean GPA of all UCSB undergraduates is reported by the University to be 2.96, and the mean GPA of a sample of 500 UCSB undergraduates was 3.01.

STOP AND THINK!

Which value is a parameter?

Which value is a statistic?

The mean GPA for the population of UCSB undergraduates is 2.96, therefore this value is a parameter and we would write $\mu = 2.96$. This value does not change depending on the sample, because it is the value for the entire population.

3.01 is the mean GPA of the sample of 500 UCSB undergraduates, so it is a statistic and we would write $\bar{x} = 3.01$. This value depends on the sample. If we took another sample of 500 UCSB undergraduates, we would not expect to get the same sample mean as before.

Now consider an example about proportions. UCSB's Office of Admissions reports that 55% of all its undergraduates are female. However, we found that 52% of a sample of 100 undergraduates surveyed were female.

STOP AND THINK!

Which value is a parameter?

Which value is a statistic?

The proportion of female undergraduates in the whole University is 0.55, therefore, this is a parameter and we would write $p = 0.55$. Since it is parameter, like μ, its value will not change depending on the sample.

In our sample, we observed a proportion of 0.52, so this is a statistic and we would write $\hat{p} = 0.52$. Like $\bar{x}$, the sample proportion *can* change depending on the sample. If we took another sample of 100 UCSB undergraduates, we would not expect to get the same sample proportion as before.

It is important to understand that since a parameter is a value describing a population, its value is not dependent on the sample. A statistic, on the other hand, is a value describing a sample, and so its value *does* depend on the sample. Each sample taken can result in a different value for a statistic, thus statistics are *random variables*.

5.2.3   SAMPLE MEAN

A sample mean $\bar{x}$ is a useful statistic to help us learn about a population mean μ. As previously discussed, the sample mean is a random variable because the value of $\bar{x}$ varies from sample to sample. We will show that under certain conditions the distribution of the sample mean is Normal.

Recall the Stanford-Binet IQ test from Unit 4. Scores from this test follow a Normal distribution with a mean of 100 and a standard deviation of 16. We can define the random variable:

$$X = \text{Score on Stanford-Binet IQ test}$$

and draw the distribution of *X*, as shown in Figure 5.6.

Figure 5.6

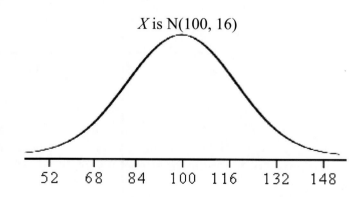

X is N(100, 16)

Suppose we sample 64 people and determine their IQ score using the Stanford-Binet test. If we are interested in the mean of this sample, the random variable is:

$$\bar{X} = \text{the sample mean score of 64 people on Stanford-Binet IQ test}$$

Since the population *X* follows a Normal distribution, the distribution of $\bar{X}$ will also be Normal. This is true no matter how large your sample size *n* is.

Important Result

A sample is taken from a population that follows a Normal distribution, with a mean of μ and a standard deviation of σ.

For *any* sample size n, the distribution of the sample mean $\bar{X}$ is also Normal, with a mean of μ and a standard deviation of $\dfrac{\sigma}{\sqrt{n}}$.

We can use this result to find the mean and standard deviation of the distribution of $\bar{X}$:

$$\text{Mean of } \bar{X}: \quad \mu = 100$$

$$\text{Standard deviation of } \bar{X}: \quad \frac{\sigma}{\sqrt{n}} = \frac{16}{\sqrt{64}} = 2$$

The distribution of $\bar{X}$ is shown in Figure 5.7.

Figure 5.7

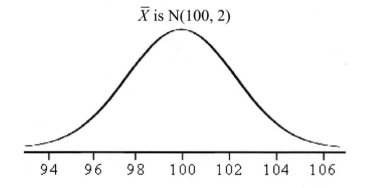

$\bar{X}$ is N(100, 2)

Even though the means of X and $\bar{X}$ are the same, there is much less spread in the distribution of $\bar{X}$. Notice from Figure 5.6 that most IQ scores range from 52 to 148. However, if we sample groups of 64 people and compute their mean IQ score, most of these means are between 94 and 106, as we see in Figure 5.7.

In the above example, we were told that the underlying population was Normal. Now consider an example in which we are *not* told the distribution of X is Normal. Suppose the average age of children in elementary school is 8.5 years and the standard deviation is 3 years. The random variable is:

$$X = \text{Ages of children in elementary school}$$

We are not told that the distribution of X is Normal, but we do know that $\mu = 8.5$ and $\sigma = 3$. Suppose we take a sample of 36 elementary school children and

---

record their ages. If we are interested in the mean age of this sample, then the random variable is:

$$\overline{X} = \text{the sample mean age of 36 elementary school children}$$

Although there is no indication that X is Normal, the distribution of $\overline{X}$ will be Normal provided the sample size is *large enough*.

Important Result

A sample is taken from a population with a mean of μ and a standard deviation of σ.

If the sample size n is at least 30, the distribution of the sample mean $\overline{X}$ is Normal, with a mean of μ and a standard deviation of $\sigma/\sqrt{n}$.

Since the sample size $n = 36$ is considered *large enough*, the distribution of $\overline{X}$ is Normal *even though* the distribution of X is not. The mean and standard deviation of the distribution of $\overline{X}$ are as follows:

$$\text{Mean of } \overline{X}: \quad \mu = 8.5$$
$$\text{Standard deviation of } \overline{X}: \quad \sigma/\sqrt{n} = 3/\sqrt{36} = 0.5$$

The distribution of $\overline{X}$ is shown in Figure 5.8.

Figure 5.8

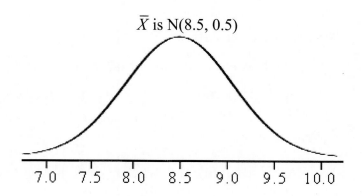

$\overline{X}$ is N(8.5, 0.5)

5.2.4 SAMPLE PROPORTION

Another useful statistic is the sample proportion $\hat{p}$. Like the sample mean, the sample proportion is also a random variable denoted by $\hat{P}$. We will show that under certain conditions, the distribution of $\hat{P}$ is Normal.

In Unit 3, we discussed the Binomial distribution, which is defined by the number of trials n and the proportion of successes p. Consider flipping a coin 100 times and suppose we are interested in the *proportion* of tails observed.

> **STOP AND THINK!**
>
> **Is this a Binomial experiment? What are the four criteria you should check?**

This is a Binomial experiment because it satisfies the four Binomial criteria:

1. There are $n = 100$ trials.
2. Each coin flip is independent of the others.
3. Since we are interested in 'tails', the coin showing 'tails' is a *success* and the coin showing 'heads' is a *failure*.
4. For each trial, the proportion of successes is $p = 0.5$.

When we first looked at the Binomial distribution, the random variable of interest was X, the *number* of successes observed in n trials. Now we are interested in $\hat{P}$, the *proportion* of successes observed in n trials. So, for this example, the random variable is:

$$\hat{P} = \text{the sample proportion of tails in 100 flips}$$

Even though this is a Binomial experiment, under the right conditions, the distribution of $\hat{P}$ is Normal.

> **Important Result**
>
> A Binomial experiment with n trials and proportion of successes p is performed.
>
> The sample proportion $\hat{P}$ follows a Normal distribution if *both*:
>
> $$np \geq 10 \quad \text{and} \quad n(1\text{-}p) \geq 10$$

We use this result to check whether $\hat{P}$ follows a Normal distribution.

$$
\begin{aligned}
np &= 100(0.5) & n(1-p) &= 100(1-0.5) \\
&= 50 & &= 50
\end{aligned}
$$

Since *both* of these values are at least 10, the distribution of $\hat{P}$ is Normal. If one or both of these values is *less* than 10, the distribution of $\hat{P}$ is *not* Normal.

To fully describe the distribution of $\hat{P}$, we need to know the mean and standard deviation of the distribution.

Mean and Standard Deviation of $\hat{P}$

Mean of $\hat{P}$: $\mu = p$

Standard Deviation of $\hat{P}$: $\sigma = \sqrt{\dfrac{p(1-p)}{n}}$

So, for our example, the mean and standard deviation of the distribution of $\hat{P}$ are as follows:

$$\text{Mean of } \hat{P}: \quad \mu = 0.5$$

$$\text{Standard deviation of } \hat{P}: \quad \sigma = \sqrt{\dfrac{p(1-p)}{n}} = \sqrt{\dfrac{0.5(1-0.5)}{100}} = 0.05$$

The distribution of $\hat{P}$ is shown in Figure 5.9.

Figure 5.9

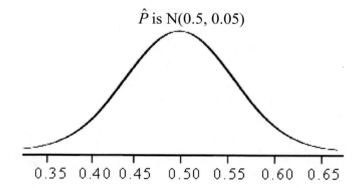

$\hat{P}$ is N(0.5, 0.05)

0.35 0.40 0.45 0.50 0.55 0.60 0.65

LESSON 5.2 EXERCISES
SAMPLE STATISTICS AS RANDOM VARIABLES

1. Which of the following values is a *parameter* and which is a *statistic*?
   a) You are interested in how easily people on your street can find parking. You talk to everybody on your street and find that 73% have difficulty finding a place to park.
   b) You are interested in how much money college students spend on average each day eating out. You talk to 30 college students and find that they spend $4.82 on average per day eating out.
   c) You are interested in the proportion of sophomores that live in dorms at a large university. You talk to 50 sophomores and find that 47% live in dorms.
   d) You are interested in the average number of hours your friends study in a week. You talk to all your friends, and determine that they spend an average of 7.2 hours per week studying.

2. You roll a fair six-sided die 20 times, and you get 5 three's.
   a) What is the sample proportion of three's that you observed?
   b) For this experiment, would it be appropriate to describe the distribution of the sample proportion as Normal? If not, explain why not. If so, explain why, define the random variable and state its distribution, including the mean and standard deviation.
   c) What if you roll a fair six-sided die 200 times. For this experiment, would it be appropriate to describe the distribution of the sample proportion of three's as Normal? If not, explain why not. If so, explain why, define the random variable and state its distribution, including the mean and standard deviation.

3. Scores on the SAT Math test are Normally distributed with a mean of 500 and a standard deviation of 100. A representative sample of 20 SAT test takers is taken. The random variable is:

$$\bar{X} = \text{the sample mean SAT Math score of 20 test takers}$$

   a) What is the mean of $\bar{X}$?
   b) What is the standard deviation of $\bar{X}$?
   c) State the distribution of $\bar{X}$.
   d) If SAT Math scores were NOT Normally distributed, but still had a mean of 500 and a standard deviation of 100, would this change your answers to parts (a) – (c)?

ANSWERS

LESSON 5.2 EXERCISES

SAMPLE STATISTICS AS RANDOM VARIABLES

Below are the answers to the exercises for Unit 5, Lesson 5.2.
For full solutions, please refer to the CD included with this textbook.

1. a) 73% is a *parameter*.
   b) $4.82 is a *statistic*.
   c) 47% is a *statistic*.
   d) 7.2 is a *parameter*.

2. a) $\hat{p} = 0.25$
   b) No, the distribution of $\hat{p}$ cannot be defined as Normal because np and $n(1-p)$ are not *both* at least 10.
   c) Yes, the distribution of $\hat{p}$ can be defined as Normal because np and $n(1-p)$ are *both* at least 10.
      The random variable is $\hat{P}$ = the sample proportion of 3's when a fair die is rolled 200 times.
      The mean of $\hat{p}$ is 1/6.
      The standard deviation of $\hat{p}$ is 0.0264.

3. a) The mean of $\overline{X}$ is 500.
   b) The standard deviation of $\overline{X}$ is 22.3607
   c) The distribution of $\overline{X}$ is N(500, 22.3607)
   d) If SAT Math scores were NOT Normally distributed, the mean and standard deviation of $\overline{X}$ would remain the same as in parts (a) and (b), but we would no longer be able to define the distribution of $\overline{X}$ as Normal.

LESSON 5.3
MORE PRACTICE IN SOLVING SAMPLE STATISTICS PROBLEMS

In this lesson we look at some more examples with full solutions. You are encouraged to work through these problems yourself if you need extra practice.

Example 1:   In a study of 1000 French adults, 300 report that they suffer from insomnia. Suppose 35% of all French adults suffer from insomnia.
a) What is the sample proportion of French adults who report that they suffer from insomnia?
b) For this experiment, would it be appropriate to describe the distribution of the sample proportion as Normal? If not, explain why not. If so, explain why, define the random variable and state its distribution, including the mean and standard deviation.

STOP AND THINK!

Is this a Binomial experiment?
What do we know about the sample proportion as a random variable?

Solution: a) Notice that this is a Binomial experiment:
1. There are $n = 1000$ trials.
2. It is reasonable to assume the French adults are independent.
3. Since we are interested in finding a 'French adult who suffers from insomnia', this is a *success* and a 'French adult who does not suffer from insomnia' is a *failure*.
4. For each trial, the proportion of successes is $p = 0.35$.

The sample proportion is $\hat{p}$. We can find it by dividing the number of successes by the number of trials:

$$\hat{p} = \frac{x}{n} = \frac{300}{1000} = 0.3$$

Solution: b) The random variable is:

$\hat{P}$ = the sample proportion of French adults who suffer from insomnia.

The distribution of $\hat{P}$ can be defined as Normal if np and $n(1-p)$ are *both* at least 10.

$$np = 1000(0.35) \qquad\qquad n(1-p) = 1000(1-0.35)$$
$$= 350 \qquad\qquad\qquad\qquad = 650$$

Since both of these values are at least 10, we can define the distribution of $\hat{P}$ as Normal.

The mean of $\hat{P}$: $p = 0.35$

The standard deviation of $\hat{P}$: $\sqrt{\dfrac{p(1-p)}{n}} = \sqrt{\dfrac{0.35(1-0.35)}{1000}} = 0.0151$

So we can say $\hat{P}$ is N(0.35, 0.0151).

Example 2: The weight of loaded railroad bogies on the Trans-Pacific Railroad is Normally distributed with a mean of 30 tons and a standard deviation of 3 tons. A sample of 10 such bogies is found to have a mean weight of 20.33 tons and a standard deviation of 2.66 tons. Identify each of the following:
a) the population of interest.
b) the sample.
c) $\bar{x}$
d) σ
e) σ^2
f) s
g) μ

STOP AND THINK!

What is the difference between a population and a sample? Which of the values are statistics and which are parameters?

Solution: a) The population of interest is *all* loaded railroad bogies on the Trans-Pacific Railroad.

Solution: b) The sample is 10 loaded railroad bogies on the Trans-Pacific Railroad.

Solution: c) $\bar{x}$ is the *sample* mean weight of the 10 bogies, so $\bar{x} = 20.33$

Solution: d) σ is the *population* standard deviation of *all* bogies, so $\sigma = 3$

Solution: e) σ^2 is the *population* variance of *all* bogies, and it is found by squaring the standard deviation, so $\sigma^2 = 9$

Solution: f) s is the *sample* standard deviation of the 10 bogies, so $s = 2.66$

Solution: g) μ is the *population* mean weight of *all* bogies, so $\mu = 30$

    ■

Example 3:   While on a fishing trip, Warren and Gabriel catch 5 brown trout and weigh each of them. They record the weights, in ounces, as follows:

$$22 \quad 15 \quad 17 \quad 28 \quad 23$$

Find the sample mean and sample standard deviation for the weights of brown trout.

STOP AND THINK!

How do you compute the sample mean?

How do you compute the sample standard deviation?

Solution: The sample mean is found by adding all the values and dividing by the number of values.

$$\bar{x} = \frac{\displaystyle\sum_{\text{for all x}} x}{n} = \frac{22+15+17+28+23}{5} = 21$$

To compute the sample standard deviation, we must first find the sample variance.

$$s^2 = \frac{\displaystyle\sum_{\text{for all x}} (x-\bar{x})^2}{n-1}$$

First calculate the numerator. We take the difference between each value of x and the sample mean, square that difference, then add them all up.

$$\sum_{\text{for all x}} (x-\bar{x})^2 = (22-21)^2 + (15-21)^2 + (17-21)^2 + (28-21)^2 + (23-21)^2$$

$$= 106$$

We can now find the sample variance:

$$s^2 = \frac{\sum\limits_{\text{for all } x} \left(x - \bar{x}\right)^2}{n-1} = \frac{106}{5-1} = 26.5$$

The sample standard deviation is the square-root of the sample variance:

$$s = \sqrt{s^2} = \sqrt{26.5} = 5.1478$$

Example 4: Eight minor earthquakes occurred in the Santa Barbara Channel one week in July. The intensities, recorded on the Richter scale, are as follows:

2.1   1.5   2.1   1.7   2.1   2.3   2.2   1.8

a) Find the mean intensity of earthquakes recorded in the Santa Barbara Channel that week.
b) Construct the five-number summary for this data.
c) What would be the most appropriate graphical display for the five-number summary?

STOP AND THINK!

How do you compute the sample mean?

How do you find the five-number summary?

We have discussed three ways to graph quantitative data. Which is appropriate here and why?

Solution: a) The sample mean is found by adding all the values and dividing by the number of values.

$$\bar{x} = \frac{\sum\limits_{\text{for all } x} x}{n} = \frac{2.1+1.5+2.1+1.7+2.1+2.3+2.2+1.8}{8} = 1.975$$

Solution: b) To find the five-number summary, first put the data in order:

1.5   1.7   1.8   2.1   2.1   2.1   2.2   2.3

The easiest values to identify first are the minimum and the maximum.

The minimum value is 1.5, so $Min = 1.5$

The maximum value is 2.3, so *Max* = 2.3

The next value you should find is the median. There are two middle values, 2.1 and 2.1, so we average these to get the median.

1.5   1.7   1.8 | 2.1   2.1 | 2.1   2.2   2.3

$$Median = \frac{2.1 + 2.1}{2} = 2.1$$

To find the first quartile, find the median of the first half of the data. The first half of the data is everything from the minimum value up to, but not including, the median.

1.5 | 1.7   1.8 | 2.1

We see that there are two middle numbers, 1.7 and 1.8, so we average these to get the first quartile.

$$Q_1 = \frac{1.7 + 1.8}{2} = 1.75 .$$

Note that we include the value 2.1 because even though it is used to *find* the median, it is not the median.

To find the third quartile, find the median of the second half of the data. The second half of the data is everything from, but not including, the median up to the maximum value.

2.1 | 2.1   2.2 | 2.3

We see that there are two middle numbers, 2.1 and 2.2, so we average these to get the third quartile.

$$Q_3 = \frac{2.1 + 2.2}{2} = 2.15 .$$

Note that we include the value 2.1 in the second half of the data because even though it is used to *find* the median, it is not the median.

So the five-number summary is: (1.5, 1.75, 2.1, 2.15, 2.3)

Solution: c) A boxplot is the most appropriate graphical display of the data.

Example 5: Here is a histogram summarizing the weekly sleep from PSTAT 5A females in Summer 2002. Note that the y-axis shows the proportion of students in each interval. Would you expect the mean hours of weekly sleep for females to be higher or lower than the median hours of weekly sleep for females? How do you know? (Do not try to calculate – REASON!)

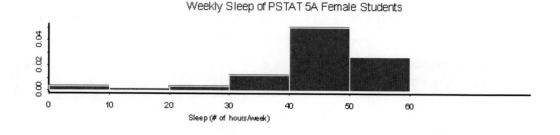

STOP AND THINK!

Do there appear to be any extreme values? Where do they occur? Do they affect the mean or the median?

Solution: The mean and median are different when there are extreme values on one end of the data. From the histogram, we see that there are some extremely small values. This indicates that the mean will be smaller than the median, because it is affected by these outliers.

Example 6: Which of the following variables are qualitative and which are quantitative?
a) A person's hair color.
b) A person's height

STOP AND THINK!

If you were to ask people their hair color, would they give you a numerical or non-numerical response?

If you were to ask people their height, would they give you a numerical or non-numerical response?

Solution: a) A person's hair color is 'brown', 'black', 'blonde', 'red', etc. This means that hair color is a *qualitative* variable.

Solution: b) A person's height is numerical, so it is a *quantitative* variable

Example 7:   Midterm scores in a large biology class had a mean of 73 and a standard deviation of 12. Suppose 36 students are sampled from this class, and their mean midterm score is computed.
a) What is the random variable of interest?
b) Can we define the distribution of the random variable of interest as Normal? Explain why or why not.
c) What is the mean of the random variable of interest?
d) What is the standard deviation of the random variable of interest?

STOP AND THINK!

What are we interested in?
Is the population Normal?

Solution: a) We are interested in the *mean* midterm score of a sample of 36 students. So the random variable of interest is:

$\overline{X}$ = the sample mean midterm score of 36 biology students.

Solution: b) The distribution of $\overline{X}$ is Normal if we either sample from a Normal population, *or* if the sample size is *at least* 30. In this case, we do not know whether the distribution of midterm scores in the whole biology class is Normal. However, since sample size is at least 30, the distribution of $\overline{X}$ is Normal.

Solution: c) We are interested in the *mean* of the sample mean, in other words, the mean of the distribution of $\overline{X}$. The mean of the distribution of $\overline{X}$ is the same as the mean of the population we sampled from. Since the average midterm score in the whole biology class was 73, then the mean of $\overline{X}$ is 73.

Solution: d) We are interested in the *standard deviation* of the sample mean, in other words, the standard deviation of the distribution of $\overline{X}$. This is found by dividing the standard deviation of the population by the square-root of the sample size. The standard deviation in the population is 12, and the sample size is 36 students. So:

$$\text{Standard deviation of } \overline{X} : \frac{\sigma}{\sqrt{n}} = \frac{12}{\sqrt{36}} = 2$$

Example 8:   You are given the following information (in inches), based on information collected from UCSB's PSTAT 5A students enrolled Summer 2002:

Females: Five Number Summary = (60, 63, 64, 65, 69.5)
             Mean = 64.405
             Standard Deviation = 1.9499

Males: Five Number Summary = (60, 68.25, 69.5, 71.75, 76)
             Mean = 69.5
             Standard Deviation = 3.9565

a) How tall is the tallest girl who answered the questionnaire?
b) Is the tallest person a male or a female?
c) On average, who are taller, the men or women who answered the questionnaire?
d) Do you expect greater variability in the heights of men or of women who answered the questionnaire? Explain.
e) What percentage of males are taller than the tallest female? Look closely at the five number summaries, and THINK!

STOP AND THINK!

What information is provided in the five-number summaries?
What information is provided by the mean?
What information is provided by the standard deviation?

Solution: a) The five-number summary for the female data indicates the maximum value is 69.5, so the tallest female is 69.5 inches.

Solution: b) Comparing the five-number summaries, we see that the maximum value for females is 69.5, while the maximum value for males is 76. Therefore, the tallest person is a male.

Solution: c) The mean of the males is higher than the mean of the females. So on average, males are taller than females.

Solution: d) The standard deviation of the males is greater than the standard deviation of the females, so there is greater variability in the heights of the men.

Solution: e) The tallest female is 69.5 inches. This corresponds with the median value in the male data. Therefore, 50% of men are taller than the tallest female.

Example 9: The heights of females at UCSB follow a Normal distribution with a mean of 64.3 inches and a standard deviation of 2.5 inches. If 58 females are sampled, describe the distribution of the sample mean height of females at UCSB. Be sure to define the random variable.

STOP AND THINK!

What is the random variable?

The population follows a Normal distribution. What does this imply about the distribution of the sample mean?

Solution: We are interested in the average height of 58 females at UCSB. Therefore, the random variable is:

$$\bar{X} = \text{the sample mean height of 58 UCSB females}$$

The distribution of $\bar{X}$ is Normal if we either sample from a Normal population, *or* if the sample size is *at least* 30. In this case, the heights in the population are Normally distributed, so this implies that the distribution of $\bar{X}$ is Normal.

To fully describe the distribution of $\bar{X}$, we need to find the mean and standard deviation of $\bar{X}$. The mean of the distribution of $\bar{X}$ is the same as the mean of the population we sampled from. Since the average height of females at UCSB is 64.3, then the mean of $\bar{X}$ is 64.3.

The standard deviation of the population is 2.5 and the sample size is 58 female students. So:

$$\text{Standard deviation of } \bar{X} : \frac{\sigma}{\sqrt{n}} = \frac{2.5}{\sqrt{58}} = 0.3283$$

We can now fully describe the distribution of $\bar{X}$ as N(64.3, 0.3283).

■

Example 10: 43% of college students have jobs during the academic year. In a random sample of 200 college students, 45% of them said they have jobs during the academic year.
a) Is this a Binomial experiment? Explain.
b) What is the observed sample proportion?
c) Define the random variable of interest and state its distribution.

> **STOP AND THINK!**
>
> What criteria must be satisfied for this to be a Binomial experiment?
> There are two proportions given; which is the sample proportion?
> How do we define the random variable?   What is its distribution?

Solution: a) This is a Binomial experiment:
1. There are $n = 200$ trials.
2. It is reasonable to assume the college students are independent.
3. Since we are interested in finding a 'college student has a job during the academic year', this is a *success* and a 'college student that does *not* have a job during the academic year' is a *failure*.
4. For each trial, the proportion of successes is $p = 0.43$.

Solution: b) The observed sample proportion is $\hat{p} = 0.45$.

Solution: c) The random variable is:

$\hat{P}$ = the sample proportion of 200 college students that have a job during the academic year

The distribution of $\hat{P}$ is Normal if np and $n(1-p)$ are *both* at least 10.

$$np = 200(0.43) \qquad\qquad n(1-p) = 200(1-0.43)$$
$$= 86 \qquad\qquad\qquad\qquad = 114$$

Since both of these values are at least 10, the distribution of $\hat{P}$ is Normal.

The mean of $\hat{P}$: $p = 0.43$

The standard deviation of $\hat{P}$: $\sqrt{\dfrac{p(1-p)}{n}} = \sqrt{\dfrac{0.43(1-0.43)}{200}} = 0.0350$

So $\hat{P}$ is N(0.43, 0.0350).

LESSON 5.3 EXERCISES
MORE PRACTICE IN SOLVING SAMPLE DATA PROBLEMS

1. A watermelon grower wants to estimate the mean weight of the watermelons he grows. He weighs a sample of 50 watermelons and finds the mean weight to be 10.23kg.
    a) Identify the population of interest.
    b) Identify the sample.
    c) Is the mean weight of 10.23kg a parameter or a statistic?

2. Which of the following variables are qualitative and which are quantitative?
    a) Age of New Zealand green lipped mussels when harvested.
    b) Scores (out of 100) on a statistics midterm.
    c) Marital status of American females between the ages of 18 and 45 years.

3. In a competition the weights lifted by 8 females in the Clean and Jerk were given (in kg's) as follows:

    $$82, \ 71, \ 83, \ 65, \ 65, \ 127, \ 80, \ 69$$

    For this Clean and Jerk competition, find:
    a) the mean.
    b) the median.
    c) the lower quartile.
    d) the upper quartile.
    e) construct the five-number summary.

4. The weights (in pounds) of four frozen turkeys were recorded as follows:

    $$12 \qquad 14 \qquad 11 \qquad 15$$

    Find the standard deviation.

5. The weights of males at UCSB follow a Normal distribution with a mean of 160 pounds and a standard deviation of 10 pounds. If 75 males are sampled, describe the distribution of the sample mean weight of males at UCSB. Be sure to define the random variable.

6. 25% of college students missed at least one class in Winter Quarter due to sickness. In a random sample of 300 college students, 28% of them said they missed at least one class in Winter Quarter due to sickness.
    a) Is this a Binomial experiment? Explain.
    b) What is the observed sample proportion?
    c) Define the random variable of interest and state its distribution.

ANSWERS
LESSON 5.3 EXERCISES
MORE PRACTICE IN SOLVING SAMPLE DATA PROBLEMS

Below are the answers to the exercises for Unit 5, Lesson 5.3.
For full solutions, please refer to the CD included with this textbook.

1. a) The population of interest is *all* watermelons grown by this watermelon grower.
   b) The sample is 50 watermelons.
   c) The mean weight of 10.23kg is a statistic.

2. a) Age of New Zealand green lipped mussels when harvested is *quantitative*.
   b) Scores (out of 100) on a Statistics midterm are *quantitative*.
   c) Marital status of American females between the ages of 18 and 45 years is *qualitative*.

3. a) $\bar{x} = 80.25$
   b) $Median = 75.5$
   c) $Q_1 = 67$
   d) $Q_3 = 82.5$
   e) Five-number summary: $(65, 67, 75.5, 82.5, 127)$

4. $s = 1.8257$

5. $\bar{X}$ = the sample mean weight of 75 males at UCSB
   $\bar{X}$ is N(160, 1.1547)

6. a) Yes, this is a Binomial experiment because it satisfies the four Binomial criteria:
      1. There are $n = 300$ trials.
      2. It is reasonable to assume the college students are independent.
      3. Since we are interested in finding a 'college student who *missed* at least one class in Winter Quarter due to sickness', this is a *success* and a 'college student who *did not* at least one class in Winter Quarter due to sickness' is a *failure*.
      4. For each trial, the proportion of successes is $p = 0.25$.
   b) $\hat{p} = 0.28$
   c) $\hat{P}$ = the sample proportion of college students that missed at least one class in Winter Quarter due to sickness.
      $\hat{P}$ is N(0.25, 0.025)

AVOIDING COMMON MISTAKES

☺ When you read the problems, think carefully as to which values are parameters and which are statistics.

☺ The distribution of $\bar{X}$ and $\hat{P}$ are *only* Normal under certain conditions. You should verify these conditions *before* stating that the distribution of either of these random variables is Normal.

☺ When you are computing the sample variance s^2, do not forget to square the differences in the numerator before you add them. If you forget, you will always get 0 for the sample variance.

☺ Do not forget that the sample standard deviation s is found by taking the square-root of the sample variance s^2.

☺ Do not include the median value when you divide the data in half to find the quartiles.

☺ Histograms resemble bar charts but bar charts are for graphing qualitative data, and histograms are for graphing quantitative data.

UNIT 5 SUMMARY

- A *population* is the entire group you are interested in studying.

- A *sample* is the subset of the population that you actually study.

- Qualitative data are non-numerical.

- Quantitative data are numerical.

- The symbol for a sample proportion is $\hat{p}$, read 'p-hat'.

$$\hat{p} = \frac{x}{n}$$

- There are three measures of center: the *sample mean*, the *median*, and the *mode*.

- The symbol for the sample mean is $\overline{x}$, read 'x-bar'.

$$\overline{x} = \frac{\displaystyle\sum_{\text{for all x}} x}{n}$$

- The median is the middle number of an ordered data set. To find the median:
  - First put the data in increasing order.
  - If the sample size is odd, the median is the exact middle number.
  - If the sample size is even, there will be 2 middle numbers, and the median is the average of these two middle numbers.

- The mode is the most frequently occurring value.
  - There may be no mode if all values occur with equal frequency.
  - There may be one mode if one value occurs more than any other.
  - There may be several modes if several values occur with equal frequency and more than other value.

- Quartiles divide the data into fourths.
  - Q_1 is the first quartile, also known as the lower quartile.
  - Q_2 is the second quartile, also known as the median.
  - Q_3 is the third quartile, also known as the upper quartile.

- The five-number summary is written: (*Min*, Q_1, *Median*, Q_3, *Max*)

- There are three measures of spread: the *range*, the *inter-quartile range* (*IQR*), and the *sample standard deviation*.

- *Range = Max – Min*

- *IQR* = $Q_3 - Q_1$

- To obtain the sample standard deviation, first compute the sample variance s^2.

$$s^2 = \frac{\displaystyle\sum_{\text{for all x}} (x - \bar{x})^2}{n-1}$$

The sample standard deviation s is the square-root of the variance.

- Qualitative data is displayed with a bar chart or a pie chart.

- Quantitative data is displayed with a histogram, boxplot, or stem-and-leaf plot.

- A *parameter* is a value that describes a population.

- A *statistic* is a value that describes a sample.

- A sample is taken from a population that follows a Normal distribution, with a mean of μ and a standard deviation of σ. For *any* sample size n, the distribution of the sample mean $\bar{X}$ will also be Normal, with a mean of μ and a standard deviation of $\sigma/\sqrt{n}$.

- A sample is taken from a population with a mean of μ and a standard deviation of σ. If the sample size n is at least 30, the distribution of the sample mean $\bar{X}$ will also be Normal, with a mean of μ and a standard deviation of $\sigma/\sqrt{n}$.

- A Binomial experiment with n trials and proportion of successes p is performed. The sample proportion $\hat{P}$ will follow a Normal distribution if *both* $np \geq 10$ and $n(1-p) \geq 10$.

- Mean of $\hat{P}$: $\mu = p$

- Standard Deviation of $\hat{P}$: $\sigma = \sqrt{\dfrac{p(1-p)}{n}}$

SELF-ASSESSMENT QUIZ

1. A researcher for a phone company wants to estimate the mean monthly phone bill of California residents. He takes a representative sample of 150 California resident phone users and finds that the mean monthly phone bill is $76.00 and the standard deviation is $15.
   a) Identify the population of interest.
   b) Identify the sample.
   c) Is the mean monthly phone bill of $76.00 a parameter or a statistic?
   d) Is the standard deviation of $15 a parameter or a statistic?

2. Which of the following variables are qualitative and which are quantitative?
   a) Number of cars sold by a dealership in the past year.
   b) The height of waves on the north shore on Oahu in December.
   c) The favorite color of 8 year old Mexican children.

3. A student recorded the number of minutes she spent each week on her cell phone for 10 consecutive weeks as follows:

   120, 160, 70, 80, 60, 110, 120, 130, 100, 120

   For the number of minutes she spent each week on her cell phone:
   a) Find the mean.
   b) Construct the five-number summary.
   c) Name the most appropriate graph for displaying the five-number summary.

4. Sales of Soda Fizz this year have declined sharply. To try to remedy this situation, the company has devised a special promotion where you stand a chance of an 'instant win' upon the purchase of a standard sized bottle of Soda Fizz. It is advertised that 1 in 5 bottles is an 'instant winner'. You and your friends buy a total of 12 bottles of Soda Fizz and 2 of them are 'instant winners'.
   a) What is the sample proportion of winning bottles of Soda Fizz?
   b) For this experiment, would it be appropriate to describe the distribution of the sample proportion as Normal? If so, explain why, define the random variable and state its distribution and determine the mean and standard deviation. If not, explain why not.
   c) What if your school buys 150 bottles and you record how many wins there are. Would it be appropriate to describe the distribution of the sample proportion as Normal? If so, explain why, define the random variable, state its distribution and determine the mean and standard deviation. If not, explain why not.

5. From data collected over several years, Berries Inc know that the actual weight of their 4 lb box of strawberries follows a Normal distribution with a mean of 3.85 lb and a standard deviation of 0.15 lb. The manager of Berries Inc takes a representative sample of 25 boxes of strawberries. Assuming that the random variable is:

$\overline{X}$ = the sample mean weight of a 4 lb box of strawberries for 25 boxes

   a) What would be the mean of $\overline{X}$?
   b) What would be the standard deviation of $\overline{X}$?

6. Elisa and Arica talked on the phone five times this week. The times each call lasted are as follows:

15   25   17   6   7

Find the standard deviation of the duration of the phone calls.

ANSWERS

SELF-ASSESSMENT QUIZ

Below are the answers to the exercises for Unit 5, Self-Assessment Quiz. For full solutions, please refer to the CD included with this textbook.

1. a) The population of interest is *all* California resident phone users.
    b) The sample is 150 California resident phone users.
    c) The mean monthly phone bill of $76.00 is a statistic.
    d) The standard deviation of $15 is a statistic.

2. a) Number of cars sold by a dealership in the past year is *quantitative*.
    b) The height of waves on the north shore on Oahu in December is *quantitative*.
    c) The favorite color of 8 year old Mexican children is *qualitative*.

3. a) $\bar{x} = 107$
    b) Five-number summary: (60, 80, 115, 120, 160)
    c) The most appropriate graph for displaying the 5-number summary is a boxplot.

4. a) $\hat{p} = \dfrac{2}{12}$

    b) $\hat{P} =$ the sample proportion of 'instant winning' bottles out of 12.
    $np = 12(0.2) = 2.4$ and $n(1-p) = 12(1-0.2) = 9.6$
    Since neither of these values are at least 10, we cannot define the distribution of $\hat{P}$ as Normal.

    c) $\hat{P} =$ the sample proportion of 'instant winning' bottles out of 150.
    $np = 150(0.2) = 30$ and $n(1-p) = 150(1-0.2) = 120$ are *both* at least 10, so we can say $\hat{P}$ is N(0.2, 0.0327).

5. a) Mean of $\bar{X}$: $\mu = 3.85$

    b) Standard deviation of $\bar{X}$: $\dfrac{\sigma}{\sqrt{n}} = \dfrac{0.15}{\sqrt{25}} = 0.03$

6. $s = 7.8102$

UNIT 6
INFERENCE ON A SAMPLE MEAN

Lesson 6.1   Confidence Intervals for a Population Mean
Exercises for Lesson 6.1
Answers to Exercises for Lesson 6.1

Lesson 6.2   Hypothesis Testing for a Population Mean
Exercises for Lesson 6.2
Answers to Exercises for Lesson 6.2

Lesson 6.3   More Practice in Solving Inference Problems
Exercises for Lesson 6.3
Answers to Exercises for Lesson 6.3

Avoiding Common Mistakes
Unit 6 Summary
Self-Assessment Quiz
Answers to Self-Assessment Quiz

LESSON 6.1
CONFIDENCE INTERVALS FOR A POPULATION MEAN

6.1.1   INTRODUCTION

At the beginning of Unit 5, we explained that there are two major branches of statistics; descriptive and inferential. Inferential statistics is concerned with analyzing *sample* data using techniques that enable us to draw conclusions about a *population* of interest. In Lesson 6.1 we learn how to estimate a population mean, and in Lesson 6.2 we show how to test a claim about a population mean.

6.1.2   ESTIMATING A POPULATION MEAN

Consider the following example. A researcher is interested in the mean height of *all* people in California. The heights of a sample of 100 Californians are recorded and the sample mean $\bar{x}$ is calculated. As long as the researcher's sample is representative of the population, the sample mean $\bar{x}$ is likely to be close to the population mean μ. However, if the researcher were to take a sample of another 100 Californians and record their heights, the sample mean would almost certainly be different. Clearly, although the sample mean is the best single value estimate of the population mean, $\bar{x}$ does not equal μ because $\bar{x}$ varies from sample to sample.

> The *point estimate* of a population mean is the sample mean.

Suppose that the researcher calculated the mean height of the sample of 100 Californians as $\bar{x} = 68$ inches. Then 68 inches is the *point estimate* of μ, the population mean height of *all* people in California.

It is very unlikely that the population mean μ will be *exactly* 68 inches, but it is likely to be reasonably close to this value. Therefore, we can be fairly sure that the population mean will lie within a *range of values* centered at 68. This *range of values* is called an *interval estimate*.

Interval Estimate

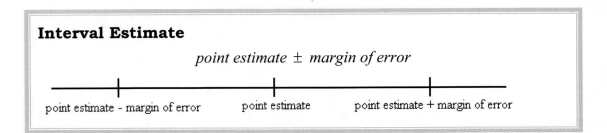

Before constructing an interval estimate, a level of confidence, usually expressed as a percentage, is chosen by the researcher. The confidence level indicates how confident you want to be that the interval estimate you construct actually contains the population parameter of interest. The most common confidence level is 95%. An interval estimate for a given level of confidence is called a *confidence interval*.

Confidence Interval for a Population Mean

sample mean $\pm$ margin of error

In order to construct a confidence interval it is essential to first define the parameter and random variable of interest. In this unit, the parameter of interest is the population mean, so $\overline{X}$ is the random variable of interest.

Consider again the researcher who is interested in the mean height of all people in California. The heights of a sample of 100 Californians are recorded.

STOP AND THINK!

What is the parameter of interest?

What is the random variable of interest?

The parameter of interest is:

μ = the population mean height of people in California

The random variable of interest is:

$\overline{X}$ = the sample mean of 100 people in California

Having defined the parameter and random variable of interest, the next task is to determine the distribution of the random variable $\overline{X}$. For estimating a population mean, there are two distributions to consider: the Z-distribution and the *t*-

distribution. In Unit 4, we discussed the Z-distribution, which has a mean of 0 and a standard deviation of 1. We now consider the t-distribution.

The t-distribution, as shown in Figure 6.1, is similar in shape to the Z-distribution, but differs in some important aspects.

Figure 6.1

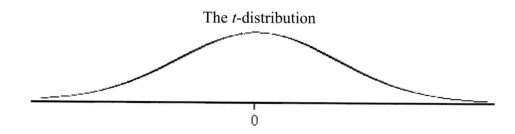

The t-distribution

0

Like the Z-distribution, the t-distribution is a symmetric, bell-shaped density curve, with a mean of 0. It differs from the Z-distribution in that its spread is determined by the number of degrees of freedom denoted by df. When using the t-distribution to estimate a population mean, the number of degrees of freedom are always equal to the sample size minus 1.

Degrees of Freedom to Estimate a Population Mean

$$df = n - 1$$

The smaller the number of degrees of freedom, the bigger the spread, making the t-distribution shorter and flatter. The larger the number of degrees of freedom, the smaller the spread, making the t-distribution taller and skinnier, as shown in Figure 6.2.

Figure 6.2

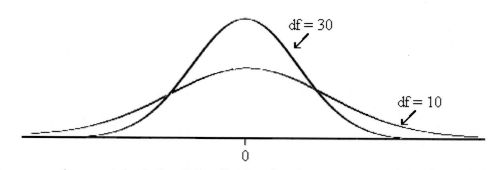

df = 30

df = 10

0

However, the spread of the t-distribution is always greater than that of the Z-distribution. As the number of degrees of freedom increase, the t-distribution looks more like the Z-distribution. The t-values can be found in the t-table in the back of this book.

To decide which distribution is appropriate for the analysis, certain conditions must be met.

Lesson 6.1: Confidence Intervals for a Population Mean

Check the Following Conditions:

- The data come from a sample that is representative of the population of interest.

- $\bar{X}$ follows a Normal distribution. That is, the data come from a Normally distributed population *or* the sample size is at least 30.

- Check if you know σ, the population standard deviation, or if you know s, the sample standard deviation.

Use the *Z*-distribution when σ is known.

Use the *t*-distribution when s is known.

If the data do not meet the above conditions, then you cannot perform the analyses discussed in this textbook.

6.1.3   **USING THE Z-DISTRIBUTION**

In Section 6.1.2, a confidence interval for the population mean was defined as:

$$sample\ mean \pm margin\ of\ error$$

Now consider how to find the margin of error, denoted by E. In Unit 5, we studied the distribution of all possible values of the sample mean, and it is to this sampling distribution that we now turn our attention. Having checked that the conditions in Section 6.1.2 hold, we know that the sampling distribution of $\bar{X}$ is Normal with a mean μ and standard deviation $\frac{\sigma}{\sqrt{n}}$. This is shown in Figure 6.3.

Figure 6.3

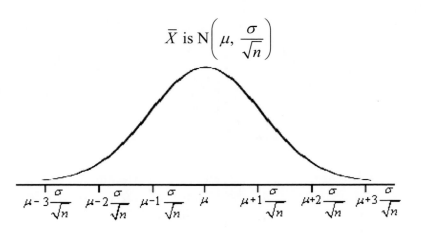

$$\bar{X}\ is\ N\left(\mu, \frac{\sigma}{\sqrt{n}}\right)$$

The *actual* value of μ is unknown, but can estimated with a confidence interval. Recall that the most common confidence level is 95%, so we will show how to find the margin of error using a 95% level of confidence. If we find *z*-scores such that the area under the curve between them is 0.95, then we have captured 95% of all values of $\overline{X}$. This is shown in Figure 6.4.

Figure 6.4

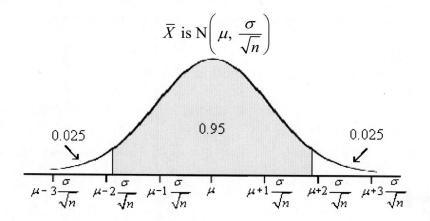

To find the z-scores, use the Standard Normal table. Look up an area of 0.0250 and read off the corresponding z-score of –1.96. Since the Normal distribution is symmetric about the mean, the other z-score is +1.96. Hence, the probability that the sample mean lies within 1.96 standard deviations of the sample mean is 0.95. The measurement of 1.96 standard deviations from the mean, called the margin of error for 95% confidence, is thus given by:

$$E = 1.96 \frac{\sigma}{\sqrt{n}}$$

and so the desired interval estimate for 95% confidence is:

$$\overline{x} \pm 1.96 \frac{\sigma}{\sqrt{n}}$$

To generalize, for any confidence level, the margin of error is:

$$E = z \frac{\sigma}{\sqrt{n}}$$

Hence,

A Confidence Interval for a Population Mean using the Z-distribution is given by:

$$\overline{x} \pm z \frac{\sigma}{\sqrt{n}}$$

- $\overline{x}$ represents the sample mean of the data.
- z is a value obtained from the last row of the t-table and is based on the confidence level.
- σ is the standard deviation of the population.
- n is the sample size.

Consider the following example. The resting pulse rate of a representative sample of 81 female students was found to have a mean of 64. If the standard deviation of resting pulse rate for the entire population of female students is 10, give a 95% confidence interval for the mean resting pulse rate in the population of female students.

The parameter of interest is:

μ = the population mean resting pulse rate of female students

To learn about μ, a sample of 81 female students was taken, and so the random variable of interest is:

$\overline{X}$ = the sample mean resting pulse rate of 81 female students

To determine the appropriate distribution to use, we need to check the conditions. We are told that the sample is representative but we are not told that the distribution of resting pulse rate in the population is Normal. However, since the sample size is at least 30 ($n = 81$), $\overline{X}$ follows a Normal distribution. The standard deviation of resting pulse rate for the *population* of female students is given, $\sigma = 10$. So the conditions required to use the Z-distribution are met.

The standard deviation of the population of female students is $\sigma = 10$, the sample size is $n = 81$, and the sample mean resting pulse rate of female students is $\overline{x} = 64$. For a 95% confidence interval, we see from the *t*-table that $z = 1.96$.

Degrees of Freedom	90%	95%	98%	99%
99	1.660	1.984	2.365	2.626
500	1.648	1.965	2.334	2.586
1000	1.646	1.962	2.330	2.581
Z-Values	1.645	1.96	2.326	2.576

Applying the formula gives the following confidence interval:

$$\overline{x} \pm z \frac{\sigma}{\sqrt{n}} = 64 \pm 1.96 \frac{10}{\sqrt{81}}$$
$$= 64 \pm 2.1778$$

The 95% confidence interval for the population mean resting pulse rate of female students is (61.8222, 66.1778). Thus we can be 95% confident that the true mean resting pulse rate of female students is between 61.8222 and 66.1778.

Confidence intervals are enclosed in parentheses, with the smaller number first, the larger number second, and a comma between the two numbers. The smaller number is called the *lower limit*, and the larger number is called the *upper limit*. So a confidence interval is written as follows:

$$(lower\ limit,\ upper\ limit)$$

Since the confidence interval is derived from sample data representative of a particular population, it can only be used to draw conclusions about that population. The results cannot be applied to other populations.

6.1.4   **FINDING THE MINIMUM SAMPLE SIZE**
If a researcher decides on the confidence level and margin of error before collecting data, then it is possible to find the minimum sample size required in order to fulfill those conditions. The following method is only appropriate when using the Z-distribution.

To find the Minimum Sample Size required to Estimate a Population Mean:

1. Verify that the population is Normally distributed and σ is known.
2. Using the formula for the margin of error E, we find that:

$$n = \left(\frac{z\sigma}{E}\right)^2$$

- z is a value obtained from the last row of the *t*-table and is based on the confidence level.
- σ is the population standard deviation
- E is the given margin of error

A sample size *must* always be reported as a whole number. If the calculation does not result in a whole number, *round up* to the next whole number.

For example, if the standard deviation of resting pulse rate for the population of female students is assumed to be 10, how large a sample would you need to estimate the population mean resting pulse rate of female students with 95% confidence and a margin of error of 2? Assume that resting pulse rate follows a Normal distribution.

The parameter of interest is:

μ = the population mean resting pulse rate for female students.

The population is assumed to be Normally distributed, with a standard deviation of resting pulse rate of $\sigma = 10$, so the conditions required to use the Z-distribution are satisfied.

To find the minimum sample size such that we can estimate the population mean with 95% confidence and a margin of error of $E = 2$, apply the formula for sample size, with $z = 1.96$.

$$n = \left(\frac{z\sigma}{E}\right)^2 = \left(\frac{1.96(10)}{2}\right)^2 = 9.8^2 = 96.04$$

So, we need to sample a minimum of 97 female students.

6.1.4   **USING THE *t*-DISTRIBUTION**

We will now discuss how to construct a confidence interval for a population mean using the *t*-distribution.

A Confidence Interval for a Population Mean using the *t*-distribution is given by:

$$\bar{x} \pm t\frac{s}{\sqrt{n}}$$

- $\bar{x}$ represents the sample mean of the data.
- t is a value obtained from the *t*-table, based on the confidence level *and* the degrees of freedom (for this method, $df = n - 1$)
- s is the standard deviation of the sample
- n is the sample size

Consider another example in which the resting pulse rate of a representative sample of 35 female students has a mean of 62 and a standard deviation of 8. Construct a 95% confidence interval for the mean resting pulse rate in the population of female students.

The parameter of interest is:

μ = the population mean resting pulse rate of female students

The random variable of interest is:

$\bar{X}$ = the sample mean resting pulse rate of 35 female students

To determine the appropriate distribution to use, check the conditions. The sample is representative but we are not told that the distribution of resting pulse rate in the population is Normal. However, the sample size is at least 30 ($n = 35$), so $\bar{X}$ follows a Normal distribution. Since the *sample* standard deviation of the resting pulse rate of female students, $s = 8$, is given, the conditions needed to use the t-distribution have been satisfied and hence the required confidence interval is found using:

$$\bar{x} \pm t \frac{s}{\sqrt{n}}$$

where $\bar{x} = 62$, $s = 8$ and $n = 35$. The value of t for a 95% confidence interval and $n - 1 = 34$ degrees of freedom is found using the t-table.

Degrees of Freedom	90%	95%	98%	99%
32	1.694	2.037	2.449	2.738
33	1.692	2.035	2.445	2.733
34	1.691	2.032	2.441	2.728
35	1.690	2.030	2.438	2.724
36	1.688	2.028	2.434	2.719

Substituting in the formula we get:

$$\bar{x} \pm t \frac{s}{\sqrt{n}} = 62 \pm 2.032 \frac{8}{\sqrt{35}}$$
$$= 62 \pm 2.7478$$

So the 95% confidence interval for the mean resting pulse rate of female students is $(59.2522, \ 64.7478)$. We are 95% confident that the population mean resting pulse rate of female students is between 59.2522 and 64.7478.

LESSON 6.1 EXERCISES
CONFIDENCE INTERVALS
FOR A POPULATION MEAN

1. The mean weight of a random sample of 50 Anna's Hummingbirds was 24 grams and the standard deviation was 0.4 grams. You want to construct a 95% confidence interval for the population mean weight. Should you use a Z-distribution, a t-distribution, or neither? Justify your answer.

2. The resting pulse rate of a representative sample of 25 female students has a mean of 64 and a standard deviation of 6. Assume the sample is from a population that follows a Normal distribution.
   a) What distribution should you use for this analysis?
   b) Define the parameter and random variable of interest.
   c) Find a 99% confidence interval for the population mean resting pulse rate of female students.
   d) Interpret the confidence interval found in part (c).

3. Army recruits are required to pass a variety of physical tests. The Army is interested in the mean time it takes a new recruit to run a mile. The mean time it takes a new recruit to run a mile for a representative sample of 68 recruits was calculated to be 7 minutes and the standard deviation was 0.5 minutes.
   a) What distribution should you use for this analysis?
   b) Define the parameter and random variable of interest.
   c) Find a 98% confidence interval for the mean time it takes a new recruit to run a mile.
   d) Interpret the confidence interval found in part (c).

4. A researcher in the Department of Computer Science wants to estimate the mean number of hours per day that computer science majors spend in the lab. A representative sample of 40 students were asked how many hours per day they spend in the lab and their answers were recorded. The researcher calculated the sample mean number of hours to be 3.45. From previous studies the researcher assumes the standard deviation for all students is 0.85.
   a) What distribution should you use for this analysis?
   b) Define the parameter and random variable of interest.
   c) Find a 95% confidence interval for the population mean number of hours per day that computer science majors spend in the lab.
   d) Interpret the confidence interval found in part (c).

5. A fruit canning company wants to estimate the mean weight of cans of peaches. Assume that the weights of the cans follow a Normal distribution with a standard deviation of 30 grams.
    a) What distribution should you use for this analysis?
    b) Define the parameter of interest.
    c) Find the minimum sample size required if the company wants to be 95% confident that the sample mean is within 5 grams of the population mean.

ANSWERS
LESSON 6.1 EXERCISES
CONFIDENCE INTERVALS
FOR A POPULATION MEAN

Below are the answers to the exercises for Unit 6, Lesson 6.1.
For full solutions, please refer to the CD included with this textbook.

1. The conditions are satisfied to use a *t*-distribution.

2. a) Conditions are satisfied to use the *t*-distribution.
    b) μ = the population mean resting pulse rate of female students

    $\overline{X}$ = the sample mean resting pulse rate of 25 female students
    c) (60.6436, 67.3564)
    d) With 99% confidence, the population mean resting pulse rate of female students is between 60.6436 and 67.3564 beats per minute.

3. a) Conditions are satisfied to use the *t*-distribution.
    b) μ = the population mean time it takes a new recruit to run a mile

    $\overline{X}$ = the sample mean time it takes 68 new recruits to run a mile
    c) (6.8555, 7.1445)
    d) With 98% confidence, the population mean time it takes a new recruit to run a mile is between 6.8555 and 7.1445 minutes.

4. a) Conditions are satisfied to use the *Z*-distribution.
    b) μ = the population mean number of hours per day that computer science majors spend in the lab

    $\overline{X}$ = the sample mean number of hours per day that 40 computer science majors spend in the lab
    c) (3.1866, 3.7134)
    d) With 95% confidence, the population mean number of hours per day that computer science majors spend in the lab is between 3.1866 and 3.7134 hours.

5. a) Conditions are satisfied to use the *Z*-distribution.
    b) μ = the population mean weight of cans of peaches
    c) The minimum sample size is 139 cans of peaches.

LESSON 6.2
HYPOTHESIS TESTING FOR A POPULATION MEAN

6.2.1   **INTRODUCTION**

Another method for learning about a population parameter is through hypothesis testing. In hypothesis testing a claim is made about the parameter of interest, and the data be used to make a decision about the claim.

6.2.2   **DECIDING WHICH DISTRIBUTION TO USE**

Recall the rules for determining the distribution to use for a confidence interval for a population mean. These also apply for a hypothesis test for a population mean. As a reminder, they are:

Check the Following Conditions:

- The data come from a sample that is representative of the population of interest.

- $\overline{X}$ follows a Normal distribution. That is, the data come from a Normally distributed population *or* the sample size is at least 30.

- Check if you know σ, the population standard deviation, or if you know s, the sample standard deviation.

Use the Z-distribution when σ is known.

Use the t-distribution when s is known.

When conducting a hypothesis test by hand, it is difficult to compute exact results with the t-distribution. Therefore, we will focus on describing the method using the Z-distribution. However, you should still determine which method is appropriate for each problem.

6.2.3   **SETTING UP HYPOTHESES**

A hypothesis test involves two hypotheses. One is called the *null hypothesis*, and is denoted by H_0. The null hypothesis must contain one of the following signs of equality, either '=', '$\leq$', or '$\geq$'. The other is the *alternative hypothesis*, denoted by H_A. The alternative hypothesis must contain the following signs of inequality, either '$\neq$', '>', or '<'. The only difference between the null and alternative hypothesis is the sign, and the signs should be complementary.

Important Idea

The null hypothesis must contain a sign of equality.

The alternative hypothesis must contain a sign of inequality.

Hypotheses are statements about the parameter of interest, which for this unit is μ, the population mean. For example, to test the claim that the population mean height of men is less than 68 inches, we can set up the hypotheses in the following way:

Let μ = the population mean height of men

Then the claim is that $\mu < 68$.

STOP AND THINK!

Is this the null or alternative hypothesis? How do you know?

Since $\mu < 68$ is a statement of inequality, it must be the alternative hypothesis.

The complementary statement to the claim is $\mu \geq 68$. Since this is a statement of equality, it must be the null hypothesis.

Thus, we can write the hypotheses and identify the claim:

$$H_0: \ \mu \geq 68 \qquad\qquad H_A: \ \mu < 68 \ \text{(claim)}$$

Example: A doctor claims that the average weight of healthy adults is 150 pounds.

Question
Write the null and alternative hypotheses to test the doctor's claim.

Solution: The parameter of interest is:

μ = the population mean weight of healthy adults

The doctor is claiming that $\mu = 150$. Since this is a statement of equality, it must be the null hypothesis.

The complementary statement to the claim is $\mu \neq 150$. Since this is a statement of inequality, it must be the alternative hypothesis.

Thus, we can write the hypotheses and identify the claim:

$$H_0: \ \mu = 150 \ \text{(claim)} \qquad H_A: \ \mu \neq 150$$

■

Consider a third example, where a magazine claims that Americans exercise at most 20 minutes a day, on average. We can set up the hypotheses in the following way to test this claim:

Let μ = the population mean time Americans exercise per day

Then the claim is that $\mu \leq 20$.

> **STOP AND THINK!**
>
> **Is this the null or alternative hypothesis? How do you know?**

Since $\mu \leq 20$ is a statement of equality, it must be the null hypothesis.

The complementary statement to the claim is $\mu > 20$. Since this is a statement of inequality, it must be the alternative hypothesis.

Thus, we can write the hypotheses and identify the claim:

$$H_0: \ \mu \leq 20 \ \text{(claim)} \qquad H_A: \ \mu > 20$$

These three scenarios illustrate the three ways in which the signs in the hypotheses can be paired together. These are summarized in Table 6.1.

Table 6.1

H_0	H_A
$=$	$\neq$
$\leq$	$>$
$\geq$	$<$

Notice from these examples that the claim can be either the null or the alternative hypothesis, depending on whether the claim is a statement of equality or inequality. Regardless of which is the claim, hypothesis testing is always done under the assumption that the *null* hypothesis is true.

Important Idea

Hypothesis testing is always done under the assumption that the *null* hypothesis is true.

The following example will be used for the remainder of the lesson to illustrate the various steps in hypothesis testing.

A representative sample of 100 students from a university were surveyed and asked their GPA. Their mean GPA was 3.57. The standard deviation for the GPA of all students at this university is known to be 0.4. The university claims the mean GPA of its students is more than 3.5. Test the university's claim at a 5% significance level.

First determine which distribution is appropriate to use.

- We are told the sample is representative.
- We are not told that the distribution of GPA in the population is Normal, however, since we sampled 100 students, this is a sufficiently large sample size to ensure that $\overline{X}$ follows a Normal distribution.
- We are told that the standard deviation of the GPA for *all* students is 0.4, therefore $\sigma = 0.4$.

Thus, the conditions needed to use the *Z*-distribution are satisfied.

Next, we define the parameter of interest and set up the hypotheses.

Let μ = the population mean GPA of students at this university

The claim is that $\mu > 3.5$.

STOP AND THINK!

Is this the null or alternative hypothesis? How do you know?

Since $\mu > 3.5$ is a statement of inequality, it must be the alternative hypothesis.

The complementary statement to the claim is $\mu \leq 3.5$. Since this is a statement of equality, it must be the null hypothesis.

Thus, we can write the hypotheses and identify the claim:

$$H_0: \ \mu \leq 3.5 \qquad\qquad H_A: \ \mu > 3.5 \ \ (claim)$$

Next we compute the test statistic, under the assumption that the null hypothesis is true.

6.2.4

CALCULATING THE TEST STATISTIC

A test statistic is simply a measure of how many standard deviations the sample statistic is from the hypothesized mean. Remember that hypothesis tests are carried out under the assumption that the null hypothesis is true.

As learned in Unit 5, under the correct conditions the sample mean $\overline{X}$ follows a Normal distribution. We have already verified that this is true in this example, and hence we can define:

$$\overline{X} = \text{the sample mean GPA of 100 students at this university}$$

The mean of $\overline{X}$ is μ, and since we are assuming the null hypothesis is true, we can assume that $\mu = 3.5$. The standard deviation of $\overline{X}$ is found as follows:

$$\text{Standard deviation of } \overline{X}: \ \frac{\sigma}{\sqrt{n}} = \frac{0.4}{\sqrt{100}} = 0.04$$

The distribution of $\overline{X}$ is shown in Figure 6.5.

Figure 6.5

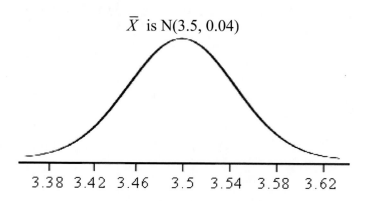

$$\overline{X} \text{ is N(3.5, 0.04)}$$

The null hypothesis states that $\mu \leq 3.5$, so it is possible that the distribution of $\overline{X}$ is centered at 3.5 *or lower*. Values of $\overline{X}$ that are 3.5 or lower will support the null hypothesis. Even values of $\overline{X}$ that are slightly larger than 3.5 will also support the null hypothesis. This is because such values are probable in the distribution shown in Figure 6.5. However, if we observe a value of $\overline{X}$ that is *much* larger than 3.5, this will lead us to doubt that the null is true.

In the example, the mean GPA of the 100 students sampled was 3.57. Figure 6.6 shows where this value falls in the distribution of $\overline{X}$:

Figure 6.6

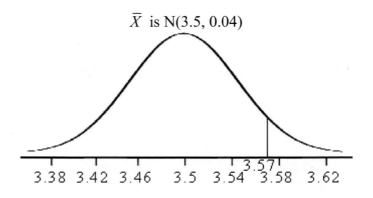

$\overline{X}$ is N(3.5, 0.04)

3.38 3.42 3.46 3.5 3.54 3.57 3.58 3.62

As we see, the sample mean we observed is larger than 3.5. In order to decide whether this supports the null hypothesis, we must first compute a test statistic.

Since we are using the Z-distribution, the test statistic is a *z*-score, and so the test statistic is computed as follows:

$$z = \frac{3.57 - 3.5}{0.04} = 1.75$$

This result can be generalized:

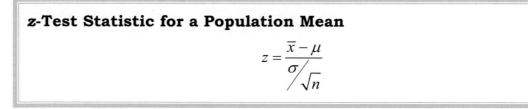

z-Test Statistic for a Population Mean

$$z = \frac{\overline{x} - \mu}{\sigma / \sqrt{n}}$$

Even though this formula looks different from the *z*-score formula we used in Unit 4, it is conceptually the same. We will now use the test statistic to obtain the *p*-value for the test.

6.2.5

FINDING THE *p*-VALUE

Recall that *z*-scores are used to find probabilities under the Normal curve. We have just computed the test statistic for the example, and obtained $z = 1.75$. What we now need to identify is the area of interest, which we call the *p*-value. We will only reject the null hypothesis if we observe a sample mean *much bigger* than 3.5. This indicates that we are interested in the area *above* the test statistic. Therefore, the *p*-value for this test is as shown in Figure 6.7.

Figure 6.7

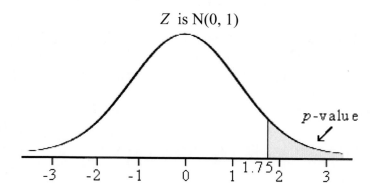

Looking up $z = 1.75$, the Standard Normal table shows that the area *below* 1.75 is 0.9599. We are interested in the area *above* $z = 1.75$, so the *p*-value is:

$$p - \text{value} = P(Z > 1.75)$$
$$= 1 - 0.9599$$
$$= 0.0401$$

Guidelines for finding *p*-values for any hypothesis test are shown below.

Finding *p*-values

To determine the *p*-value, first look at the sign in the alternative hypothesis:

If the sign is '<', then the *p*-value for the test is the area *below* the test statistic.

If the sign is '>', then the *p*-value for the test is the area *above* the test statistic.

If the sign is '≠', then the *p*-value for the test is the area *below* the negative value of the test statistic *plus* the area *above* the positive value of the test statistic.

Having found the *p*-value, next we decide whether the data supports the null or the alternative hypothesis.

6.2.6

THE DECISION

The null hypothesis is assumed to be true *unless* there is enough evidence to believe it is *not* true. This evidence is found in the *p*-value. A large *p*-value indicates that we have a high probability of observing the data if we believe the null. A large *p*-value then indicates that you should *not* reject the null hypothesis. When a *p*-value becomes too small, this indicates that the data is *unlikely* to occur if we believe the null. So a small *p*-value indicates that you should reject the null hypothesis.

The guideline for deciding whether a *p*-value is small or large is called the significance level, denoted by α, and it is established before any testing is done. A 5% significance level is the most common.

In the example, we were told to use a 5% significance level. So we have enough evidence to reject the null if we observe a *p*-value that is *less* than 0.05, and we do *not* have enough evidence to reject the null if we observe a *p*-value that is *more* than 0.05. The *p*-value for the test is 0.0401, which is *less* than the significance level. Therefore, we have enough evidence to reject the null hypothesis. In other words, the sample mean that we observed was *much* greater than 3.5, and so it does not support the null hypothesis.

To generalize:

Deciding Whether to Reject H₀

If the *p*-value is smaller than the significance level α, there is enough evidence to reject the null hypothesis.

Otherwise, there is not enough evidence to reject the null hypothesis.

Now that a decision has been made, we must offer an interpretation of our results.

6.2.7   **INTERPRETING THE RESULTS**

The final step in hypothesis testing is to state the conclusion. This means we need to address the original claim. Does the data support the claim, or does it not? Recall the hypotheses for this example:

$$H_0: \ \mu \le 3.5 \qquad\qquad H_A: \ \mu > 3.5 \ \text{(claim)}$$

Since the decision was to reject the null, the data supports the alternative, which is the claim. Therefore, at a 5% significance level, we can conclude that the mean GPA of students at this university is greater than 3.5.

LESSON 6.2 EXERCISES
HYPOTHESIS TESTING
FOR A POPULATION MEAN

1. A study was done on how much time kids spend watching television each day. A random sample of 400 kids found that they spend an average of 3.8 hours watching television each day. The standard deviation for the whole population is 1.2 hours per day. The claim is that on average kids watch less than 4 hours of television each day. Use a significance level of 0.01.
   a) Determine the appropriate distribution to use.
   b) Define the parameter and random variable of interest.
   c) State the null and alternative hypotheses, and identify the claim.
   d) Calculate the test statistic.
   e) Determine the p-value.
   f) State your decision.
   g) State your conclusion.

2. Every year, more and more people have to commute to work. A survey of 100 commuters in southern California determined that their average commute time is 1.6 hours. Suppose that the commute time for southern Californians is Normally distributed with a standard deviation of 1.25 hours, and that the sample is representative of all southern Californians. The claim is that commuters in southern California spend more than 1.5 hours commuting to work on average. Use a significance level of 0.05.
   a) Determine the appropriate distribution to use.
   b) Define the parameter and random variable of interest.
   c) State the null and alternative hypotheses, and identify the claim.
   d) Calculate the test statistic.
   e) Determine the p-value.
   f) State your decision.
   g) State your conclusion.

3. A sample of 133 college students were asked how many hours they work each week. The sample mean was 14.2 hours per week and the sample standard deviation was 2.5. Assume that the sample is representative of all college students. The claim is that the mean time college students spend working per week is 15 hours. Use a 5% significance level.
   a) Determine the appropriate distribution to use.
   b) Define the parameter and random variable of interest.
   c) State the null and alternative hypotheses and identify the claim.
   d) The p-value for this test is 0.0003. Use this p-value to make your decision.
   e) State your conclusion.

ANSWERS

LESSON 6.2 EXERCISES

HYPOTHESIS TESTING

FOR A POPULATION MEAN

Below are the answers to the exercises for Unit 6, Lesson 6.2.
For full solutions, please refer to the CD included with this textbook.

1. a) Conditions are satisfied to use the Z-distribution.
    b) μ = the population mean time kids watch TV each day
       $\overline{X}$ = the sample mean time 400 kids spend watching TV each day
    c) H_0: $\mu \geq 4$ H_A: $\mu < 4$ (claim)
    d) $z = -3.33$
    e) $p-\text{value} = 0.0004$
    f) There is enough evidence to reject H_0.
    g) There is enough evidence to support the claim that on average kids watch less than 4 hours of television each day.

2. a) Conditions are satisfied to use the Z-distribution.
    b) μ = the population mean time commuters in southern California spend commuting to work
       $\overline{X}$ = the sample mean time 100 commuters in southern California spend commuting to work
    c) H_0: $\mu \leq 1.5$ H_A: $\mu > 1.5$ (claim)
    d) $z = 0.80$
    e) $p-\text{value} = 0.2119$
    f) There is *not* enough evidence to reject H_0.
    g) There is *not* enough evidence to support the claim that the mean time commuters in southern California spend commuting to work is more than 1.5 hours.

3. a) Conditions are satisfied to use the t-distribution.
    b) μ = the population mean time college students spend working per week
       $\overline{X}$ = the sample mean time 133 college students spend working per week
    c) H_0: $\mu = 15$ (claim) H_A: $\mu \neq 15$
    d) There is enough evidence to reject H_0.
    e) There is evidence to reject the claim that the mean time all college students spend working per week is 15 hours

LESSON 6.3
MORE PRACTICE IN SOLVING INFERENCE PROBLEMS

In this lesson we look at some more examples with full solutions. You are encouraged to work through these problems yourself if you need extra practice.

Example 1: Silky Yarns produces spools of thread. A random sample of 36 spools is taken and the length of thread on each spool is measured. The sample mean is 1000 yards. Experience suggests that the population standard deviation is 50.
a) What distribution should you use for this analysis?
b) Define the parameter and random variable of interest.
c) Construct a 95% confidence interval for the true mean length of thread on each spool.

> **STOP AND THINK!**
>
> **Is the sample representative?**
>
> **Is the distribution of the sample mean Normal?**
>
> **Do we know the standard deviation of the population or of the sample?**

Solution: a) First determine which distribution is appropriate to use.
- We are told the sample is random, so we can assume it is representative.
- We are not told that the distribution of the population is Normal, however, since we sampled 36 spools, this is a sufficiently large sample size to ensure that $\bar{X}$ follows a Normal distribution.
- We are told that the standard deviation in the population is 50, therefore $\sigma = 50$.

Thus, the conditions needed to use the Z-distribution are satisfied.

Solution: b) We are testing a claim about a population mean, so the parameter of interest is:

$$\mu = \text{the population mean length of thread on a spool}$$

The random variable of interest is the sample mean:

$$\overline{X} = \text{the sample mean length of thread on 36 spools}$$

Solution: c) Since we are using the Z-distribution, the formula for a confidence interval is:

$$\overline{x} \pm z \frac{\sigma}{\sqrt{n}}$$

$\overline{x} = 1000$, $\sigma = 50$, $n = 36$, and 95% confidence implies that $z = 1.96$.

$$1000 \pm 1.96 \frac{50}{\sqrt{36}} = 1000 \pm 16.3333$$

The 95% confidence interval for the population mean length of thread on a spool is (983.6667, 1016.3333).

Example 2:   After a certain number of games, a tennis ball loses its bounce and is discarded. By taking a random sample of 16 tennis balls, a researcher finds that on average, a tennis ball loses its bounce after 6 hrs use. She calculated a sample standard deviation $s = 0.5$ hr. Assume the data come from a Normal distribution.
a) What distribution should you use for this analysis?
b) Define the parameter and random variable of interest.
c) Construct a 95% confidence interval for the true mean time it takes a tennis ball to lose its bounce.
d) Interpret the confidence interval you found in part (c).

> **STOP AND THINK!**
>
> **Is the sample representative?**
>
> **Is the distribution of the sample mean Normal?**
>
> **Do we know the standard deviation of the population or of the sample?**

Solution: a) First determine which distribution is appropriate to use.
- We are told the sample is random, so we can assume it is representative.
- The distribution of the population is Normal, so $\overline{X}$ follows a Normal distribution.
- We are told that the standard deviation in the sample is 0.5, therefore $s = 0.5$.

Thus, the conditions needed to use the t-distribution are satisfied.

Solution: b) We are testing a claim about a population mean, so the parameter of interest is:

μ = the population mean time it takes a tennis ball to lose its bounce

The random variable of interest is the sample mean:

$\bar{X}$ = the sample mean time it takes 16 tennis balls to lose their bounce

Solution: c) Since we are using the *t*-distribution, the formula for a confidence interval is:

$$\bar{x} \pm t \frac{s}{\sqrt{n}}$$

$\bar{x} = 6$, $s = 0.5$, $n = 16$, and 95% confidence with 15 degrees of freedom implies that $t = 2.131$.

$$6 \pm 2.131 \frac{0.5}{\sqrt{16}} = 6 \pm 0.2664$$

The 95% confidence interval for the population mean time it takes a tennis ball to lose its bounce is (5.7336, 6.2664).

Solution: d) We are 95% confident that the mean time it takes a tennis ball to lose its bounce lies between 5.7336 and 6.2664 hours.

Example 3: When constructing a confidence interval it is usual to choose a confidence level of 95%, 98% or 99%. Why would you choose 95% rather than 99%.

> **STOP AND THINK!**
>
> **How does the confidence level affect the interval?**

Solution: The higher the confidence level of the interval, the wider the interval will be. Therefore, you would choose 95% rather than 99% if you wanted a narrower interval which would provide more useful information.

Example 4: A random sample of 49 UCSB students were found to have a mean GPA of 3.0 with a standard deviation of 0.2. Assuming that the GPA of UCSB students are Normally distributed, find a 95% confidence interval for the population mean.
a) What distribution should you use for this analysis?
b) Define the parameter and random variable of interest.
c) Construct a 95% confidence interval for the population mean GPA of UCSB students.
d) Interpret the confidence interval you found in part c.

> **STOP AND THINK!**
>
> **Is the sample representative?**
>
> **Is the distribution of the sample mean Normal?**
>
> **Do we know the standard deviation of the population or of the sample?**

Solution:　　a)　First determine which distribution is appropriate to use.
- We are told the sample is random, so we can assume it is representative.
- The distribution of GPA's in the population is Normal, so $\bar{X}$ follows a Normal distribution.
- We are told that the standard deviation in the sample is 0.2, therefore $s = 0.2$.

Thus, the conditions needed to use the t-distribution are satisfied.

Solution:　　b)　We are testing a claim about a population mean, so the parameter of interest is:

$$\mu = \text{the population mean GPA of UCSB students}$$

The random variable of interest is the sample mean:

$$\bar{X} = \text{the sample mean GPA of 49 UCSB students}$$

Solution:　　c)　Since we are using the t-distribution, the formula for a confidence interval is:

$$\bar{x} \pm t \frac{s}{\sqrt{n}}$$

$\bar{x} = 3.0$, $s = 0.2$, $n = 49$, and 95% confidence with 48 degrees of freedom implies that $t = 2.011$.

$$3.0 \pm 2.011 \frac{0.2}{\sqrt{49}} = 3.0 \pm 0.0575$$

The 95% confidence interval for the population mean GPA of UCSB students is (2.9425, 3.0575).

Solution:　　d)　We are 95% confident that the mean GPA of UCSB students lies between 2.9425 and 3.0575.

Example 5: What is the minimum sample size required if you want to be 98% confident that the sample mean GPA of community college students is within 0.02 of the population mean? Assume that the GPA of all community college students is Normally distributed with a standard deviation of 0.18.

> **STOP AND THINK!**
>
> **What is the population standard deviation?**
>
> **What is the confidence level?**
>
> **What is the margin of error?**

Solution: This method is always done with the Z-distribution provided the data follows a Normal distribution and the population standard deviation is known. We do have the population standard deviation, it is $\sigma = 0.18$, and we are told to assume the GPA follows a Normal distribution. The confidence level is 98%, which implies $z = 2.326$, and the margin of error is $E = 0.02$. So we apply the formula:

$$n = \left(\frac{z\sigma}{E}\right)^2 = \left(\frac{2.326(0.18)}{0.02}\right)^2 = 438.2324$$

Therefore, the minimum sample size needed is 439 community college students.

■

Example 6: Doctors recommend getting 8 hours of sleep each night to avoid feeling tired during the day. College students regularly complain of being tired, and it is thought that it is because they do not get the recommended amount of sleep. A sample of 100 college students were asked how many hours they slept the night before. They averaged 7.62 hours of sleep. Assume the standard deviation for the hours slept each night for all college students is 1.5, and that the sample is representative of all college students. Test the claim that college students on average sleep less than the recommended 8 hours each night. Use a 5% significance level.
a) Determine the appropriate distribution to use.
b) Define the parameter and random variable of interest.
c) State the null and alternative hypotheses.
d) Calculate the test statistic.
e) Determine the *p*-value.
f) State your decision.
g) State your conclusion.

Solution:

a) First determine which distribution is appropriate to use.
   - We are told the sample is representative.
   - We are not told that the distribution of hours slept in the population is Normal, however, since we sampled 100 college students, this is a sufficiently large sample size to ensure that $\overline{X}$ follows a Normal distribution.
   - We are told that the standard deviation for *all* college students is 1.5, therefore $\sigma = 1.5$.

   Thus, the conditions needed to use the Z-distribution are satisfied.

Solution:

b) We are testing a claim about a population mean, so the parameter of interest is:

   μ = the population mean hours college students sleep each night

   The random variable of interest is the sample mean:

   $\overline{X}$ = the sample mean hours 100 college students sleep each night

Solution:

c) The claim is that $\mu < 8$. Since this is a statement of inequality, it must be the alternative hypothesis.

   The complementary statement to the claim is $\mu \geq 8$. Since this is a statement of equality, it must be the null hypothesis.

   Thus, we can write the hypotheses and identify the claim:

   $$H_0:\ \mu \geq 8 \qquad H_A:\ \mu < 8 \ \text{(claim)}$$

Solution:

d) The mean of $\overline{X}$ is μ, and since we are assuming the null hypothesis is true, we can assume that $\mu = 8$. The standard deviation of $\overline{X}$ is found as follows:

Standard deviation of $\bar{X}$: $\dfrac{\sigma}{\sqrt{n}} = \dfrac{1.5}{\sqrt{100}} = 0.15$

The observed sample mean was 7.62. The distribution of $\bar{X}$ is shown below, with the observed value of $\bar{x}$ marked.

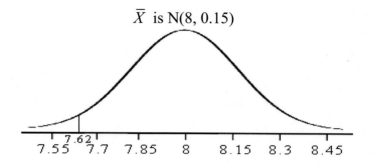

$\bar{X}$ is N(8, 0.15)

As we see, the sample mean we observed is smaller than 8. In order to decide whether this supports the null hypothesis, we must first compute a test statistic:

$$z = \dfrac{7.62 - 8}{0.15} = -2.53$$

Solution: e)   We will only reject the null hypothesis if we observe a sample mean *much smaller* than 8. This indicates that we are interested in the area *below* the test statistic. Therefore, the *p*-value for this test is as shown below:

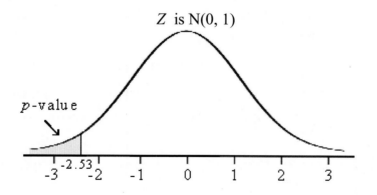

Z is N(0, 1)

p-value

This area is found in the Standard Normal table.

$$p-\text{value} = P(Z < -2.53) = 0.0057$$

Solution: f)   In the example, we were told to use a 5% significance level. So we have enough evidence to reject the null if we observe a *p*-value that is *less* than 0.05, and we do *not* have enough evidence to reject the null if we observe a *p*-value that is *more* than 0.05. The *p*-value for the test is 0.0057, which is *less* than the significance level. Therefore, we have enough evidence to reject the null hypothesis. In other words, the sample mean that we observed was *much* smaller than 8, and so it does not support the null hypothesis.

Solution: g) The final step in hypothesis testing is to state the conclusion. This means we need to address the original claim. Does the data support the claim, or does it not? Recall the hypotheses for this example:

$$H_0: \ \mu \geq 8 \qquad\qquad H_A: \ \mu < 8 \ \text{(claim)}$$

Since the decision was to reject the null, the data supports the alternative, which is the claim. Therefore, at a 5% significance level, we can conclude that the mean time college students sleep each night is less than 8 hours.

Example 7:   Previous studies have indicated the weights of dwarf rabbits follow a Normal distribution with a standard deviation of 0.32 pounds. A random sample of 16 dwarf rabbits showed an average weight was 4.1 pounds. The claim is that the mean weight of dwarf rabbits is 3.9 pounds. Use a 5% significance level.
a) Determine the appropriate distribution to use.
b) Define the parameter and random variable of interest.
c) State the null and alternative hypotheses.
d) Calculate the test statistic.
e) Determine the *p*-value.
f) State your decision.
g) State your conclusion.

> **STOP AND THINK!**
>
> **Is the sample representative?**
>
> **Is the distribution of the sample mean Normal?**
>
> **Do we know the standard deviation of the population or of the sample?**
>
> **What is the claim? Is it the null or alternative hypothesis? How do you know?**

Solution: a) First determine which distribution is appropriate to use.
- We are told the sample is random, which means we can assume it is representative.
- We are told that the distribution of weights in the population is Normal, so $\bar{X}$ follows a Normal distribution.
- We are told that the standard deviation for *all* dwarf rabbits is 0.32, therefore $\sigma = 0.32$.

Thus, the conditions needed to use the *Z*-distribution are satisfied.

Solution: b) We are testing a claim about a population mean, so the parameter of interest is:

$$\mu = \text{the population mean weight of dwarf rabbits}$$

The random variable of interest is the sample mean:

$$\bar{X} = \text{the sample mean weight of 16 dwarf rabbits}$$

Solution: c) The claim is that $\mu = 3.9$. Since this is a statement of equality, it must be the null hypothesis.

The complementary statement to the claim is $\mu \neq 3.9$. Since this is a statement of inequality, it must be the alternative hypothesis.

Thus, we can write the hypotheses and identify the claim:

$$H_0: \ \mu = 3.9 \ \text{(claim)} \qquad\qquad H_A: \ \mu \neq 3.9$$

Solution: d) The mean of $\bar{X}$ is μ, and since we are assuming the null hypothesis is true, we can assume that $\mu = 3.9$. The standard deviation of $\bar{X}$ is found as follows:

$$\text{Standard deviation of } \bar{X}: \quad \frac{\sigma}{\sqrt{n}} = \frac{0.32}{\sqrt{16}} = 0.08$$

The observed sample mean was 4.1. The distribution of $\bar{X}$ is shown below, with the observed value of $\bar{x}$ marked.

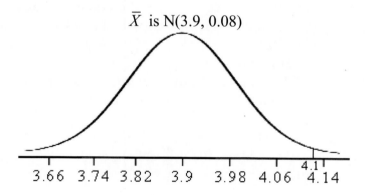

$\bar{X}$ is N(3.9, 0.08)

As we see, the sample mean we observed is larger than 3.9. In order to decide whether this supports the null hypothesis, we must first compute a test statistic:

$$z = \frac{4.1 - 3.9}{0.08} = 2.50$$

Solution: e) When the sign in the alternative is '≠', the *p*-value is defined to be the area *below* the negative value of the test statistic *plus* the area *above* the positive value of the test statistic. This is because we will find evidence to reject the null hypothesis if the observed sample mean is much larger *or* much smaller than 3.9. Therefore, the *p*-value for this test is as shown below:

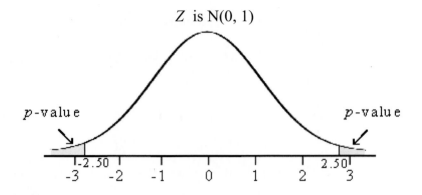

This area is found in the Standard Normal table.

$$p - \text{value} = P(Z < -2.50) + P(Z > 2.50)$$
$$= 0.0062 + (1 - 0.9938)$$
$$= 0.0062 + 0.0062$$
$$= 0.0124$$

Notice that the two areas are equal. This will always be the case for such a test.

Solution: f) In the example, we were told to use a 5% significance level. So we have enough evidence to reject the null if we observe a *p*-value that is *less* than 0.05, and we do *not* have enough evidence to reject the null if we observe a *p*-value that is *more* than 0.05. The *p*-value for the test is 0.0124, which is *less* than the significance level. Therefore, we have enough evidence to reject the null hypothesis. In other words, the sample mean that we observed was *much* larger than 3.9, and so it does not support the null hypothesis.

Solution: g) The final step in hypothesis testing is to state the conclusion. This means we need to address the original claim. Does the data support the claim, or does it not? Recall the hypotheses for this example:

$$H_0: \mu = 3.9 \text{ (claim)} \qquad H_A: \mu \neq 3.9$$

Since the decision was to reject the null, the data supports the alternative, which is *not* the claim. Therefore, at a 5% significance level, we can conclude that the mean weight of dwarf rabbits is *not* 3.9 pounds.

Example 8: The vocabulary of students learning French was tested after 1 year of study. A random sample of 11 students were tested after 1 year of study and the results recorded. The mean number of words understood by a student was 800 and the standard deviation was 30. Assume the data come from a Normal distribution. The claim is that the mean number of words understood by a student learning French is more than 750. The appropriate hypothesis test was carried out, and the p-value was 0.0001. State your decision and conclusion for the test, using a 1% significance level.

> **STOP AND THINK!**
>
> **What are the null and alternative hypotheses that were tested?**
>
> **How does the p-value help you make a decision?**

Solution: Let μ = the population mean number of words understood by a student learning French

The claim is that $\mu > 750$. This is a statement of inequality, so it is the alternative hypothesis.

The complementary statement to the claim is that $\mu \leq 750$. Since this is a statement of equality, this is the null hypothesis.

Thus, the hypotheses are:

$$H_0: \ \mu \leq 750 \qquad\qquad H_A: \ \mu > 750 \ \text{(claim)}$$

The p-value is 0.0001, which is smaller than the significance level of 0.01. Therefore, there is enough evidence to reject the null hypothesis. This indicates that there is enough evidence to support the claim that the mean number of words understood by a student learning French is more than 750.

■

Example 9: Mike loves movies, and has heard that the average movie length is 100 minutes. He decides to test this claim, so he randomly selects 50 movies and records how long they last. He tests the following hypotheses:

$$H_0: \ \mu = 100 \ \text{(claim)} \qquad\qquad H_A: \ \mu \neq 100$$

where μ = the population mean movie length in minutes. He obtains a p-value of 0.002.

a) Using a 5% level of significance, what does Mike decide?
b) State the conclusion of Mike's test.
c) Mike then constructs a 95% confidence interval for the population mean movie length using the data he collected. Which of these intervals is the one Mike constructed? Explain.
   Interval A: (93.4, 104.9)
   Interval B: (109.2, 120.7)

STOP AND THINK!

How does the *p*-value help you make a decision?

Which interval supports the conclusion from the hypothesis test?

Solution: a) Since the *p*-value is smaller than 0.05, there is enough evidence to reject the null hypothesis.

Solution: b) Mike can conclude that the population mean movie length is *not* 100 minutes.

Solution: c) Interval B is the one Mike constructed. It supports the results of the hypothesis test because it indicates that the population mean movie length is *not* 100 minutes.

Example 10: When people purchase a new car, they have the option of trading in their old car to cover part of the cost. A used car dealer claims that the average mileage of these trade-ins is below 80,000 miles. To test this claim, 100 trade-ins were randomly inspected and their mileage recorded.
a) Define the parameter and random variable of interest.
b) State the null and alternative hypotheses, and identify the claim.
c) The *p*-value for the test is 0.7832. What is the decision of the test? Use a 5% significance level.
d) What can we conclude?

STOP AND THINK!

What are we interested in?

What is the claim? Is it the null or the alternative? How do you know?

We are not given a significance level to use, but it does not matter? Why not?

Is the claim supported?

Solution: a) We are testing a claim about a population mean, so the parameter of interest is:

$$\mu = \text{the population mean mileage of trade-ins}$$

The random variable of interest is the sample mean:

$$\overline{X} = \text{the sample mean mileage of 100 trade-ins}$$

Solution: b) The claim is that $\mu < 80,000$. Since this is a statement of inequality, it must be the alternative hypothesis.

The complementary statement to the claim is $\mu \geq 80,000$. Since this is a statement of equality, it must be the null hypothesis.

Thus, we can write the hypotheses and identify the claim:

$$H_0: \ \mu \geq 80,000 \qquad\qquad H_A: \ \mu < 80,000 \ \text{(claim)}$$

Solution: c) The p-value is 0.7832, which is much larger than the significance level, so we have no evidence to reject the null hypothesis.

Solution: d) The final step in hypothesis testing is to state the conclusion. This means we need to address the original claim. Does the data support the claim, or does it not? Recall the hypotheses for this example:

$$H_0: \ \mu \geq 80,000 \qquad\qquad H_A: \ \mu < 80,000 \ \text{(claim)}$$

Since the decision was *not* to reject the null, the data supports the null, which is *not* the claim. Therefore, we can conclude that the mean mileage of trade-ins is *not* less than 80,000

■

LESSON 6.3 EXERCISES
MORE PRACTICE IN SOLVING INFERENCE ON A SAMPLE MEAN PROBLEMS

1. After a storm, Bob needs to get the roof of his home repaired. He phones 9 roofing specialists and asks how much they would charge for the repair. The mean price is $230 and the standard deviation is $24. Bob wants to construct a confidence interval for the population mean price of repairing his roof. Assume the sample comes from a Normal population.
   a) What distribution should he use for this analysis?
   b) Define the parameter and random variable of interest.
   c) Find a 95% confidence interval for the population mean price of repairing Bob's roof.
   d) Interpret the confidence interval found in part (c).

2. Peter keeps a record of the fuel consumption of his car. Weekly records for the past 36 weeks show that the mean number of miles per gallon for Peter's car is 40. Assume the standard deviation is known to be 5 and the sample comes from a Normal distribution.
   a) What distribution should you use for this analysis?
   b) Define the parameter and random variable of interest.
   c) Find a 98% CI for the mean number of miles per gallon for Peter's car.
   d) Interpret the confidence interval found in part (c).
   e) Find the minimum number of weeks that Peter should record the fuel consumption of his car if he wants to estimate the population mean fuel consumption within 1.5 miles per gallon with 98% confidence.

3. Ten pages of "Pride and Prejudice" are chosen at random and the number of words per page recorded. The mean number of words per page is 500 and the sample standard deviation is 25. Assume the sample comes from a Normal population.
   a) What distribution should you use for this analysis?
   b) Define the parameter and random variable of interest.
   c) Find a 95% confidence interval for the mean number of words per page.
   d) Interpret the confidence interval found in part (c).

4. A random sample of $n = 45$ was taken from a Normal distribution and the following statistics were calculated: $\bar{x} = 125$ and $s = 5$. The claim is that the population mean is less than 125. An appropriate hypothesis test was carried out and the p-value was 0.1234. State your decision and conclusion for the test, using a 5% significance level.

5. A manufacturer of refrigerators knows from data collected over a long time that the lifetime of their refrigerators is Normal distributed with a standard deviation of 1.5 years. A random sample of 20 refrigerators was found to have an average lifetime of 9.5 years. The manufacturers claim that the mean lifetime of their refrigerators is 10 years. You are not convinced that this claim is correct and decide to test it. Use a 5% significance level.
   a) Determine the appropriate distribution to use.
   b) Define the parameter and random variable of interest.
   c) State the null and alternative hypotheses, and identify the claim.
   d) Calculate the test statistic.
   e) Determine the p-value.
   f) State your decision.
   g) State your conclusion.

6. A shoe factory manager knows from records kept for many years that the number of pairs of shoes produced by the factory each day is on average 500. The manager claims that this rate of production may have changed recently. She randomly samples 35 days and finds that the mean production rate is 450 pairs of shoes. She computes the standard deviation for the sample to be 20. Test the manager's claim. Use a 5% significance level.
   a) Determine the appropriate distribution to use.
   b) Define the parameter and random variable of interest.
   c) State the null and alternative hypotheses, and identify the claim.
   d) The p-value for the test is almost 0.   Use this p-value to make your decision.
   e) State your conclusion.

ANSWERS
LESSON 6.3 EXERCISES
MORE PRACTICE IN SOLVING INFERENCE ON A SAMPLE MEAN PROBLEMS

Below are the answers to the exercises for Unit 6, Lesson 6.3.
For full solutions, please refer to the CD included with this textbook.

1. a) Conditions are satisfied to use the t-distribution.
    b) $\mu =$ the population mean price of repairing Bob's roof from roofing specialists
        $\overline{X} =$ the sample mean price of repairing Bob's roof from 9 roofing specialist
    c) (211.55, 248.45)
    d) We can be 95% confident that the population mean price of repairing Bob's roof is between $211.55 and $248.45.

2. a) Conditions are satisfied to use the Z-distribution.
    b) $\mu =$ the population mean weekly fuel consumption of Peter's car
        $\overline{X} =$ the sample mean weekly fuel consumption of Peter's car for the past 36 weeks
    c) (38.0617, 41.9383)
    d) We can be 98% confident that the population mean weekly fuel consumption of Peter's car is between 38.0617 and 41.9383 gallons.
    e) $n = 61$

3. a) Conditions are satisfied to use the t-distribution.
    b) $\mu =$ the population mean number of words per page in "Pride and Prejudice"
        $\overline{X} =$ the sample mean number of words per page on 10 pages of "Pride and Prejudice"
    c) (482.1173, 517.8827)
    d) We can be 95% confident that the population mean number of words per page in "Pride and Prejudice" is between 482.1173 and 517.8827.

4. Decision: There is not enough evidence to reject the null hypothesis.
    Conclusion: There is not enough evidence to show that the population mean is less than 125.

5. a) Conditions are satisfied to use the Z-distribution.
    b) μ = the population mean lifetime of refrigerators

        $\overline{X}$ = the sample mean lifetime of 20 refrigerators
    c) H_0: $\mu = 10$ (claim) H_A: $\mu \neq 10$
    d) $z = -1.49$
    e) $p-\text{value} = 0.1362$
    f) There is not enough evidence to reject H_0.
    g) There is enough evidence to support the claim that the average lifetime of refrigerators is 10 years.

6. a) Conditions are satisfied to use the t-distribution.
    b) μ = the population mean number of pairs of shoes produced by the factory each day

        $\overline{X}$ = the sample mean number of pairs of shoes produced by the factory in 35 days
    c) H_0: $\mu = 500$ H_A: $\mu \neq 500$ (claim)
    d) There is enough evidence to reject H_0.
    e) There is enough evidence to support the claim that the average number of pairs of shoes produced by the factory each day is not 500.

AVOIDING COMMON MISTAKES

☺ A common mistake is to leave the parameter out of the hypotheses. For example, to test a claim that the true mean height of men is less than 68 inches, people often write the hypotheses like this:

THIS IS WRONG!!! $H_0 \geq 68$ $H_A < 68$ **THIS IS WRONG!!!**

☺ Other common mistakes are to include sample values or point estimates in your hypotheses. **THIS IS WRONG!!!!!** The claim drives your hypothesis, and the claim is based on the parameter you are trying to learn about, and NOT on the sample data. Setting up your hypotheses right is the key, do not do it incorrectly.

☺ Always verify which distribution you should use *before* computing any confidence intervals or conducting any hypothesis testing. If you use the wrong distribution, you are solving the problem incorrectly.

UNIT 6 SUMMARY

- The *point estimate* of a population mean is the sample mean.

- Interval estimate

  point estimate $\pm$ margin of error

- Confidence Interval for a Population Mean

  sample mean $\pm$ margin of error

- Check the Following Conditions:
  - The data come from a sample that is representative of the population of interest.
  - $\overline{X}$ follows a Normal distribution. That is, the data come from a Normally distributed population *or* the sample size is at least 30.
  - Check if you know σ, the population standard deviation, or if you know s, the sample standard deviation.

  Use the Z-distribution when σ is known.

  Use the t-distribution when s is known.

- A Confidence Interval for a Population Mean using the Z-distribution is given by:

$$\overline{x} \pm z \frac{\sigma}{\sqrt{n}}$$

  - $\overline{x}$ represents the sample mean of the data.
  - z is a value obtained from the last row of the t-table and is based on the confidence level.
  - σ is the standard deviation of the population.
  - n is the sample size.

- To find the Minimum Sample Size required to Estimate a Population Mean:
  - Verify that the population is Normally distributed and σ is known.
  - Using the formula for the margin of error E, we find that:

$$n = \left(\frac{z\sigma}{E} \right)^2$$

  - z is a value obtained from the last row of the t-table and is based on the confidence level.
  - σ is the standard deviation of the population.
  - E is the margin of error.
  - Sample size *must* always be reported as a whole number. If the calculation does not result in a whole number, *round up* to the next whole number.

- A Confidence Interval for a Population Mean using the *t*-distribution is given by:

$$\bar{x} \pm t \frac{s}{\sqrt{n}}$$

  - $\bar{x}$ represents the sample mean of the data.
  - *t* is a value obtained from the *t*-table, based on the confidence level *and* the degrees of freedom (for this method, $df = n - 1$)
  - *s* is the standard deviation of the sample
  - *n* is the sample size

- The null hypothesis must contain a sign of equality. The alternative hypothesis must contain a sign of inequality.

- Hypothesis testing is always done under the assumption that the *null* hypothesis is true.

- *z*-Test Statistic for a Population Mean

$$z = \frac{\bar{x} - \mu}{\sigma / \sqrt{n}}$$

- To determine the *p*-value, first look at the sign in the alternative hypothesis:

  - If the sign is '<', then the *p*-value for the test is the area *below* the test statistic.

  - If the sign is '>', then the *p*-value for the test is the area *above* the test statistic.

  - If the sign is '≠', then the *p*-value for the test is the area *below* the negative value of the test statistic *plus* the area *above* the positive value of the test statistic.

- Deciding Whether to Reject H_0
  - If the *p*-value is smaller than the significance level α, there is enough evidence to reject the null hypothesis.
  - Otherwise, there is not enough evidence to reject the null hypothesis.

SELF-ASSESSMENT QUIZ

1. Seven random samples of water are taken from a creek and the concentration of phosphates in mg per liter is measured. The 95% confidence interval for the mean concentration of phosphates (mg/l) in the water from this creek is (1.3398, 1.8889). Interpret this confidence interval.

2. A researcher is interested in estimating the population mean circumference of aspen trees in a local forest. A random sample of 50 aspen trees was found to have a mean circumference of 17 inches and a standard deviation of 10.
   a) What distribution should you use for this analysis?
   b) Define the parameter and random variable of interest.
   c) Construct a 95% confidence interval for the population mean.
   d) Interpret the confidence interval found in part c.
   e) If you were to use the data to construct a 98% confidence interval for the population mean, would it be wider or narrower than the interval constructed in part (c)? Explain your answer (don't construct the interval).

3. What is the minimum sample size required if the researcher wants to be 95% confident that the sample mean weight of golden retrievers is within 2 pounds of the population mean? Assume the weights of golden retrievers are Normally distributed with a standard deviation of 7.5 pounds.

4. A local primary care physician claims that the mean time patients wait before being treated is less than 25 minutes. Previous studies have indicated that waiting times follow a Normal distribution with a standard deviation of 3 minutes. A random sample of 12 patients had a mean waiting time of 24 minutes. Test the physicians claim using a 1% significance level.
   a) Determine the appropriate distribution to use.
   b) Define the parameter and random variable of interest.
   c) State the null and alternative hypotheses, and identify the claim.
   d) Calculate the test statistic.
   e) Determine the p-value.
   f) State your decision.
   g) State your conclusion.

5. Carla is studying abroad in Spain. She claims that the mean number of Euros she spends each day is no more than 30. She records here spending for 15 representative days and finds the sample mean is 31.4 Euros and the standard deviation is 3.3. Assume the data comes from a Normal population. Test Carla's claim using a 5% significance level.
   a) Determine the appropriate distribution to use.
   b) Define the parameter and random variable of interest.
   c) State the null and alternative hypotheses, and identify the claim.
   d) The p-value for the test is 0.0613. Use this p-value to make your decision.
   e) State your conclusion.

ANSWERS
SELF-ASSESSMENT QUIZ

Below are the answers to the exercises for Unit 6, Self-Assessment Quiz. For full solutions, please refer to the CD included with this textbook.

1. We can be 95% confident that the population mean concentration of phosphates in the water from this creek is between 1.3398 and 1.8889 mg/l.

2. a) Conditions are satisfied to use the t-distribution.
    b) $\mu =$ the population mean circumference of aspen trees in a local forest

    $\overline{X} =$ the sample mean circumference of 50 aspen trees in a local forest
    c) (14.1574, 19.8426)
    d) We can be 95% confident that the population mean circumference of aspen trees in a local forest is between 14.1574 and 19.8426 inches.
    e) The 98% confidence interval would be wider than the 95% confidence interval because increasing the confidence level increases the width of the interval.

3. $n = 55$

4. a) Conditions are satisfied to use the Z-distribution.
    b) $\mu =$ the population mean waiting time of patients

    $\overline{X} =$ the sample mean waiting time of 12 patients
    c) $H_0: \mu \geq 25$ $H_A: \mu < 25$ (claim)
    d) $z = -1.15$
    e) $p - \text{value} = 0.1251$
    f) There is not enough evidence to reject H_0.
    g) There is not enough evidence to support the claim that the average waiting time of patients is less than 25 minutes.

5. a) Conditions are satisfied to use the t-distribution.
    b) $\mu =$ the population mean number of Euros Carla spends each day

    $\overline{X} =$ the sample mean number Euros Carla spends on 15 days
    c) $H_0: \mu \leq 30$ (claim) $H_A: \mu > 30$
    d) There is not enough evidence to reject H_0.
    e) There is enough evidence to support Carla's claim that the average number Euros she spends each day is no more than 30.

UNIT 7
INFERENCE ON A SAMPLE PROPORTION

Lesson 7.1   Confidence Intervals for a Population Proportion
Exercises for Lesson 7.1
Answers to Exercises for Lesson 7.1

Lesson 7.2   Hypothesis Testing for a Population Proportion
Exercises for Lesson 7.2
Answers to Exercises for Lesson 7.2

Lesson 7.3   More Practice in Solving Inference Problems
Exercises for Lesson 7.3
Answers to Exercises for Lesson 7.3

Avoiding Common Mistakes
Unit 7 Summary
Self-Assessment Quiz
Answers to Self-Assessment Quiz

LESSON 7.1
CONFIDENCE INTERVALS
FOR A POPULATION PROPORTION

7.1.1

INTRODUCTION

In Lesson 7.1 we continue our study of inferential statistics by learning how to estimate a population proportion p, the probability of a success in a population. In Lesson 7.2 we show how to test a claim about a population proportion.

7.1.2

ESTIMATING A POPULATION PROPORTION

As we saw in Unit 6, an interval estimate is defined as:

> **Interval Estimate**
>
> $$point\ estimate\ \pm\ margin\ of\ error$$

The parameter of interest now is the population proportion, and so:

> The *point estimate* of a population proportion is the sample proportion.

Recall, an interval estimate for a given level of confidence is called a *confidence interval*.

> **Confidence Interval for a Population Proportion**
>
> $$sample\ proportion\ \pm\ margin\ of\ error$$

Consider the following example. A researcher is interested in the proportion of American adults that are unemployed. A representative sample of 1,000 American adults are asked if they are unemployed and their answers recorded.

The parameter of interest is:

> p = the population proportion of American adults that are unemployed

and the random variable of interest:

> $\hat{P}$ = the sample proportion of 1,000American adults that are unemployed

Having defined the parameter and random variable of interest, the next task is to determine the distribution of the random variable $\hat{P}$. For estimating a population proportion the Z-distribution is always used, provided certain assumptions have been met.

Check the Following Conditions:

Use the *Z*-distribution for the analysis if all of the following are true:

All four Binomial criteria are met in the experiment.
1. There is a fixed number of trials
2. The trials are independent
3. The outcome of each trial is a success or a failure
4. The proportion of success remains constant from trial to trial

The sample size is sufficiently large to define the distribution of $\hat{P}$ as Normal. This is true if $np \geq 10$ and $n(1-p) \geq 10$ but since the value of p is unknown:

- If a claim is made about the value of p, check that $np \geq 10$ and $n(1-p) \geq 10$
- If *no* claim is made about the value of p, check that $n\hat{p} \geq 10$ and $n(1-\hat{p}) \geq 10$

If these assumptions are *not* met, then you cannot perform the analyses discussed here.

7.1.3   **USING THE NORMAL DISTRIBUTION**

Having checked that the conditions in Section 7.1.2 hold, we know that the sampling distribution of $\hat{P}$ is Normal, centered at p and with a standard deviation of :

$$\sqrt{\frac{p(1-p)}{n}}$$

Since we do not know the *actual* value of p, we use $\hat{p}$ instead of p in the formula for the standard deviation of $\hat{P}$. The result is called the standard error of $\hat{P}$:

$$\sqrt{\frac{\hat{p}(1-\hat{p})}{n}}$$

In Section 7.1.2, a confidence interval for the population proportion was defined as:

$$sample\ proportion \pm margin\ of\ error$$

In Unit 6 we saw that the margin of error, denoted by E, is given by the z-score for a desired level of confidence multiplied by the standard deviation of the sampling distribution. In the case of proportions, we use the standard error, so when estimating a population proportion:

$$E = z\sqrt{\frac{\hat{p}(1-\hat{p})}{n}}$$

and hence:

A Confidence Interval for a Population Proportion using the Z-distribution is given by:

$$\hat{p} \pm z\sqrt{\frac{\hat{p}(1-\hat{p})}{n}}$$

- $\hat{p}$ represents the sample proportion of successes observed in the experiment
- z is a value obtained from the last row of the t-table and is based on the confidence level.
- n is the sample size

For example, suppose that in a random sample of 800 teenagers, it was determined that 408 had parents who were divorced. Find a 95% confidence interval for the population proportion of teenagers that have divorced parents.

The parameter of interest is:

p = the population proportion of teenagers with divorced parents

The random variable of interest is:

$\hat{P}$ = the sample proportion of 800 teenagers with divorced parents

---

To check that it is appropriate to use the Z-distribution, first verify the conditions for a Binomial experiment:

1. There are $n = 800$ trials.
2. The trials are independent since the teenagers were randomly selected.
3. Since we are interested in finding a 'teenager whose parents are divorced', this is a *success*, and finding a 'teenager whose parents are not divorced is a *failure*.
4. Although we do not know the value of p, it is reasonable to assume it is constant.

All four conditions for a Binomial experiment have been met. Next, we verify that the sample size is large enough to define the distribution of $\hat{P}$ as Normal. Since *no* claim is made about the value of p, we check that $n\hat{p} \geq 10$ and $n(1-\hat{p}) \geq 10$.

$$\hat{p} = \frac{408}{800} = 0.51$$

So,

$$n\hat{p} = 800(0.51) \qquad n(1-\hat{p}) = 800(1-0.51)$$
$$= 408 \qquad\qquad\qquad = 392$$

Since both of these values are at least 10, the distribution of $\hat{P}$ is Normal and thus the conditions required to use the Z-distribution are met. So, a 95% confidence interval for the population proportion of teenagers with divorced parents is found using:

$$\hat{p} \pm z\sqrt{\frac{\hat{p}(1-\hat{p})}{n}}$$

We have already found that $\hat{p} = 0.51$. The value of z is based on the desired level of confidence and is found in the last row of the t-table. Since we want to construct a 95% confidence interval, $z = 1.96$. The sample size is $n = 800$. Substituting these values in the formula gives:

$$\hat{p} \pm z\sqrt{\frac{\hat{p}(1-\hat{p})}{n}} = 0.51 \pm 1.96\sqrt{\frac{0.51(1-0.51)}{800}}$$
$$= 0.51 \pm 0.0346$$

and so the desired confidence interval is $(0.4754, 0.5446)$. So we can be 95% confident that the population proportion of teenagers with divorced parents is between 0.4754 and 0.5446.

7.1.4   **FINDING THE MINIMUM SAMPLE SIZE**

If a researcher decides on the confidence level and margin of error before collecting data, then it is possible to find the minimum sample size required in order to fulfill those conditions. The following method is only appropriate when using the Z-distribution.

> **To find the Minimum Sample Size required to Estimate a Population Proportion:**
>
> Using the formula for the margin of error E, we find that the sample size is:
>
> $$n = \left(\frac{z}{E}\right)^2 p(1-p)$$
>
> - z is a value obtained from the last row of the t-table and is based on the confidence level.
> - use $p = 0.5$ since this ensures that the margin of error is no larger than desired
> - E is the given margin of error
>
> A sample size *must* always be reported as a whole number. If the calculation does not result in a whole number, *round up* to the next whole number.

Consider the following example. How many college would need to be sampled to produce a 90% confidence interval for the population proportion of college students on academic probation, with a margin of error of 0.02?

The formula for sample size is:

$$n = \left(\frac{z}{E}\right)^2 p(1-p)$$

where $z = 1.645$, $p = 0.5$, $E = 0.02$. Hence:

$$n = \left(\frac{1.645}{0.02}\right)^2 (0.5)(1-0.5) = 1691.2656$$

Thus, we need to sample 1692 college students.

LESSON 7.1 EXERCISES
CONFIDENCE INTERVALS
FOR A POPULATION PROPORTION

1. In a survey of 1000 American adults, 200 say that they take at least one vacation a year. Assume the sample is representative of all American adults, and that we are interested in estimating the proportion of all American adults who take at least one vacation a year.
    a) What distribution should you use for this analysis?
    b) Define the parameter and random variable of interest.
    c) Construct a 95% confidence interval for the proportion of American adults who say that they take at least one vacation a year.
    d) Interpret the confidence interval found in part (c).

2. In a survey of 800 randomly selected UCSB students, 150 said that they supported election candidate Ms. Jones. We are interested in estimating the proportion of all UCSB students who say they support Ms. Jones.
    a) What distribution should you use for this analysis?
    b) Define the parameter and random variable of interest.
    c) Construct a 98% confidence interval for the proportion of UCSB students who say they support election candidate Ms. Jones.
    d) Interpret the confidence interval found in part (c).

3. You want to estimate, with 95% confidence, the population proportion of computers that crash within three days of installing a new software product. Find the minimum sample size needed to be sure that your estimate is within 3% of the population proportion.

4. In a survey conducted by a local bookstore, 30% of 100 customers said that they would like to receive special offers by e-mail. We are interested in estimating the proportion of all customers that would like to receive special offers by e-mail.
    a) What distribution should you use for this analysis?
    b) Define the parameter and random variable of interest.
    c) Construct a 90% confidence interval for the proportion of customers who said they would like to receive special offers by e-mail.
    d) Interpret the confidence interval found in part (c).

5. A local veterinarian wants to estimate, with 95% confidence, the proportion of dogs who have fleas within 10 weeks of receiving a flea treatment. Find the minimum sample size needed if the veterinarian wants to be sure that his estimate is within 5% of the population proportion.

ANSWERS

LESSON 7.1 EXERCISES

CONFIDENCE INTERVALS

FOR A POPULATION PROPORTION

Below are the answers to the exercises for Unit 7, Lesson 7.1.
For full solutions, please refer to the CD included with this textbook.

1. a) Conditions are satisfied to use the Z-distribution.
    b) p = the population proportion of American adults who take at least one vacation a year
       $\hat{P}$ = the sample proportion of 1000 American adults who take at least one vacation a year
    c) (0.1752, 0.2248)
    d) With 95% confidence, the population proportion of American adults who say that they take at least one vacation a year is between 0.1752 and 0.2248.

2. a) Conditions are satisfied to use the Z-distribution.
    b) p = the population proportion of UCSB students who say they support Ms. Jones
       $\hat{P}$ = the sample proportion of 800 UCSB students who say they support Ms. Jones
    c) (0.1554, 0.2196)
    d) With 98% confidence, the population proportion of UCSB students who say they support Ms. Jones is between 0.1554 and 0.2196.

3. $n = 1068$

4. a) Conditions are satisfied to use the Z-distribution.
    b) p = the population proportion of customers that would like to receive special offers by e-mail
       $\hat{P}$ = the sample proportion of 100 customers that would like to receive special offers by e-mail
    c) (0.2246, 0.3754)
    d) With 90% confidence, the population proportion of customers that would like to receive special offers by e-mail is between 0.2246 and 0.3754.

5. $n = 385$

LESSON 7.2
HYPOTHESIS TESTING FOR A POPULATION PROPORTION

7.2.1   INTRODUCTION

We will now discuss how to learn about a population proportion through hypothesis testing. It is important to keep in mind that conceptually, hypothesis testing for a population proportion is the same as for a population mean.

7.2.2   DECIDING WHICH DISTRIBUTION TO USE

Hypothesis testing for a population proportion is done with the Z-distribution, provided that certain conditions are met. These are the same as those for a confidence interval for a population proportion. As a reminder, these are:

Check the Following Conditions:

Use the Z-distribution for the analysis if all of the following are true:

All four Binomial criteria are met in the experiment.
1. There is a fixed number of trials
2. The trials are independent
3. The outcome of each trial is a success or a failure
4. The proportion of success remains constant from trial to trial

The sample size is sufficiently large to define the distribution of $\hat{P}$ as Normal. This is true if $np \geq 10$ and $n(1-p) \geq 10$ but since the value of p is unknown, use the value of p that is made in the claim.

7.2.3   SETTING UP HYPOTHESES

The same rules for setting up hypotheses that we learned in Lesson 6.2 apply here. The difference is that now the claim will be about a population proportion p rather than a population mean μ. For example, to test the claim that over half of American adults own cars, we can set up the hypotheses as follows:

Let p = the population proportion of American adults who own cars

Then the claim is that $p > 0.5$.

STOP AND THINK!

Is this the null or alternative hypothesis? How do you know?

Since $p > 0.5$ is a statement of inequality, it must be the alternative hypothesis.

The complementary statement to the claim is $p \leq 0.5$. Since this is a statement of equality, it must be the null hypothesis.

Thus, we can write the hypotheses and identify the claim:

$$H_0: \ p \leq 0.5 \qquad\qquad H_A: \ p > 0.5 \ \text{(claim)}$$

The following example will be used for the remainder of the lesson to illustrate the various steps in hypothesis testing. We will explain all parts of the problem in the following sections.

A random sample of 100 teenagers were asked if they were afraid of the dark, and 8% said yes. Test the claim that less than 10% of teenagers are afraid of the dark using a 5% significance level.

To verify that it is appropriate to use the Z-distribution, first check that the experiment is Binomial:
1. There are $n = 100$ trials.
2. The trials are independent because they come from a random sample.
3. We are interested in finding 'a teenager who is afraid of the dark', so this is a *success*, and finding 'a teenager who is not afraid of the dark' is a *failure*.
4. The actual value of p is unknown, but we will assume it is constant.

Next verify that $np \geq 10$ and $n(1-p) \geq 10$:

$$np = 100(0.10) \qquad\qquad n(1-p) = 100(1-0.10)$$
$$= 10 \qquad\qquad\qquad\qquad = 90$$

Thus, the conditions needed to use the Z-distribution are satisfied.

Next, we define the parameter of interest and set up the hypotheses.

Let $p =$ the population proportion of teenagers who are afraid of the dark.

Then the claim is that $p < 0.10$.

> **STOP AND THINK!**
>
> **Is this the null or alternative hypothesis? How do you know?**

Since $p < 0.10$ is a statement of inequality, it must be the alternative hypothesis.

The complementary statement to the claim is $p \geq 0.10$. Since this is a statement of equality, it must be the null hypothesis.

Thus, we can write the hypotheses and identify the claim:

$$H_0: \ p \geq 0.10 \qquad\qquad H_A: \ p < 0.10 \ \ (\text{claim})$$

Next we compute the test statistic, under the assumption that the null hypothesis is true.

7.2.4

CALCULATING THE TEST STATISTIC

The same concepts we learned in Lesson 6.2 apply here, except now we are using the distribution of $\hat{P}$. Since we have already verified that the distribution of $\hat{P}$ is Normal, we now need to find the mean and standard deviation. The random variable of interest is:

$\hat{P} =$ the sample proportion of 100 teenagers who are afraid of the dark

The mean of $\hat{P}$ is p, and since we are assuming the null hypothesis is true, we can assume that $p = 0.10$. The standard deviation of $\hat{P}$ is found as follows:

$$\text{Standard deviation of } \hat{P}: \ \sqrt{\frac{p(1-p)}{n}} = \sqrt{\frac{0.10(1-0.10)}{100}} = 0.03$$

The distribution of $\hat{P}$ is shown in Figure 7.1.

Figure 7.1

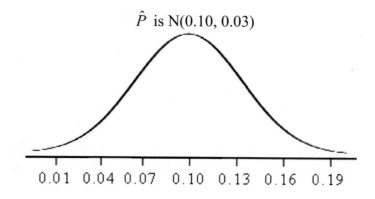

$\hat{P}$ is N(0.10, 0.03)

The null hypothesis states that $p \geq 0.10$, so it is possible that the distribution of $\hat{P}$ is centered at 0.10 *or higher*. Values of $\hat{P}$ that are 0.10 or higher will support the null hypothesis. Even values of $\hat{P}$ that are slightly smaller than 0.10 will also support the null hypothesis. This is because such values are probable in the distribution shown in Figure 7.1. However, if we get values of $\hat{P}$ that are *much* smaller than 0.10, this will lead us to doubt that the null is true.

In the example, the proportion of teenagers in the sample who are afraid of the dark is 0.08. Figure 7.2 shows where this value falls in the distribution of $\hat{P}$:

Figure 7.2

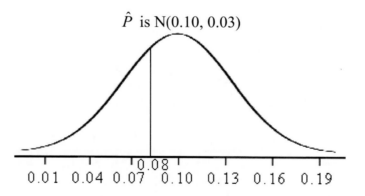

$\hat{P}$ is N(0.10, 0.03)

As we see, the sample proportion we observed is smaller than 0.10. In order to decide whether this supports the null hypothesis, we first compute a test statistic.

Since we are using the Z-distribution, the test statistic is a z-score, and so the test statistic is computed as follows:

$$z = \frac{0.08 - 0.10}{0.03} = -0.67$$

This result can be generalized:

z-Test Statistic for a Population Proportion

$$z = \frac{\hat{p} - p}{\sqrt{\dfrac{p(1-p)}{n}}}$$

Even though this formula looks different from the z-score formula we used in Unit 4, it is conceptually the same. We will now use the test statistic to obtain the p-value for the test.

7.2.5   **FINDING THE p-VALUE**

Recall that z-scores are used to find probabilities under the Normal curve. We have just computed the test statistic for the example, and obtained $z = -0.67$. What we now need to identify is the area of interest, called the p-value. The null hypothesis will only be rejected if we observe a sample proportion *much smaller* than 0.10. So we are interested in the area *below* the test statistic, and therefore, the p-value for this test is as shown in Figure 7.3.

Figure 7.3

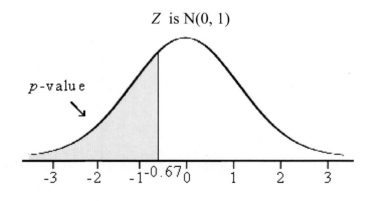

Looking up $z = -0.67$, the Standard Normal table shows that the area *below* -0.67 is 0.2514. Since this corresponds to the shaded area, the p-value is:

$$p - \text{value} = P(Z < -0.67)$$
$$= 0.2514$$

Guidelines for finding p-values given in Section 6.2.5 are repeated here.

> **Finding *p*-values**
>
> To determine the *p*-value, first look at the sign in the alternative hypothesis:
>
> If the sign is '<', then the *p*-value for the test is the area *below* the test statistic.
>
> If the sign is '>', then the *p*-value for the test is the area *above* the test statistic.
>
> If the sign is '≠', then the *p*-value for the test is the area *below* the negative value of the test statistic *plus* the area *above* the positive value of the test statistic.

Having found the *p*-value, next we decide whether the data supports the null or the alternative hypothesis.

7.2.6   **THE DECISION**

Recall a small *p*-value indicates that you should reject the null hypothesis. The decision process here is the same as in Section 6.2.6.

In the example, we were told to use a 5% significance level. So we have enough evidence to reject the null if we observe a *p*-value that is *less* than 0.05, and we do *not* have enough evidence to reject the null if we observe a *p*-value that is *more* than 0.05. The *p*-value for our test is 0.2514, which is *more* than the significance level. Therefore, we *do not* have enough evidence to reject the null hypothesis. In other words, the sample proportion that we observed was *not* much less than 0.10, and so it does support the null hypothesis.

Now that a decision has been made, we must offer an interpretation of our results.

7.2.7   **INTERPRETING THE RESULTS**

The final step in hypothesis testing is to state the conclusion. This means we need to address the original claim. Does the data support the claim, or does it not? Recall the hypotheses for this example:

$$H_0: \ p \geq 0.10 \qquad H_A: \ p < 0.10 \ \text{(claim)}$$

Since the decision was *not* to reject the null, this means that the data supports the null, which is *not* the claim. Therefore, at a 5% significance level, we conclude that the proportion of all teenagers who are afraid of the dark is *not* less than 0.10.

LESSON 7.2 EXERCISES
HYPOTHESIS TESTING
FOR A POPULATION PROPORTION

1. In a survey of 1000 randomly selected high school students, 18% have a private tutor. Test the claim that less than 20% of high school students have a private tutor. Use a 1% significance level.
   a) Determine the appropriate distribution to use.
   b) Define the parameter and random variable of interest.
   c) State the null and alternative hypotheses, and identify the claim.
   d) Calculate the test statistic.
   e) Determine the p-value.
   f) State your decision.
   g) State your conclusion.

2. David claims that he eats in the dining commons for 80% of his meals. Out of a sample of 63 meals, he ate at the dining commons for 55 of them. Test David's claim at a 1% significance level.
   a) Determine the appropriate distribution to use.
   b) Define the parameter and random variable of interest.
   c) State the null and alternative hypotheses, and identify the claim.
   d) Calculate the test statistic.
   e) Determine the p-value.
   f) State your decision.
   g) State your conclusion.

3. Danelle claims that when she goes surfing with her friends, she drives over half the time. Out of sample of 30 surfing trips with her friends, Danelle drove 23 times. Test Danelle's claim at a 5% significance level.
   a) Determine the appropriate distribution to use.
   b) Define the parameter and random variable of interest.
   c) State the null and alternative hypotheses, and identify the claim.
   d) Calculate the test statistic.
   e) Determine the p-value.
   f) State your decision.
   g) State your conclusion.

ANSWERS

LESSON 7.2 EXERCISES

HYPOTHESIS TESTING

FOR A POPULATION PROPORTION

Below are the answers to the exercises for Unit 7, Lesson 7.2.
For full solutions, please refer to the CD included with this textbook.

1. a) Conditions are satisfied to use the Z-distribution.
   b) p = the population proportion of high school students with a private tutor

   $\hat{P}$ = the sample proportion of 1000 high school students with a private tutor
   c) H_0: $p \geq 0.20$ H_A: $p < 0.20$ (claim)
   d) $z = -1.58$
   e) $p - \text{value} = 0.0571$
   f) There is *not* enough evidence to reject H_0.
   g) There is *not* enough evidence to support the claim that less than 20% of high school students have a private tutor.

2. a) Conditions are satisfied to use the Z-distribution.
   b) p = the population proportion of meals David eats in the dining commons

   $\hat{P}$ = the sample proportion of 63 meals David eats in the dining commons
   c) H_0: $p = 0.8$ (claim) H_A: $p \neq 0.8$
   d) $z = 1.45$
   e) $p - \text{value} = 0.1470$
   f) There is *not* enough evidence to reject H_0.
   g) There is enough evidence to support David's claim that he eats 80% of his meals in the dining commons.

3. a) Conditions are satisfied to use the Z-distribution.
   b) p = the population proportion of surf trips where Danelle drives

   $\hat{P}$ = the sample proportion of 30 surf trips where Danelle drives
   c) H_0: $p \leq 0.5$ H_A: $p > 0.5$ (claim)
   d) $z = 2.92$
   e) $p - \text{value} = 0.0018$
   f) There is enough evidence to reject H_0.
   g) There is enough evidence to support Danelle's claim that she drives over half the time when she surfs with her friends.

LESSON 7.3
MORE PRACTICE IN SOLVING INFERENCE PROBLEMS

In this lesson we look at some more examples with full solutions. You are encouraged to work through these problems yourself if you need extra practice.

Example 1:   In a survey of 2500 randomly selected visitors to Yosemite, 400 said that this was their first visit. Construct a 95% confidence interval for the proportion of visitors to Yosemite.

> **STOP AND THINK!**
>
> **What distribution should be used for the analysis?**
>
> **What are the parameter and random variable of interest?**

Solution: To check that it is appropriate to use the *Z*-distribution, first verify the conditions for a Binomial experiment:

1. There are $n = 2500$ trials.
2. The trials are independent because they are randomly selected.
3. Since we are interested in finding 'a first-time visitor to Yosemite', this is a *success* and finding 'a visitor who is not there for the first time' is a *failure*.
4. Although we do not know the value of p, it is reasonable to assume it is constant.

All four conditions for a Binomial experiment have been met. Next, we verify that the sample size is large enough to define the distribution of $\hat{P}$ as Normal. Since *no* claim is made about the value of p, we check that $n\hat{p} \geq 10$ and $n(1 - \hat{p}) \geq 10$.

$$\hat{p} = \frac{400}{2500} = 0.16$$

So,

$$n\hat{p} = 2500(0.16) \qquad n(1-\hat{p}) = 2500(1-0.16)$$
$$= 400 \qquad\qquad\qquad = 2100$$

Since both of these values are at least 10, the distribution of $\hat{P}$ is Normal and thus the conditions required to use the Z-distribution are met.

The parameter of interest is:

p = the population proportion of visitors to Yosemite who are there for the first time

The random variable of interest is:

$\hat{P}$ = the sample proportion of 2500 visitors to Yosemite who are there for the first time

So, a 95% confidence interval for p is found using:

$$\hat{p} \pm z\sqrt{\frac{\hat{p}(1-\hat{p})}{n}}$$

Where $\hat{p} = 0.16$, $z = 1.96$, and $n = 2500$. Substituting these values in the formula gives:

$$\hat{p} \pm z\sqrt{\frac{\hat{p}(1-\hat{p})}{n}} = 0.16 \pm 1.96\sqrt{\frac{0.16(1-0.16)}{2500}}$$
$$= 0.16 \pm 0.0144$$

and so the desired confidence interval is $(0.1456, 0.1744)$. So we can be 95% confident that the population proportion of visitors to Yosemite who are there for the first time 0.1456 and 0.1744.

■

Example 2:   Of 500 randomly selected UCSB students surveyed, 275 said that they always read the Daily Nexus. Construct a 90% confidence interval for the proportion of UCSB students who say they always read the Daily Nexus.

> **STOP AND THINK!**
>
> **What distribution should be used for the analysis?**
>
> **What are the parameter and random variable of interest?**

Solution: To check that it is appropriate to use the *Z*-distribution, first verify the conditions for a Binomial experiment:

1. There are $n = 500$ trials
2. It is reasonable to believe that the trials are independent
3. Since we are interested in finding 'a UCSB student who always reads the Daily Nexus', this is a *success* and finding 'a UCSB student who does not always reads the Daily Nexus' is a *failure*.
4. Although we do not know the value of p, it is reasonable to assume it is constant.

All four conditions for a Binomial experiment have been met. Next, we verify that the sample size is large enough to define the distribution of $\hat{P}$ as Normal. Since *no* claim is made about the value of p, we check that $n\hat{p} \geq 10$ and $n(1-\hat{p}) \geq 10$.

$$\hat{p} = \frac{275}{500} = 0.55$$

So,

$$n\hat{p} = 500(0.55) \qquad n(1-\hat{p}) = 500(1-0.55)$$
$$= 275 \qquad\qquad\qquad = 225$$

Since both of these values are at least 10, the distribution of $\hat{P}$ is Normal and thus the conditions required to use the *Z*-distribution are met.

The parameter of interest is:

p = the population proportion of UCSB students who always read the Daily Nexus

The random variable of interest is:

$\hat{P}$ = the sample proportion of 500 UCSB students who always read the Daily Nexus

So, a 90% confidence interval for p is found using:

$$\hat{p} \pm z\sqrt{\frac{\hat{p}(1-\hat{p})}{n}}$$

Where $\hat{p} = 0.55$, $z = 1.645$, and $n = 500$. Substituting these values in the formula gives:

$$\hat{p} \pm z \sqrt{\frac{\hat{p}(1-\hat{p})}{n}} = 0.55 \pm 1.645 \sqrt{\frac{0.55(1-0.55)}{500}}$$

$$= 0.55 \pm 0.0366$$

and so the desired confidence interval is $(0.5134, 0.5866)$. So we can be 90% confident that the population proportion of UCSB students who always read the Daily Nexus is between 0.5134 and 0.5866.

■

Example 3: A researcher wants to estimate the proportion of high school students whose favorite subject is math using a 95% confidence level. What is the minimum sample size needed if the researcher wants to be sure that his estimate is within 5% of the population proportion.

STOP AND THINK!

What is the level of confidence?

What is the margin of error?

Solution: The formula for sample size is:

$$n = \left(\frac{z}{E}\right)^2 p(1-p)$$

where $z = 1.96$, $p = 0.5$, $E = 0.05$. Hence:

$$n = \left(\frac{1.96}{0.05}\right)^2 (0.5)(1-0.5) = 384.16$$

Thus, we need to sample 385 high school students.

■

Example 4: A survey conducted by a local public health inspector found that 10% of 200 randomly chosen restaurants failed to meet hygiene regulations. Construct a 99% confidence interval for the proportion of restaurants that fail to meet hygiene regulations.

STOP AND THINK!

What distribution should be used for the analysis?

What are the parameter and random variable of interest?

Lesson 7.3: More Practice in Solving Inference Problems

Solution: To check that it is appropriate to use the Z-distribution, first verify the conditions for a Binomial experiment:

1. There are $n = 200$ trials
2. The trials are independent since the restaurants are randomly selected.
3. Since we are interested in finding 'a restaurant that fails to meet hygiene regulations', this is a *success* and finding 'a restaurant that does not fail to meet hygiene regulations' is a *failure*.
4. Although we do not know the value of p, it is reasonable to assume it is constant.

All four conditions for a Binomial experiment have been met. Next, we verify that the sample size is large enough to define the distribution of $\hat{P}$ as Normal. Since *no* claim is made about the value of p, we check that $n\hat{p} \geq 10$ and $n(1-\hat{p}) \geq 10$.

$$\hat{p} = 0.10$$

So,

$$n\hat{p} = 200(0.10) \qquad n(1-\hat{p}) = 200(1-0.10)$$
$$= 20 \qquad\qquad\qquad = 180$$

Since both of these values are at least 10, the distribution of $\hat{P}$ is Normal and thus the conditions required to use the Z-distribution are met.

The parameter of interest is:

p = the population proportion of restaurants that fail to meet hygiene regulations

The random variable of interest is:

$\hat{P}$ = the sample proportion of 200 restaurants that fail to meet hygiene regulation

So, a 99% confidence interval for p is found using:

$$\hat{p} \pm z\sqrt{\frac{\hat{p}(1-\hat{p})}{n}}$$

Where $\hat{p} = 0.10$, $z = 2.576$, and $n = 500$. Substituting these values in the formula gives:

$$\hat{p} \pm z\sqrt{\frac{\hat{p}(1-\hat{p})}{n}} = 0.10 \pm 2.576\sqrt{\frac{0.10(1-0.10)}{200}}$$
$$= 0.10 \pm 0.0546$$

and so the desired confidence interval is $(0.0454, 0.1546)$. So we can be 99% confident that the population proportion of restaurants that fail to meet hygiene regulations is between 0.0454 and 0.1546.

■

Example 5: Maria likes to walk on the beach with her daughter. Out of 50 walks on the beach, Maria found at least one abalone shell on 11 separate occasions. The 95% confidence interval for the proportion of times Maria finds at least one abalone shell on the beach is $(0.1052, 0.3348)$. Maria claims she finds at least one abalone shell on the beach 25% of the time. Does the confidence interval support her claim, or provide evidence against it? Explain.

> **STOP AND THINK!**
>
> **What value should be in the confidence interval if it supports her claim?**

Solution: If the confidence interval does *not* contain the value in the claim, then the interval provides evidence *against* the claim. Otherwise, the interval supports the claim. Maria claims that $p = 0.25$, so the confidence interval supports Maria's claim because it contains this value.

■

Example 6: In a random sample of 1000 adults, it was found that 32% are afraid of flying. Test the claim that over 25% of adults are afraid of flying. Use a 1% significance level.
a) Determine the appropriate distribution to use.
b) Define the parameter and random variable of interest.
c) State the null and alternative hypotheses and identify the claim.
d) Calculate the test statistic.
e) Determine the *p*-value.
f) State your decision.
g) State your conclusion.

> **STOP AND THINK!**
>
> **Is it appropriate to use the Z-distribution?**
>
> **What is the claim? Is it the null or alternative hypothesis? How do you know?**

Solution: a) To verify that it is appropriate to use the Z-distribution, first check that the experiment is Binomial:

1. There are $n = 1000$ trials.
2. The trials are independent because they come from a random sample.
3. We are interested in finding 'an adult who is afraid of flying', so this is a *success*, and finding 'an adult who is not afraid of flying' is a *failure*.
4. The actual value of p is unknown, but we will assume it is constant.

Next verify that $np \geq 10$ and $n(1-p) \geq 10$:

$$np = 1000(0.25) \qquad\qquad n(1-p) = 1000(1-0.25)$$
$$= 250 \qquad\qquad\qquad\qquad = 750$$

Thus, the conditions needed to use the Z-distribution are satisfied.

Solution: b) The parameter of interest is:

p = the population proportion of adults who are afraid of flying

The random variable of interest is:

$\hat{P}$ = the sample proportion of 1000 adults who are afraid of flying

Solution: c) The claim is that $p > 0.25$. Since this is a statement of inequality, it must be the alternative hypothesis.

The complementary statement to the claim is $p \leq 0.25$. Since this is a statement of equality, it must be the null hypothesis.

Thus, we can write the hypotheses and identify the claim:

$$\text{H}_0: \ p \leq 0.25 \qquad\qquad \text{H}_A: \ p > 0.25 \ \text{(claim)}$$

Solution: d) The mean of $\hat{P}$ is p, and since we are assuming the null hypothesis is true, we can assume that $p = 0.25$. The standard deviation of $\hat{P}$ is found as follows:

$$\text{Standard deviation of } \hat{P}: \ \sqrt{\frac{p(1-p)}{n}} = \sqrt{\frac{0.25(1-0.25)}{1000}} = 0.0137$$

The observed sample proportion is 0.32. The distribution of $\hat{P}$ is shown below, with the observed value of $\hat{p}$ marked. Note that the right side of the curve had to be extended to be able to mark the value of $\hat{p}$.

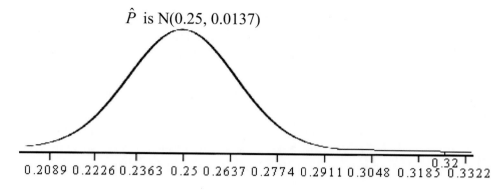

$\hat{P}$ is N(0.25, 0.0137)

0.2089 0.2226 0.2363 0.25 0.2637 0.2774 0.2911 0.3048 0.3185 0.32 0.3322

As we see, the sample proportion we observed is *much* larger than 0.25. In order to decide whether this supports the null hypothesis, we first compute a test statistic:

$$z = \frac{0.32 - 0.25}{0.0137} = 5.11$$

Solution: e) We will only reject the null hypothesis if we observe a sample proportion *much larger* than 0.25. This indicates that we are interested in the area *above* the test statistic. Therefore, the *p*-value for this test is as shown below:

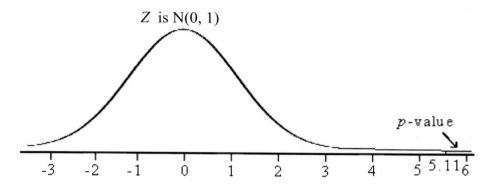

Z is N(0, 1)

p-value

-3   -2   -1   0   1   2   3   4   5 5.11 6

This area is not found in the Standard Normal table, because the highest *z*-score included in the table is 3.49. Such extreme *z*-scores are not uncommon in hypothesis tests, and when they occur, the *p*-value is reasoned out. The probability of an extreme *z*-score is almost 1 if the shaded area is practically the entire curve, and it is almost 0 is the shaded area is practically none of the curve. From the above picture, we can see that the shaded area is practically none of the curve, so:

$$p - \text{value} = P(Z > 5.11) \approx 0$$

Solution: f) In the example, we were told to use a 1% significance level. So there is enough evidence to reject the null if we observe a *p*-value that is *less* than 0.01, and there is *not* have enough evidence to reject the null if we observe a *p*-value that is *more* than 0.01. The *p*-value for the test is almost 0, which is *less* than the significance level. Therefore, we have enough evidence to reject the null hypothesis. In other words, the sample proportion that we observed was *much* larger than 0.25, and so it does not support the null hypothesis.

Solution: g) The final step in hypothesis testing is to state the conclusion. This means we need to address the original claim. Does the data support the claim, or does it not? Recall the hypotheses for this example:

$$H_0: \ p \leq 0.25 \qquad\qquad H_A: \ p > 0.25 \ \text{(claim)}$$

Since the decision was to reject the null, the data supports the alternative, which is the claim. Therefore, at a 1% significance level, we can conclude that over 25% of all adults are afraid of flying.

■

Example 7:   Suppose that 82% of 100 randomly selected UCSB students love to watch scary movies. Test the claim that 75% of UCSB students love to watch scary movies. Use a 5% significance level.
a) Determine the appropriate distribution to use.
b) Define the parameter and random variable of interest.
c) State the null and alternative hypotheses, and identify the claim.
d) Calculate the test statistic.
e) Determine the p-value.
f) State your decision.
g) State your conclusion.

> **STOP AND THINK!**
>
> **Is it appropriate to use the Z-distribution?**
>
> **What is the claim? Is it the null or alternative hypothesis? How do you know?**

Solution: a) To verify that it is appropriate to use the Z-distribution, first check that the experiment is Binomial:
1. There are $n = 100$ trials.
2. The trials are independent because they come from a random sample.
3. We are interested in finding 'a UCSB student that loves to watch scary movies', so this is a *success*, and finding 'a UCSB student that does not love to watch scary movies' is a *failure*.
4. The actual value of p is unknown, but we will assume it is constant.

Next verify that $np \geq 10$ and $n(1-p) \geq 10$:

$$np = 100(0.75) \qquad\qquad n(1-p) = 100(1-0.25)$$
$$= 75 \qquad\qquad\qquad\qquad = 25$$

Thus, the conditions needed to use the Z-distribution are satisfied.

Solution: b) The parameter of interest is:

p = the population proportion of UCSB students that love to watch scary movies

The random variable of interest is:

$\hat{P}$ = the sample proportion of 100 of UCSB students that love to watch scary movies

Solution: c) The claim is that $p = 0.75$. Since this is a statement of equality, it must be the null hypothesis.

The complementary statement to the claim is $p \neq 0.75$. Since this is a statement of inequality, it must be the alternative hypothesis.

Thus, we can write the hypotheses and identify the claim:

$$H_0: \ p = 0.75 \ \text{(claim)} \qquad\qquad H_A: \ p \neq 0.75$$

Solution: d) The mean of $\hat{P}$ is p, and since we are assuming the null hypothesis is true, we can assume that $p = 0.75$. The standard deviation of $\hat{P}$ is found as follows:

$$\text{Standard deviation of } \hat{P}: \ \sqrt{\frac{p(1-p)}{n}} = \sqrt{\frac{0.75(1-0.75)}{100}} = 0.0433$$

The observed sample proportion is 0.82. The distribution of $\hat{P}$ is shown below, with the observed value of $\hat{p}$ marked.

$\hat{P}$ is N(0.75, 0.0433)

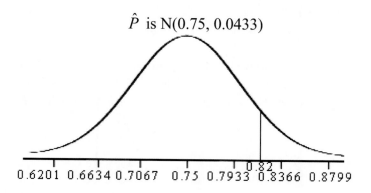

0.6201 0.6634 0.7067   0.75 0.7933 0.8366 0.8799

As we see, the sample proportion we observed is *much* larger than 0.75. In order to decide whether this supports the null hypothesis, we first compute a test statistic:

$$z = \frac{0.82 - 0.75}{0.0433} = 1.62$$

Solution: e) When the sign in the alternative is ' ≠ ', the p-value is defined to be the area *below* the negative value of the test statistic *plus* the area *above* the positive value of the test statistic. This is because we will find evidence to reject the null hypothesis if the observed sample proportion is much larger *or* much smaller than 0.75. Therefore, the p-value for this test is as shown below:

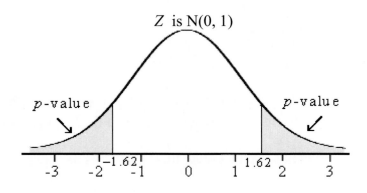

This area is found in the Standard Normal table.

$$p - \text{value} = P(Z < -1.62) + P(Z > 1.62)$$
$$= 0.0526 + (1 - 0.9474)$$
$$= 0.0526 + 0.0526$$
$$= 0.1052$$

Solution: f) In the example, we were told to use a 5% significance level. So there is enough evidence to reject the null if we observe a p-value that is *less* than 0.05, and there is *not* have enough evidence to reject the null if we observe a p-value that is *more* than 0.05. The p-value for the test is 0.1052, which is *more* than the significance level. Therefore, there is not enough evidence to reject the null hypothesis.

Solution: g) The final step in hypothesis testing is to state the conclusion. This means we need to address the original claim. Does the data support the claim, or does it not? Recall the hypotheses for this example:

Ho: $p = 0.75$ (claim)   HA: $p \neq 0.75$

Since the decision was to not reject the null, the data supports the null, which is the claim. Therefore, at a 5% significance level, we can conclude that 75% of UCSB students love to watch scary movies.

Example 8: Chris plays his favorite video game 50 times against his friends and wins 36 times. He verifies that it is appropriate to use the Z-distribution for the analysis, and finds a confidence interval for the population proportion of his wins with this video game to be (0.5956, 0.8445). Chris next conducts a hypothesis test to determine if he wins the game 75% of the time. Based on the information given by the confidence interval, what will Chris conclude?

> **STOP AND THINK!**
>
> **If Chris wins 75% of the time, what value should be contained in the interval?**

Solution: If Chris wins 75% of the time, then $p = 0.75$. The confidence interval Chris constructed contains this value, thus, it suggests that he wins 75% of the time. Therefore, this is the same conclusion Chris will reach by conducting a hypothesis test.

■

Example 9: Suppose you conduct a Binomial experiment with n = 100 trials. Is it true that a sample size of 100 will ALWAYS be large enough to allow you to use the Z-distribution estimate the population proportion?

> **STOP AND THINK!**
>
> **What are the conditions necessary to use the Z-distribution?**

Solution: In order to use the Z-distribution, the four Binomial criteria must be satisfied. In addition, $np \geq 10$ and $n(1-p) \geq 10$. Therefore, simply having a Binomial experiment is not enough to ensure that it is appropriate to use the Z-distribution. Furthermore, a sample size of 100 is not always large enough. As an example, if $p = 0.07$, then $np = 100(0.07) = 7$, and it would not be appropriate to use the Z-distribution.

■

Example 10: Krystal talked to 50 people who live in San Diego and found that 62% of them surf. Assume the sample is representative of all people who live in San Diego. From this information alone, which is the more reasonable conclusion Krystal can make? Briefly explain your answer.

Conclusion 1:   The population proportion of people in San Diego who surf is 0.62.

Conclusion 2:   The population proportion of people in San Diego who surf is close to 0.62.

> **STOP AND THINK!**
>
> Is 62% a parameter or a statistic?

Solution: The sample proportion is 0.62. From this information alone, Krystal cannot conclude that the population proportion is equal to 0.62, but she can conclude that the population proportion is *close* to 0.62.

LESSON 7.3 EXERCISES
MORE PRACTICE IN SOLVING INFERENCE PROBLEMS

1. In a survey of 1500 visitors to Santa Barbara, 200 say that their favorite cuisine is Thai. Assume the sample is representative of all visitors to Santa Barbara, and that we are interested in estimating the population proportion of visitors to Santa Barbara whose favorite cuisine is Thai.
   a) What distribution should you use for the analysis?
   b) Define the parameter and random variable of interest.
   c) Construct a 95% confidence interval for the proportion of all visitors to Santa Barbara who say their favorite cuisine is Thai.
   d) Interpret the confidence interval found in part (c).
   e) Test the claim that 15% of visitors to Santa Barbara say Thai is their favorite cuisine. Use a 5% significance level and perform all steps of the test.

2. Of 600 UCSB students surveyed, 50 said that they never read a daily newspaper. Assume the sample is representative of all UCSB students, and that we are interested in estimating the population proportion of UCSB students who say they never read a daily newspaper.
   a) What distribution should you use for the analysis?
   b) Define the parameter and random variable of interest.
   c) Construct a 98% confidence interval for the proportion of UCSB students who say they never read a daily newspaper.
   d) Interpret the confidence interval found in part (c).

3. A medical researcher wants to estimate the proportion of adults over the age of 65 who receive an annual flu vaccination. What is the minimum sample size needed if the researcher wants to be 90% confident and be sure that his estimate is within 3% of the population proportion.

4. In a survey conducted by a local library 40% of 100 customers said that they would like to be able to renew their library books online. Assume the sample is representative of all customers to the local library, and that we are interested in estimating the population proportion of customers that say they would like to be able to renew their library books online.
   a) What distribution should you use for the analysis?
   b) Define the parameter and random variable of interest.
   c) Construct a 90% confidence interval for the proportion of customers who said they would like to be able to renew their library books online
   d) Interpret the confidence interval found in part (c).

5. Of 500 randomly surveyed adults, 9% said they get enough sleep. Test the claim that less than 10% of adults say they get enough sleep. Use a 5% significance level
    a) Determine the appropriate distribution to use.
    b) Define the parameter and random variable of interest.
    c) State the null and alternative hypotheses, and identify the claim.
    d) Calculate the test statistic.
    e) Determine the p-value.
    f) State your decision.
    g) State your conclusion.

ANSWERS

LESSON 7.3 EXERCISES

MORE PRACTICE IN SOLVING INFERENCE PROBLEMS

Below are the answers to the exercises for Unit 7, Lesson 7.3.
For full solutions, please refer to the CD included with this textbook.

1. a) Conditions are satisfied to use the Z-distribution.
    b) p = the population proportion of visitors to Santa Barbara whose favorite cuisine is Thai
    $\hat{P}$ = the sample proportion of 1500 visitors to Santa Barbara whose favorite cuisine is Thai
    c) $(0.1161, 0.1505)$
    d) We can be 95% confident that the proportion of all visitors to Santa Barbara whose favorite cuisine is Thai is between 0.1161 and 0.1505.
    e) H_0: $p = 0.15$ (claim) H_A: $p \neq 0.15$
    $z = -1.81$
    $p-\text{value} = 0.0702$
    There is not enough evidence to reject H_0.
    There is enough evidence to support the claim that 15% of visitors to Santa Barbara say Thai is their favorite cuisine.

2. a) Conditions are satisfied to use the Z-distribution.
    b) p = the population proportion of UCSB students who say they never read a daily newspaper
    $\hat{P}$ = the sample proportion of 600 UCSB students who say they never read a daily newspaper
    c) $(0.0571, 0.1095)$
    d) We can be 98% confident that the population proportion of UCSB students who say they never read a daily newspaper is between 0.0571 and 0.1095.

3. $n = 752$

4. a) Conditions are satisfied to use the Z-distribution.
    b) p = the population proportion of customers that say they would like to be able to renew their library books online

        $\hat{P}$ = the sample proportion of 100 customers that say they would like to be able to renew their library books online
    c) (0.3194, 0.4806)
    d) We can be 90% confident that the population proportion of customers that say they would like to be able to renew their library books online is between 0.3194 and 0.4806.

5. a) Conditions are satisfied to use the Z-distribution.
    b) p = the population proportion of adults who say they get enough sleep

        $\hat{P}$ = the sample proportion of 500 adults who say they get enough sleep
    c) H_0: $p \geq 0.1$ H_A: $p < 0.1$ (claim)
    d) $z = -0.75$
    e) $p - \text{value} = 0.2266$
    f) There is *not* enough evidence to reject H_0.
    g) There is *not* enough evidence to support the claim that less than 10% of adults say they get enough sleep.

AVOIDING
COMMON MISTAKES

☺ A common mistake is to leave the parameter out of the hypotheses. For example, to test a claim that the population proportion is less than 0.7, people often write the hypotheses like this:

THIS IS WRONG!!! $H_0 \geq 0.7$ $H_A < 0.7$ **THIS IS WRONG!!!**

☺ Other common mistakes are to include sample values or point estimates in your hypotheses. **THIS IS WRONG!!!!!** The claim drives your hypothesis, and the claim is based on the parameter you are trying to learn about, and NOT on the sample data. Setting up your hypotheses right is the key, do not do it incorrectly.

☺ Always verify which distribution you should use *before* computing any confidence intervals or conducting any hypothesis testing. If you use the wrong distribution, you are solving the problem incorrectly.

UNIT 7 SUMMARY

- The *point estimate* of a population proportion is the sample proportion.

- Interval estimate

  point estimate $\pm$ *margin of error*

- Confidence Interval for a Population Proportion

  sample proportion $\pm$ *margin of error*

- Check the Following Conditions:

  Use the *Z*-distribution for the analysis if all of the following are true:

  □ All four Binomial criteria are met in the experiment.
  1. There is a fixed number of trials
  2. The trials are independent
  3. The outcome of each trial is a success or a failure
  4. The proportion of success remains constant from trial to trial

  □ The sample size is sufficiently large to define the distribution of $\hat{P}$ as Normal. This is true if $np \geq 10$ and $n(1-p) \geq 10$ but since the value of p is unknown:
  - If a claim is made about the value of p, check that $np \geq 10$ and $n(1-p) \geq 10$
  - If *no* claim is made about the value of p, check that $n\hat{p} \geq 10$ and $n(1-\hat{p}) \geq 10$

- A Confidence Interval for a Population Proportion using the *Z*-distribution is given by:

$$\hat{p} \pm z \sqrt{\frac{\hat{p}(1-\hat{p})}{n}}$$

  □ $\hat{p}$ represents the sample proportion
  □ z is a value obtained from the last row of the *t*-table and is based on the confidence level.
  □ n is the sample size.

- To find the Minimum Sample Size required to Estimate a Population Proportion:

  Using the formula for the margin of error E, we find that:

  $$n = \left(\frac{z}{E}\right)^2 p(1-p)$$

  - □ z is a value obtained from the last row of the t-table and is based on the confidence level.
  - □ use $p = 0.5$ since this ensures that the margin of error is no larger than desired
  - □ E is the given margin of error

  A sample size *must* always be reported as a whole number. If the calculation does not result in a whole number, *round up* to the next whole number.

- The null hypothesis must contain a sign of equality. The alternative hypothesis must contain a sign of inequality.

- Hypothesis testing is always done under the assumption that the *null* hypothesis is true.

- z-Test Statistic for a Population Proportion

  $$z = \frac{\hat{p} - p}{\sqrt{\dfrac{p(1-p)}{n}}}$$

- To determine the p-value, first look at the sign in the alternative hypothesis:
  - □ If the sign is '<', then the p-value for the test is the area *below* the test statistic.

  - □ If the sign is '>', then the p-value for the test is the area *above* the test statistic.

  - □ If the sign is '≠', then the p-value for the test is the area *below* the negative value of the test statistic *plus* the area *above* the positive value of the test statistic.

- Deciding Whether to Reject H_0
  - □ If the p-value is smaller than the significance level α, there is enough evidence to reject the null hypothesis.
  - □ Otherwise, there is not enough evidence to reject the null hypothesis.

SELF-ASSESSMENT QUIZ

1. In a study of 500 athletes, 20 say that they train 7 days a week. Assume the sample is representative of all athletes, and that we are interested in estimating the population proportion of athletes who say that they train 7 days a week.
   a) What distribution should you use for the analysis?
   b) Define the parameter and random variable of interest.
   c) Construct a 95% confidence interval for the proportion of athletes who say that they train 7 days a week.
   d) Interpret the confidence interval found in part c.

2. In a survey conducted by the airline SuperPlanes, 65% of 1000 travelers said that they would like food to be served during flights lasting 4 hours or longer. Assume the sample is representative of all travelers, and that we are interested in estimating the population proportion of travelers said that they would like food to be served during flights lasting 4 hours or longer.
   a) What distribution should you use for the analysis?
   b) Define the parameter and random variable of interest.
   c) Construct a 98% confidence interval for the proportion of travelers who said they would like food to be served during flights lasting 4 hours or longer.
   d) Interpret the confidence interval found in part c.

3. A researcher wants to estimate the proportion of Californian adults who are fluent in Spanish using a 95% confidence level. What is the minimum sample size needed if the researcher wants to be sure that his estimate is within 2.5% of the population proportion.

4. Paula claims that more than 50% of UCSB students go home for Memorial holiday weekend. In a random sample of 150 UCSB students, 65% say that they went home for Memorial holiday weekend. Is there sufficient evidence to support Paula's claim? Use $\alpha = 0.05$.
   a) Determine the appropriate distribution to use.
   b) Define the parameter and random variable of interest.
   c) State the null and alternative hypotheses, and identify the claim.
   d) Calculate the test statistic.
   e) Determine the p-value.
   f) State your decision.
   g) State your conclusion.

5. A researcher claims that fewer than 25% of adults in the United States watch more than 4 hours television per day. In a random sample of 100 American adults, 20% say that they watch more than 4 hours television per day. Is there sufficient evidence to support the researcher's claim? Use a 1% significance level.

a) Determine the appropriate distribution to use.
b) Define the parameter and random variable of interest.
c) State the null and alternative hypotheses, and identify the claim.
d) Calculate the test statistic.
e) Determine the p-value.
f) State your decision.
g) State your conclusion.

ANSWERS
SELF-ASSESSMENT QUIZ

Below are the answers to the exercises for Unit 7, Self-Assessment Quiz. For full solutions, please refer to the CD included with this textbook.

1. a) Conditions are satisfied to use the Z-distribution.
   b) p = the population proportion of athletes who say that they train 7 days a week

      $\hat{P}$ = the sample proportion of 500 athletes who say that they train 7 days a week
   c) (0.0228, 0.0572)
   d) We can be 95% confident that the population proportion of athletes who say that they train 7 days a week is between 0.0228 and 0.0572.

2. a) Conditions are satisfied to use the Z-distribution.
   b) p = the population proportion of travelers who say that they would like food to be served during flights lasting 4 hours or longer

      $\hat{P}$ = the sample proportion of 1000 travelers who say that they would like food to be served during flights lasting 4 hours or longer
   c) (0.6149, 0.6851)
   d) We can be 98% confident that the population proportion of travelers who say that they would like food to be served during flights lasting 4 hours or longer is between 0.6149 and 0.6851.

3. $n = 1537$

4. a) Conditions are satisfied to use the Z-distribution.
   b) p = the population proportion of UCSB students who go home for Memorial holiday weekend

      $\hat{P}$ = the sample proportion of 150 UCSB students who go home for Memorial holiday weekend
   c) H_0: $p \leq 0.5$ H_A: $p > 0.5$ (claim)
   d) $z = 3.67$
   e) $p - \text{value} \approx 0$
   f) There is enough evidence to reject H_0.
   g) There is enough evidence to support Paula's claim that more than half of UCSB students go home for Memorial holiday weekend.

5. a) Conditions are satisfied to use the *Z*-distribution.
    b) p = the population proportion of adults in the United States who watch more than 4 hours television per day

    $\hat{P}$ = the sample proportion of 100 adults in the United States who watch more than 4 hours television per day
    c) H$_0$: $p \geq 0.25$ H$_A$: $p < 0.25$ (claim)
    d) $z = -1.15$
    e) $p - \text{value} = 0.1251$
    f) There is *not* enough evidence to reject H$_0$.
    g) There is *not* enough evidence to support the claim that fewer than 25% of adults in the United States watch more than 4 hours television per day.

UNIT 8
INFERENCE ON TWO SAMPLE PROPORTIONS

Lesson 8.1 Confidence Intervals for Comparing Two Population Proportions
Exercises for Lesson 8.1
Answers to Exercises for Lesson 8.1

Lesson 8.2 Hypothesis Testing for Comparing Two Population Proportions
Exercises for Lesson 8.2
Answers to Exercises for Lesson 8.2

Lesson 8.3 More Practice in Solving Inference Problems
Exercises for Lesson 8.3
Answers to Exercises for Lesson 8.3

Avoiding Common Mistakes
Unit 8 Summary
Self-Assessment Quiz
Answers to Self-Assessment Quiz

LESSON 8.1
CONFIDENCE INTERVALS FOR COMPARING TWO POPULATION PROPORTIONS

8.1.1   **INTRODUCTION**

In Units 6 and 7 we learned how to estimate a single parameter by constructing a confidence interval. We also learned how to test a hypothesis about a population parameter. In Unit 8 we will compare two populations proportions; first, by constructing a confidence interval for the difference in proportions and second, by carrying out a hypothesis test.

8.1.2   **ESTIMATING THE DIFFERENCE BETWEEN TWO POPULATION PROPORTIONS**

All the concepts introduced in Unit 7 for estimating a single population proportion are also applicable when estimating the difference between two population proportions. Suppose we are interested in estimating the difference between Population 1 and Population 2. Define:

$$p_1 = \text{the proportion of successes in Population 1}$$

and

$$p_2 = \text{the proportion of successes in Population 2}$$

then the parameter of interest is $p_1 - p_2$, the difference between the two population proportions. The best estimate of $p_1 - p_2$ is the difference between the two *sample* proportions $\hat{p}_1 - \hat{p}_2$.

$\hat{p}_1 - \hat{p}_2$ is the *point estimate* of $p_1 - p_2$

Recall, an interval estimate for a given level of confidence is called a *confidence interval*.

> ### Confidence interval for the difference between two population proportions is:
>
> *difference between two sample proportions ± margin of error*

Consider the following example. Suppose that in a random sample of 800 American high school students, it was determined that 350 had parents who were divorced and in a random sample of 700 Mexican high school students, it was determined that 140 had parents who were divorced.

Using the techniques in Unit 7, we can find the 95% confidence interval for the population proportion of American high school students with divorced parents and we can also find the 95% confidence interval for the population proportion of Mexican high school students with divorced parents. However, from these individual intervals, we may not be able to reach a conclusion about whether there is a *difference* in the proportion of American and Mexican high school students with divorced parents. We now show how to reach a conclusion about the difference in the population proportions by constructing a confidence interval.

> ### STOP AND THINK!
>
> **Define Population 1 and Population 2.**
>
> **What is the parameter of interest?**
>
> **What is the random variable of interest?**
>
> **What is the point estimate?**

It does not matter how Population 1 and Population 2 are assigned, but once you have made the assignment, you must keep it throughout the problem.

Define:

Population 1 = American high school students
Population 2 = Mexican high school students

Then:

p_1 = the population proportion of American high school students with divorced parents

p_2 = the population proportion of Mexican high school students with divorced parents

The parameter of interest is:

$$p_1 - p_2$$

Similarly:

$\hat{P}_1$ = the sample proportion of 800 American high school students with divorced parents

$\hat{P}_2$ = the sample proportion of 700 Mexican high school students with divorced parents

The random variable of interest is:

$$\hat{P}_1 - \hat{P}_2$$

The next task is to determine the distribution of the random variable $\hat{P}_1 - \hat{P}_2$. For estimating the difference between two population proportions the Z-distribution is always used, provided certain conditions are met.

CHECK THE FOLLOWING CONDITIONS:

Use the Z-distribution for the analysis if all of the following are true for *both* samples:

All four Binomial criteria are met in the experiment.
1. There is a fixed number of trials: n_1 for Population 1 and n_2 for Population 2
2. The trials are independent
3. The outcome of each trial is a success or a failure
4. The proportion of successes remains constant from trial to trial

The sample size is sufficiently large to define the distribution of $\hat{P}_1 - \hat{P}_2$ as Normal. This is true if:

$$n_1 p_1 \geq 10 \text{ and } n_1(1 - p_1) \geq 10$$
$$n_2 p_2 \geq 10 \text{ and } n_2(1 - p_2) \geq 10$$

but since the value of p_1 and p_2 is unknown, use $\hat{p}_1$ and $\hat{p}_2$.

If these assumptions are *not* met, then you cannot perform the analyses discussed here.

8.1.3

USING THE NORMAL DISTRIBUTION

Having checked that the conditions given in Section 8.1.2 hold, we know that the sampling distribution of $\hat{P}_1 - \hat{P}_2$ is Normal, centered at $p_1 - p_2$ and with standard error of :

$$\sqrt{\frac{\hat{p}_1(1 - \hat{p}_1)}{n_1} + \frac{\hat{p}_2(1 - \hat{p}_2)}{n_2}}$$

Thus, the margin of error is:

$$E = z\sqrt{\frac{\hat{p}_1(1-\hat{p}_1)}{n_1} + \frac{\hat{p}_2(1-\hat{p}_2)}{n_2}}$$

Hence,

Confidence Interval for the Difference between Two Population Proportions using the Z-distribution is:

$$(\hat{p}_1 - \hat{p}_2) \pm z\sqrt{\frac{\hat{p}_1(1-\hat{p}_1)}{n_1} + \frac{\hat{p}_2(1-\hat{p}_2)}{n_2}}$$

- $\hat{p}_1$ is the sample proportion of successes observed from Population 1
- $\hat{p}_2$ is the sample proportion of successes observed from Population 2
- z is a value obtained from the last row of the t-table and is based on the confidence level
- n_1 is the sample size from Population 1
- n_2 is the sample size from Population 2

Continuing the example in Section 8.1.2: Suppose that in a random sample of 800 American high school students, it was determined that 350 had parents who were divorced and in a random sample of 700 Mexican high school students, it was determined that 140 had parents who were divorced. Find a 95% confidence interval for the difference between the two population proportions of high school students with divorced parents.

In Section 8.1.2 we defined the parameter and random variable of interest. To determine whether it is appropriate to use the Z-distribution, verify that the experiment is Binomial for *both* samples:

Population 1: American high school students
1. There are $n_1 = 800$ trials.
2. The trials are independent since the American high school students were randomly selected.
3. Since we are interested in finding 'an American high school student with divorced parents', this is a *success*, and finding 'an American high school student who does not have divorced parents' is a *failure*.
4. Although we do not know the value of p_1, it is reasonable to assume it is constant.

So for the sample from Population 1 the experiment is Binomial.

Population 2: Mexican high school student
1. There are $n_2 = 700$ trials.
2. The trials are independent since the Mexican high school students were randomly selected.
3. Since we are interested in finding 'a Mexican high school student with divorced parents', this is a *success*, and finding 'a Mexican high school student who does not have divorced parents' is a *failure*.
4. Although we do not know the value of p_2, it is reasonable to assume it is constant.

So for the sample from Population 2 the experiment is Binomial.

We also need to verify the sample size is large enough to define the distribution of $\hat{P}_1$ and $\hat{P}_2$ as Normal. Since the values of p_1 and p_2 are unknown, we use the value of $\hat{p}_1$ and $\hat{p}_2$ observed in the samples.

For American high school students:

$$n_1\hat{p}_1 = (800)\left(\frac{350}{800}\right) \qquad\qquad n_1(1-\hat{p}_1) = (800)\left(1 - \frac{350}{800}\right)$$

$$= 350 \qquad\qquad\qquad\qquad\qquad = 450$$

Since both of these values are at least 10, we can define the distribution of $\hat{P}_1$ as Normal.

For Mexican high school students:

$$n_2\hat{p}_2 = (700)\left(\frac{140}{700}\right) \qquad\qquad n_2(1-\hat{p}_2) = (700)\left(1 - \frac{140}{700}\right)$$

$$= 140 \qquad\qquad\qquad\qquad\qquad = 560$$

Since both of these values are at least 10, we can define the distribution of $\hat{P}_2$ as Normal.

Thus, the conditions required to use the Z-distribution have been satisfied.

So, a 95% confidence interval for the difference in the two population proportions of high school students with divorced parents is found using:

$$(\hat{p}_1 - \hat{p}_2) \pm z \sqrt{\frac{\hat{p}_1(1-\hat{p}_1)}{n_1} + \frac{\hat{p}_2(1-\hat{p}_2)}{n_2}}$$

We have already found that:

$$\hat{p}_1 = \frac{350}{800} = 0.4375 \qquad \hat{p}_2 = \frac{140}{700} = 0.2$$

Since we want to construct a 95% confidence interval, $z = 1.96$. Substituting these values in the formula gives:

$$(\hat{p}_1 - \hat{p}_2) \pm z \sqrt{\frac{\hat{p}_1(1-\hat{p}_1)}{n_1} + \frac{\hat{p}_2(1-\hat{p}_2)}{n_2}}$$

$$= (0.4375 - 0.2) \pm 1.96 \sqrt{\frac{0.4375(1-0.4375)}{800} + \frac{0.2(1-0.2)}{700}}$$

$$= 0.2375 \pm 0.0454$$

and so the desired confidence interval is $(0.1921, 0.2829)$. This confidence interval is interpreted as follows:

We can be 95% confident that the true difference in proportion of divorced parents for American and Mexican high school students is between 0.1921 and 0.2829.

From this interval, how do we know if there is a difference in the two population proportions? We have found a confidence interval for $p_1 - p_2$, the difference between the population proportions. If $p_1 - p_2 = 0$, then $p_1 = p_2$, and so there is no difference between the population proportions. Thus, if the confidence interval contains 0, we conclude that there is no difference in the two population proportions.

STOP AND THINK!

Does the confidence interval constructed contain 0?

In the above example, the confidence interval we constructed does not contain 0. This means that there is a difference in the two population proportions. Furthermore, since the interval only contains positive values, this tells us that the difference $p_1 - p_2$ is positive.

STOP AND THINK!

If p_1-p_2 is positive, which population proportion is larger, p_1 or p_2?

So, we can conclude that p_1 is larger than p_2, which means that a higher proportion of American high school students have divorced parents compared with Mexican high school students.

LESSON 8.1 EXERCISES
CONFIDENCE INTERVALS FOR COMPARING TWO POPULATION PROPORTIONS

1. In a random sample of 500 male American college students, 60 went on to graduate school. In a random sample of 500 female American college students, 50 went on to graduate school. A college administrator wants to determine whether there is any difference between the two populations.
   a) Define Population 1 and Population 2.
   b) Identify the parameter of interest.
   c) Identify the random variable of interest.
   d) Determine the appropriate distribution for the analysis.
   e) Find a 95% confidence interval for the difference between the two population proportions.
   f) Interpret the confidence interval you found in part (e).
   g) Is there a difference between the two population proportions? Use the confidence interval you found in part (e) to support your decision.

2. A memory chip manufacturer operates two plants, one in Japan and one in the UK. In a random sample of 300 memory chips made at the Japanese plant, 15 were found to be defective. In a random sample of 200 memory chips made at the UK plant, 18 were found to be defective.
   a) Define Population 1 and Population 2.
   b) Identify the parameter of interest.
   c) Identify the random variable of interest.
   d) Determine the appropriate distribution for the analysis.
   e) Find a 95% confidence interval for the difference between the two population proportions of defective memory chips.
   f) Interpret the confidence interval you found in part (e).
   g) Is there a difference between the two population proportions? Use the confidence interval you found in part (e) to support your decision.

3. At Happy Skiers Resort, 270 accidents were reported during one season, 30 of which resulted in a broken leg. At Snowy Mountain Resort, 220 accidents were reported during one season, 20 of which resulted in a broken leg.
   a) Define Population 1 and Population 2.
   b) Identify the parameter of interest.
   c) Identify the random variable of interest.
   d) Determine the appropriate distribution for the analysis.
   e) Find a 90% confidence interval for the difference between the two population proportions of skiing accidents resulting in a broken leg.
   f) Interpret the confidence interval you found in part (e).
   g) Is there a difference between the two population proportions? Use the confidence interval you found in part (e) to support your decision.

ANSWERS

LESSON 8.1 EXERCISES

CONFIDENCE INTERVALS FOR COMPARING TWO POPULATION PROPORTIONS

Below are the answers to the exercises for Unit 8, Lesson 8.1.
For full solutions, please refer to the CD included with this textbook.

1. a) Population 1 = Male American college students
        Population 2 = Female American college students

    b) p_1 = the population proportion of male American college students who go to graduate school

        p_2 = the population proportion of female American college students who go to graduate school

        The parameter of interest is $p_1 - p_2$.

    c) $\hat{P}_1$ = the sample proportion of 500 male American college students who go to graduate school

        $\hat{P}_2$ = the sample proportion of 500 female American college students who go to graduate school

        The random variable of interest is $\hat{p}_1 - \hat{p}_2$.

    d) Conditions are satisfied to use the Z-distribution.

    e) (-0.0188, 0.0588)

    f) With 95% confidence, the difference between the population proportions of male and female American college students who go to graduate school is between -0.0188 and 0.0588.

    g) The interval indicates that the population proportion of male American college students that go to graduate school is the same as the population proportion of female American college students that go to graduate school.

2. a) Population 1 = Memory chips from Japanese plant
        Population 2 = Memory chips from UK plant

    b) p_1 = the population proportion of memory chips made in the Japanese plant that are defective

        p_2 = the population proportion of memory chips made in the UK plant that are defective

        The parameter of interest is $p_1 - p_2$.

c) $\hat{P}_1 =$ the sample proportion of 300 memory chips made in the Japanese plant that are defective

$\hat{P}_2 =$ the sample proportion of 200 memory chips made in the UK plant that are defective

The random variable of interest is $\hat{p}_1 - \hat{p}_2$.

d) Conditions are satisfied to use the Z-distribution.

e) (-0.0867, 0.0067)

f) With 95% confidence, the difference between the population proportions of defective memory chips in the Japanese plant and the UK plant is between -0.0867 and 0.0067.

g) The interval indicates that the population proportion of defective memory chips is the same in the Japanese plant as in the UK plant.

3. a) Population 1 = Accidents at Happy Skiers Resort
   Population 2 = Accidents at Snowy Mountain Resort

   b) $p_1 =$ the population proportion of accidents at Happy Skiers Resort that result in a broken leg

   $p_2 =$ the population proportion of accidents at Snowy Mountain Resort that result in a broken leg

   The parameter of interest is $p_1 - p_2$.

   c) $\hat{P}_1 =$ the sample proportion of 270 accidents at Happy Skiers Resort that result in a broken leg

   $\hat{P}_2 =$ the sample proportion of 220 accidents at Snowy Mountain Resort that result in a broken leg

   The random variable of interest is $\hat{p}_1 - \hat{p}_2$.

   d) Conditions are satisfied to use the Z-distribution.

   e) (-0.0246, 0.0650)

   f) With 90% confidence, the difference between the population proportions of accidents resulting in a broken leg at Happy Skiers Resort and Snowy Mountain Resort is between -0.0246 and 0.0650.

   g) The interval indicates that the population proportion of accidents that result in broken legs is the same at the two resorts.

LESSON 8.2
HYPOTHESIS TESTING FOR COMPARING TWO POPULATION PROPORTIONS

8.2.1

INTRODUCTION

The third hypothesis test we will learn is for comparing two population proportions. It is important to keep in mind that the same concepts learned in Lessons 7.2 and 8.2 apply here.

8.2.2

DECIDING WHICH DISTRIBUTION TO USE

Hypothesis testing for comparing two population proportions uses the Z-distribution, provided that certain conditions are met. They are the same as those for a confidence interval for the difference between two population proportions. As a reminder, they are:

CHECK THE FOLLOWING CONDITIONS:

Use the Z-distribution for the analysis if all of the following are true for *both* samples:

All four Binomial criteria are met in the experiment.
1. There is a fixed number of trials: n_1 for Population 1 and n_2 for Population 2
2. The trials are independent
3. The outcome of each trial is a success or a failure
4. The proportion of successes remains constant from trial to trial

The sample size is sufficiently large to define the distribution of $\hat{P}_1 - \hat{P}_2$ as Normal. This is true if:

$$n_1 p_1 \geq 10 \text{ and } n_1(1 - p_1) \geq 10$$
$$n_2 p_2 \geq 10 \text{ and } n_2(1 - p_2) \geq 10$$

but since the value of p_1 and p_2 is unknown, use $\hat{p}_1$ and $\hat{p}_2$.

8.2.3   **SETTING UP HYPOTHESES**

The same rules for setting up hypotheses that we learned in Lesson 6.2 apply here. The difference is that the claim is about comparing two population proportions, p_1 and p_2, rather than about a population mean μ or a single population proportion p. For example, to test the claim that a higher proportion of adults suffer from insomnia than children, we first assign Population 1 as the adults and Population 2 as the children. The hypotheses are set up as follows.

The parameters of interest are:

p_1 = the population proportion of adults who suffer from insomnia

p_2 = the population proportion of children who suffer from insomnia

The claim is $p_1 > p_2$.

STOP AND THINK!

Is this the null or alternative hypothesis? How do you know?

Since $p_1 > p_2$ is a statement of inequality, it is the alternative hypothesis.

The complementary statement to the claim is $p_1 \leq p_2$, and since this is a statement of equality, it is the null hypothesis.

Thus, we write the hypotheses and identify the claim:

$$H_0: \ p_1 \leq p_2 \qquad\qquad H_A: \ p_1 > p_2 \ \text{(claim)}$$

The following example will be used for the remainder of the lesson to illustrate the various steps in hypothesis testing.

A random sample of 150 employed men and 200 employed women were asked if they enjoy their jobs. Of the men, 78 said they enjoy their job, and of the women, 122 said they enjoy their job. Test the claim that a higher proportion of women enjoy their job. Use a 5% significance level.

First verify that it is appropriate to use the Z-distribution by checking the conditions hold for both samples.

Population 1: Employed men
1. There are $n_1 = 150$ trials.
2. The trials are independent because they come from a random sample.
3. We are interested in finding 'an employed man who enjoys his job', so this is a *success*, and finding 'an employed man who does not enjoy his job' is a *failure*.
4. We do not know the actual value of p_1, but we will assume it is constant.

So for the sample from Population 1 the experiment is Binomial.

Population 2: Employed women
1. There are $n_2 = 200$ trials.
2. The trials are independent because they come from a random sample.
3. We are interested in finding 'an employed woman who enjoys her job', so this is a *success*, and finding 'an employed woman who does not enjoy her job' is a *failure*.
4. We do not know the actual value of p_2, but we will assume it is constant.

So for the sample from Population 2 the experiment is Binomial.

We also need to verify the sample size is large enough to define the distribution of $\hat{P}_1$ and $\hat{P}_2$ as Normal. Since the values of p_1 and p_2 are unknown, we use the value of $\hat{p}_1$ and $\hat{p}_2$ observed in the samples.

For employed men:

$$n\hat{p}_1 = 150\left(\frac{78}{150}\right) \qquad\qquad n(1-\hat{p}_1) = 150\left(1-\frac{78}{150}\right)$$
$$= 78 \qquad\qquad\qquad\qquad\qquad\qquad = 72$$

Since both of these values are at least 10, we can define the distribution of $\hat{P}_1$ as Normal.

For employed women:

$$n\hat{p}_2 = 200\left(\frac{122}{200}\right) \qquad\qquad n(1-\hat{p}_2) = 200\left(1-\frac{122}{200}\right)$$
$$= 122 \qquad\qquad\qquad\qquad\qquad\qquad = 78$$

Since both of these values are at least 10, we can define the distribution of $\hat{P}_2$ as Normal.

Thus, the conditions required to use the Z-distribution have been satisfied.

Next, we define the parameters of interest and set up the hypotheses.

Let p_1 = the population proportion of employed men who enjoy their job

p_2 = the population proportion of employed women who enjoy their job

The claim is that $p_1 < p_2$.

STOP AND THINK!

Is this the null or alternative hypothesis? How do you know?

Since $p_1 < p_2$ is a statement of inequality, it is the alternative hypothesis.

The complementary statement to the claim is $p_1 \geq p_2$, and since this is a statement of equality, it is the null hypothesis.

Thus, we write the hypotheses and identify the claim:

$$H_0: \ p_1 \geq p_2 \qquad\qquad H_A: \ p_1 < p_2 \ \text{(claim)}$$

Next compute the test statistic, under the assumption that the null hypothesis is true.

8.2.4

CALCULATING THE TEST STATISTIC

The same concepts we learned in Lesson 6.2 apply here, except that now we are using the distribution of the *difference* between two population proportions, $\hat{P}_1 - \hat{P}_2$. Since in this example, the distribution of $\hat{P}_1 - \hat{P}_2$ is Normal, we need to find the mean and standard deviation. We define the random variables of interest:

$\hat{P}_1$ = the sample proportion of 150 employed men who enjoy their job

$\hat{P}_2$ = the sample proportion of 200 employed women who enjoy their job

The mean of $\hat{P}_1 - \hat{P}_2$ is $p_1 - p_2$, and since we assume that the null hypothesis is true, this implies that $p_1 = p_2$, and hence, $p_1 - p_2 = 0$. The standard deviation of $\hat{P}_1 - \hat{P}_2$ is:

$$\text{Standard deviation of } \hat{P}_1 - \hat{P}_2: \ \sqrt{\bar{p}(1-\bar{p})\left(\frac{1}{n_1} + \frac{1}{n_2}\right)}$$

---

where n_1 and n_2 are the sample sizes taken from the two populations, and $\overline{p}$, read 'p-bar', is found by dividing the *total* number of successes in the two samples by the *total* number of trials.

$$\overline{p} = \frac{x_1 + x_2}{n_1 + n_2} = \frac{78 + 122}{150 + 200} = \frac{4}{7}$$

So the standard deviation of $\hat{P}_1 - \hat{P}_2$ is:

$$\sqrt{\overline{p}(1-\overline{p})\left(\frac{1}{n_1} + \frac{1}{n_2}\right)} = \sqrt{\left(\frac{4}{7}\right)\left(1 - \frac{4}{7}\right)\left(\frac{1}{150} + \frac{1}{200}\right)} = 0.0535$$

The distribution of $\hat{P}_1 - \hat{P}_2$ is shown in Figure 8.1.

Figure 8.1

$$\hat{P}_1 - \hat{P}_2 \text{ is } N(0, 0.0535)$$

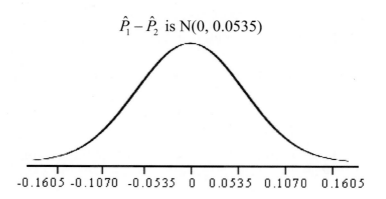

-0.1605 -0.1070 -0.0535 0 0.0535 0.1070 0.1605

The null hypothesis states that $p_1 \geq p_2$, so it is possible that the distribution of $\hat{P}_1 - \hat{P}_2$ is centered at 0 *or higher*. Values of $\hat{p}_1 - \hat{p}_2$ that are 0 or higher support the null hypothesis. Even values of $\hat{p}_1 - \hat{p}_2$ that are slightly less than 0 will also support the null hypothesis because such values are probable in the distribution shown in Figure 8.1. However, values of $\hat{p}_1 - \hat{p}_2$ that are *much* less than 0 leads us to doubt that the null is true.

In the example, the proportion of employed men in the sample who enjoy their job is:

$$\hat{p}_1 = \frac{x_1}{n_1} = \frac{78}{150} = 0.52$$

The proportion of employed women in the sample who enjoy their job is:

$$\hat{p}_2 = \frac{x_2}{n_2} = \frac{122}{200} = 0.61$$

Therefore, the difference in the sample proportions is:

$$\hat{p}_1 - \hat{p}_2 = 0.52 - 0.61 = -0.09$$

Figure 8.2 shows where this value falls in the distribution of $\hat{P}_1 - \hat{P}_2$:

Figure 8.2

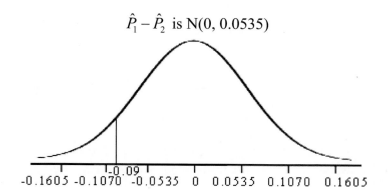

$\hat{P}_1 - \hat{P}_2$ is N(0, 0.0535)

As we see, the sample difference observed is less than 0. In order to decide whether this supports the null hypothesis, we first compute a test statistic.

Since we are using the Z-distribution, the test statistic is a z-score, and so the test statistic is computed as follows:

$$z = \frac{-0.09 - 0}{0.0535} = -1.68$$

This result can be generalized:

---

z-Test Statistic for Comparing Two Population Proportions

$$z = \frac{\left(\hat{p}_1 - \hat{p}_2\right) - \left(p_1 - p_2\right)}{\sqrt{\overline{p}\left(1 - \overline{p}\right)\left(\dfrac{1}{n_1} + \dfrac{1}{n_2}\right)}}$$

Even though this formula looks different from the z-score formula used in Unit 4, it is conceptually the same. We will now use the test statistic to obtain the p-value for the test.

8.2.5   **FINDING THE *p*-VALUE**

Having computed the test statistic for the example and obtained $z = -1.68$, we now identify the area of interest. This area is called the p-value. We will only reject the null hypothesis if we observe a difference in sample proportions *much less* than 0. So we are interested in the area *below* the test statistic, and therefore, the *p*-value for this test is as shown in Figure 8.3.

Figure 8.3

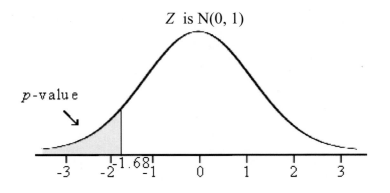

Looking up $z = -1.68$, the Standard Normal table shows that the area *below* it is 0.0465. Since this corresponds with the shaded area, the *p*-value is:

$$p-\text{value} = P(Z < -1.68)$$
$$= 0.0465$$

Guidelines for finding *p*-values given in Sections 6.2.5 and 7.25 are repeated here.

Finding *p*-values

To determine the *p*-value, first look at the sign in the alternative hypothesis:

If the sign is '<', then the *p*-value for the test is the area *below* the test statistic

If the sign is '>', then the *p*-value for the test is the area *above* the test statistic

If the sign is '≠', then the *p*-value for the test is the area *below* the negative value of the test statistic *plus* the area *above* the positive value of the test statistic.

Having found the *p*-value, next we decide whether the data supports the null or the alternative hypothesis.

8.2.6   **THE DECISION**

Recall a small *p*-value indicates that you should reject the null hypothesis. The decision process here is the same as in Sections 6.2.6 and 7.2.6.

In the example, we were told to use a 5% significance level. So there is enough evidence to reject the null if we observe a *p*-value that is *less* than 0.05, and there is *not* enough evidence to reject the null if we observe a *p*-value that is *more* than 0.05. The *p*-value for our test is 0.0465, which is *less* than the significance level. Therefore, there is enough evidence to reject the null hypothesis. In other words, the difference in sample proportions that we observed was *much* less than 0, and so it does *not* support the null hypothesis.

Now that a decision has been made, we must offer an interpretation of our results.

8.2.7   **INTERPRETING THE RESULTS**

The final step in hypothesis testing is to state the conclusion. This means we need to address the original claim. Does the data support the claim, or does it not? Recall the hypotheses for this example:

$$H_0: \; p_1 \geq p_2 \qquad\qquad H_A: \; p_1 < p_2 \;\; \text{(claim)}$$

Since the decision was to reject the null, the data supports the alternative, which is the claim. Therefore, at a 5% significance level, we conclude that the p_2, the proportion of all employed women who enjoy their job is higher than p_1, the proportion of all employed men who enjoy their job.

LESSON 8.2 EXERCISES
HYPOTHESIS TESTING FOR COMPARING TWO POPULATION PROPORTIONS

1. In a random sample of 400 blue-collar workers, it was found that 50 were saving for a pension. In a random sample of 500 white-collar workers, it was found that 150 were saving for a pension. A human resources manager wants to determine whether there is any difference between the two populations. Use $\alpha=0.01$
    a) Define Population 1 and Population 2.
    b) Determine the appropriate distribution to use.
    c) Define the parameters and random variables of interest.
    d) State the null and alternative hypotheses, and identify the claim.
    e) Calculate the test statistic.
    f) Determine the p-value.
    g) State your decision.
    h) State your conclusion.

2. An ocean fish farmer is concerned about the number of fish being damaged or eaten by seals at two farming locations, Cod Cove and Cockle Cove. The farm owner wants to test the claim that a higher proportion of fish being are being mauled by seals at Cockle Cove. In a random sample of 120 fish taken from Cod Cove, 15 were mauled by seals. In a random sample of 150 fish taken from Cockle Cove, 25 were mauled by seals. Use $\alpha=0.05$.
    a) Define Population 1 and Population 2.
    b) Determine the appropriate distribution to use.
    c) Define the parameters and random variables of interest.
    d) State the null and alternative hypotheses, and identify the claim.
    e) Calculate the test statistic.
    f) Determine the p-value.
    g) State your decision.
    h) State your conclusion.

ANSWERS
LESSON 8.2 EXERCISES
HYPOTHESIS TESTING FOR COMPARING TWO POPULATION PROPORTIONS

Below are the answers to the exercises for Unit 8, Lesson 8.2.
For full solutions, please refer to the CD included with this textbook.

1. a) Population 1 = Blue-collar workers
        Population 2 = White-collar workers
    b) Conditions are satisfied to use the Z-distribution.
    c) The parameters of interest are:

    p_1 = the population proportion of blue-collar workers saving for a pension

    p_2 = the population proportion of white-collar workers saving for pension

    The random variables of interest are:

    $\hat{P}_1$ = the sample proportion of 400 blue-collar workers saving for a pension

    $\hat{P}_2$ = the sample proportion of 500 white-collar workers saving for pension

    d) H_0: $p_1 = p_2$ $\qquad$ H_A: $p_1 \neq p_2$ (claim)
    e) $z = -6.27$
    f) $p-\text{value} \approx 0$
    g) There is enough evidence to reject the null hypothesis.
    h) There is a difference between the two population proportions of workers saving for a pension.

2. a) Population 1 = Fish at Cod Cove
        Population 2 = Fish at Cockle Cove
    b) Conditions are satisfied to use the Z-distribution.
    c) The parameters of interest are:

    p_1 = the population proportion of fish at Cod Cove mauled by seals

    p_2 = the population proportion of fish at Cockle Cove mauled by seals

    The random variables of interest are:

    $\hat{P}_1$ = the sample proportion of 120 fish at Cod Cove mauled by seals

    $\hat{P}_2$ = the sample proportion of 150 fish at Cockle Cove mauled by seals

    d) H_0: $p_1 \geq p_2$ $\qquad$ H_A: $p_1 < p_2$ (claim)
    e) $z = -0.96$
    f) $p-\text{value} = 0.1685$
    g) There is not enough evidence to reject the null hypothesis.
    h) There is not enough evidence to support the claim that a higher proportion of fish are mauled by seals at Cockle Cove.

LESSON 8.3
MORE PRACTICE IN SOLVING INFERENCE PROBLEMS

In this lesson we look at some more examples with full solutions. You are encouraged to work through these problems yourself if you need extra practice.

Example 1: In a survey of 100 randomly selected adult farm workers in, 5 were overweight. In a survey of 100 randomly selected adult office workers, 20 were overweight. If we wanted to construct a 95% confidence interval for the difference between the population proportions of adult farm and office workers that are overweight, is it appropriate to use the Z-distribution?

> **STOP AND THINK!**
>
> **How are Population 1 and 2 defined?**
>
> **How do we verify that it is appropriate to use the Z-distribution?**

Solution:
Define:
Population 1 = Adult farm workers
Population 2 = Adult office workers

Then:
$p_1 =$ the population proportion of adult farm workers that are overweight
$p_2 =$ the population proportion of adult office workers that are overweight

The parameter of interest is $p_1 - p_2$.

Similarly:
$\hat{P}_1 =$ the sample proportion of 100 adult farm workers that are overweight
$\hat{P}_2 =$ the sample proportion of 100 adult office workers that are overweight

The random variable of interest is $\hat{P}_1 - \hat{P}_2$.

To determine whether it is appropriate to use the Z-distribution, verify that the experiment is Binomial for *both* samples:

Population 1: Adult farm workers
1. There are $n_1 = 100$ trials.
2. The trials are independent since the adult farm workers were randomly selected.
3. Since we are interested in finding 'an adult farm worker who is overweight', this is a *success*, and finding 'an adult farm worker who is not overweight' is a *failure*.
4. Although we do not know the value of p_1 , it is reasonable to assume it is constant.

So for the sample from Population 1 the experiment is Binomial.

Population 2: Adult office workers
1. There are $n_2 = 100$ trials.
2. The trials are independent since the adult office workers were randomly selected.
3. Since we are interested in finding 'an adult office worker who is overweight', this is a *success*, and finding 'an adult office worker who is not overweight' is a *failure*.
4. Although we do not know the value of p_2 , it is reasonable to assume it is constant.

So for the sample from Population 2 the experiment is Binomial.

We also need to verify the sample size is large enough to define the distribution of $\hat{P}_1$ and $\hat{P}_2$ as Normal. Since the values of p_1 and p_2 are unknown, we use the value of $\hat{p}_1$ and $\hat{p}_2$ observed in the samples.

For adult farm workers:

$$n_1\hat{p}_1 = (100)\left(\frac{5}{100}\right) \qquad\qquad n_1(1-\hat{p}_1) = (100)\left(1-\frac{5}{100}\right)$$
$$= 5 \qquad\qquad\qquad\qquad\qquad = 95$$

Since one of these values is less than 10, we *cannot* define the distribution of $\hat{P}_1$ as Normal.

For adult office workers:

$$n_2\hat{p}_2 = (100)\left(\frac{20}{100}\right) \qquad\qquad n_2(1-\hat{p}_2) = (100)\left(1-\frac{20}{100}\right)$$
$$= 20 \qquad\qquad\qquad\qquad\qquad = 80$$

Lesson 8.3: More Practice in Solving Inference Problems

Since both of these values are at least 10, we can define the distribution of $\hat{P}_2$ as Normal.

Since the distribution of $\hat{P}_1$ cannot be defined as Normal, it is not appropriate to use the Z-distribution for this analysis.

■

Example 2:   Kevin is running for office as State Senator. In one district, a poll of 100 randomly selected registered voters was taken and 45% favored Kevin. In a second district, a poll of 100 randomly selected registered voters was taken and 55% favored Kevin.
a) Find a 95% confidence interval for the difference between the two population proportions of registered voters that favor Kevin.
b) Interpret the confidence interval you found in part (a).

> **STOP AND THINK!**
>
> **Define Population 1 and 2.**
>
> **Identify the parameter and random variable of interest.**
>
> **Determine the appropriate distribution for the analysis.**

Solution: a) Define:
Population 1 = Registered voters in the first district
Population 2 = Registered voters in the second district

Then:
p_1 = the population proportion of registered voters in the first district that favor Kevin
p_2 = the population proportion of registered voters in the second district that favor Kevin

The parameter of interest is $p_1 - p_2$.

Similarly:
$\hat{P}_1$ = the sample proportion of 100 registered voters in the first district that favor Kevin
$\hat{P}_2$ = the sample proportion of 100 registered voters in the second district that favor Kevin

The random variable of interest is $\hat{P}_1 - \hat{P}_2$.

To determine whether it is appropriate to use the Z-distribution, verify that the experiment is Binomial for *both* samples:

Population 1: Registered voters in the first district
1. There are $n_1 = 100$ trials.
2. The trials are independent since the registered voters were randomly selected.
3. Since we are interested in finding 'a registered voter who favors Kevin', this is a *success*, and finding 'a registered voter who does not favor Kevin' is a *failure*.
4. Although we do not know the value of p_1, it is reasonable to assume it is constant.

So for the sample from Population 1 the experiment is Binomial.

Population 2: Registered voters in the second district
1. There are $n_2 = 100$ trials.
2. The trials are independent since the registered were randomly selected.
3. Since we are interested in finding 'a registered voter who favors Kevin', this is a *success*, and finding 'a registered voter who does not favor Kevin' is a *failure*.
4. Although we do not know the value of p_2, it is reasonable to assume it is constant.

So for the sample from Population 2 the experiment is Binomial.

We also need to verify the sample size is large enough to define the distribution of $\hat{P}_1$ and $\hat{P}_2$ as Normal. Since the values of p_1 and p_2 are unknown, we use the value of $\hat{p}_1$ and $\hat{p}_2$ observed in the samples.

For registered voters in the first district:

$$n_1 \hat{p}_1 = (100)(0.45) \qquad\qquad n_1(1 - \hat{p}_1) = (100)(1 - 0.45)$$
$$= 45 \qquad\qquad\qquad\qquad\qquad = 55$$

Since both of these values are at least 10, we can define the distribution of $\hat{P}_1$ as Normal.

For registered voters in the second district:

$$n_2 \hat{p}_2 = (100)(0.55) \qquad\qquad n_2(1 - \hat{p}_2) = (100)(1 - 0.55)$$
$$= 55 \qquad\qquad\qquad\qquad\qquad = 45$$

Since both of these values are at least 10, we can define the distribution of $\hat{P}_2$ as Normal.

So it is appropriate to use the Z-distribution for this analysis.

A 95% confidence interval for the difference in the two population proportions of is found using:

$$(\hat{p}_1 - \hat{p}_2) \pm z \sqrt{\frac{\hat{p}_1(1-\hat{p}_1)}{n_1} + \frac{\hat{p}_2(1-\hat{p}_2)}{n_2}}$$

We have already found that:

$$\hat{p}_1 = 0.45 \text{ and } \hat{p}_2 = 0.55$$

Since we want to construct a 95% confidence interval, $z = 1.96$. Substituting these values in the formula gives:

$$(\hat{p}_1 - \hat{p}_2) \pm z \sqrt{\frac{\hat{p}_1(1-\hat{p}_1)}{n_1} + \frac{\hat{p}_2(1-\hat{p}_2)}{n_2}}$$

$$= (0.45 - 0.55) \pm 1.96 \sqrt{\frac{0.45(1-0.45)}{100} + \frac{0.55(1-0.55)}{100}}$$

$$= -0.1 \pm 0.1379$$

and so the desired confidence interval is $(-0.2379, \ 0.0379)$.

Solution: b) This confidence interval is interpreted as follows:

We can be 95% confident that the true difference in proportion of registered voters in the first and second district that favor Kevin is between –0.2379 and 0.0379.

■

Example 3: A survey of 75 French adults found that 50 of them regularly drink wine at lunchtime. A similar survey found that 50 out of 100 Spanish adults regularly drink wine at lunchtime. Let Population 1 represent French adults, and Population 2 represent Spanish adults. The 95% confidence interval constructed for $p_1 - p_2$ is (0.0218, 0.3115).

a) Interpret the confidence interval.
b) Can we conclude that a higher proportion of French adults regularly drink wine at lunchtime compared with Spanish adults? Explain.

> **STOP AND THINK!**
>
> Define p_1 and p_2. What do the values in the interval indicate about the population proportions?

Solution: a) $p_1 =$ the population proportion of French adults that regularly drink wine at lunchtime

$p_2 =$ the population proportion of Spanish adults that regularly drink wine at lunchtime

With 95% confidence, the difference between the population proportion of French and Spanish adults that regularly drink wine at lunchtime is between 0.0218 and 0.3115.

Solution: b) Since the interval only contains positive values, this indicates that the difference $p_1 - p_2$ is positive. Thus, p_1 must be greater than p_2, which means we can conclude that a higher proportion of French adults regularly drink wine at lunchtime compared with Spanish adults

Example 4:   The injuries incurred by professional football teams and professional baseball teams were documented. Let Population 1 represent professional football teams and Population 2 represent professional baseball teams. Brian thinks that there is a higher proportion of injuries in professional football than there are in professional baseball. What type of confidence interval will support his belief: one that contains only positive values, only negative values, or the value 0? Explain.

> **STOP AND THINK!**
>
> If all the values in the interval are positive, what does this indicate about the population proportions?
>
> If all the values in the interval are negative, what does this indicate about the population proportions?
>
> If the interval contains 0, what does this indicate about the population proportions?

Solution: If there is a higher proportion of injuries in professional football than in professional baseball, then $p_1 > p_2$. Therefore, the difference $p_1 - p_2$ will be positive, and so an interval that contains only positive values will support Brian's belief.

Example 5: Two furniture manufacturers, Newbridge Joinery and Amazon Dining Suites use renewable resource hardwoods. Samples were taken from the timber yard of Newbridge Joinery and it was found that 22% of the timber was renewable hardwood. Samples taken from the timber yard of Amazon Dining Suites revealed that 18% of the timber was renewable hardwood. From this information alone, can we conclude that Newbridge Joinery has a higher population proportion of renewable hardwood than Amazon Dining Suites? Explain.

STOP AND THINK!

Are the proportions given statistics or parameters?

Can we construct a confidence interval based on the given information?

Solution: Define:
Population 1 = Timber from Newbridge Joinery
Population 2 = Timber from Amazon Dining Suites

Then:
$p_1 =$ the population proportion of renewable hardwood at Newbridge Joinery
$p_2 =$ the population proportion of renewable hardwood at Amazon Dining Suites

We want to know whether $p_1 > p_2$. The values given in the problem are sample proportions, $\hat{p}_1 = 0.22$ and $\hat{p}_2 = 0.18$. From these values alone, we cannot conclude that $p_1 > p_2$. To make such a conclusion we would need to construct a confidence interval for the difference $p_1 - p_2$. Since we are not given the sample sizes for the two samples, we cannot actually construct a confidence interval.

■

Example 6: Data is collected from 1000 randomly selected community college students and 2000 randomly selected university students. The students are asked whether they receive financial support from their parents, and 56% of the community college students and 62% of the university students say they do. Test the claim that the proportion of students that receive financial support from their parents differs in the two populations. Use a 1% significance level.
a) State the null and alternative hypotheses, and identify the claim.
b) Calculate the test statistic.
c) Determine the *p*-value.
d) State your decision.
e) State your conclusion.

> **STOP AND THINK!**
>
> Define Population 1 and 2.
>
> Identify the parameters and random variables of interest.
>
> Determine the appropriate distribution for the analysis.
>
> What is the claim? Is it the null or alternative hypothesis? How do you know?

Solution:

a) Define:
   Population 1 = Community college students
   Population 2 = University students

   Then the parameters of interest are:

   p_1 = the population proportion of community college students who receive financial support from their parents

   p_2 = the population proportion of university students who receive financial support from their parents

   The random variables of interest are:

   $\hat{P}_1$ = the sample proportion of 1000 community college students who receive financial support from their parents

   $\hat{P}_2$ = the sample proportion of 2000 university students who receive financial support from their parents

   Verify that it is appropriate to use the Z-distribution by checking the conditions hold for both samples.

   Population 1: Community college students
   1. There are $n_1 = 1000$ trials.
   2. The trials are independent because they come from a random sample.
   3. We are interested in finding 'a community college student who receives financial support from his/her parents', so this is a *success*, and finding 'a community college student who does not receive financial support from his/her parents' is a *failure*.
   4. We do not know the actual value of p_1, but we will assume it is constant.

   So for the sample from Population 1 the experiment is Binomial.

Population 2: University students

1. There are $n_2 = 2000$ trials.
2. The trials are independent because they come from a random sample.
3. We are interested in finding 'a university student who receives financial support from his/her parents', so this is a *success*, and finding 'a university student who does not receive financial support from his/her parents' is a *failure*.
4. We do not know the actual value of p_2, but we will assume it is constant.

So for the sample from Population 2 the experiment is Binomial.

We also need to verify the sample size is large enough to define the distribution of $\hat{P}_1$ and $\hat{P}_2$ as Normal. Since the values of p_1 and p_2 are unknown, we use the value of $\hat{p}_1$ and $\hat{p}_2$ observed in the samples.

For community college students:

$$n\hat{p}_1 = 100(0.56) \qquad n(1 - \hat{p}_1) = 1000(1 - 0.56)$$
$$= 560 \qquad\qquad\qquad = 440$$

Since both of these values are at least 10, we can define the distribution of $\hat{P}_1$ as Normal.

For university students:

$$n\hat{p}_2 = 2000(0.62) \qquad n(1 - \hat{p}_2) = 2000(1 - 0.62)$$
$$= 1240 \qquad\qquad\qquad = 760$$

Since both of these values are at least 10, we can define the distribution of $\hat{P}_2$ as Normal.

Thus, the conditions required to use the Z-distribution have been satisfied.

Next, set up the hypotheses.

The claim is that $p_1 \neq p_2$. Since this is a statement of inequality, it is the alternative hypothesis.

The complementary statement to the claim is $p_1 = p_2$, and since this is a statement of equality, it is the null hypothesis.

Thus, we write the hypotheses and identify the claim:

$$\text{H}_0\colon\ p_1 = p_2 \qquad\qquad \text{H}_\text{A}\colon\ p_1 \neq p_2 \ \text{(claim)}$$

Solution: b) The mean of $\hat{P}_1 - \hat{P}_2$ is $p_1 - p_2$, and since we assume that the null hypothesis is true, this implies that $p_1 = p_2$, and hence, $p_1 - p_2 = 0$. The standard deviation of $\hat{P}_1 - \hat{P}_2$ is:

$$\text{Standard deviation of } \hat{P}_1 - \hat{P}_2 : \sqrt{\overline{p}(1-\overline{p})\left(\frac{1}{n_1} + \frac{1}{n_2}\right)}$$

where n_1 and n_2 are the sample sizes taken from the two populations, and $\overline{p}$, read 'p-bar', is found by dividing the *total* number of successes in the two samples by the *total* number of trials. To find $\overline{p}$, we must first find x_1 and x_2.

$$x_1 = n_1 \hat{p}_1 \qquad\qquad x_2 = n_2 \hat{p}_2$$
$$= 1000(0.56) \qquad\qquad = 2000(0.62)$$
$$= 560 \qquad\qquad\qquad = 1240$$

Thus, $\overline{p}$ is:

$$\overline{p} = \frac{x_1 + x_2}{n_1 + n_2} = \frac{560 + 1240}{1000 + 2000} = 0.6$$

So the standard deviation of $\hat{P}_1 - \hat{P}_2$ is:

$$\sqrt{\overline{p}(1-\overline{p})\left(\frac{1}{n_1} + \frac{1}{n_2}\right)} = \sqrt{(0.6)(1-0.6)\left(\frac{1}{1000} + \frac{1}{2000}\right)} = 0.019$$

The difference in the sample proportions is:

$$\hat{p}_1 - \hat{p}_2 = 0.56 - 0.62 = -0.06$$

The distribution of $\hat{P}_1 - \hat{P}_2$ is shown below, with the observed sample difference marked.

$\hat{P}_1 - \hat{P}_2$ is N(0, 0.019)

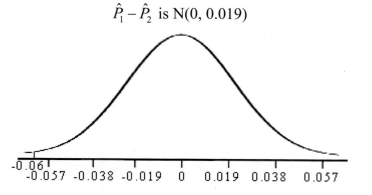

-0.06
-0.057 -0.038 -0.019   0   0.019 0.038   0.057

As we see, the sample difference observed is less than 0. In order to decide whether this supports the null hypothesis, we first compute a test statistic:

$$z = \frac{-0.06 - 0}{0.019} = -3.16$$

Solution: c) When the sign in the alternative is '≠', the *p*-value is defined to be the area *below* the negative value of the test statistic *plus* the area *above* the positive value of the test statistic. Therefore, the *p*-value for this test is as shown below:

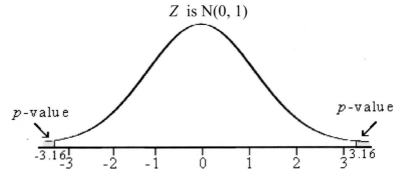

This area is found in the Standard Normal table.

$$p - \text{value} = P(Z < -3.16) + P(Z > 3.16)$$
$$= 0.0008 + (1 - 0.9992)$$
$$= 0.0008 + 0.0008$$
$$= 0.0016$$

Solution: d) In the example, we were told to use a 1% significance level. So there is enough evidence to reject the null if we observe a *p*-value that is *less* than 0.01, and there is *not* have enough evidence to reject the null if we observe a *p*-value that is *more* than 0.01. The *p*-value for the test is 0.0016, which is *less* than the significance level. Therefore, there is enough evidence to reject the null hypothesis.

Solution: e) The final step in hypothesis testing is to state the conclusion. This means we need to address the original claim. Does the data support the claim, or does it not? Recall the hypotheses for this example:

$$H_0: \ p_1 = p_2 \qquad\qquad H_A: \ p_1 \neq p_2 \ \text{(claim)}$$

Since the decision was to reject the null, the data supports the alternative, which is the claim. Therefore, at a 1% significance level, we can conclude that the proportion of community college students that receive financial support from their parents differs from that of university students.

Example 7: A random sample of 100 males who live in southern California found that 33 of them surf. Of 100 randomly selected females who live in southern California, 27 of them surf. Test the claim that a higher proportion of males who live in southern California surf compared with females. Use a 5% significance level.
a) State the null and alternative hypotheses, and identify the claim.
b) Calculate the test statistic.
c) Determine the *p*-value.
d) State your decision.
e) State your conclusion.

> **STOP AND THINK!**
>
> **Define Population 1 and 2.**
>
> **Identify the parameters and random variables of interest.**
>
> **Determine the appropriate distribution for the analysis.**
>
> **What is the claim? Is it the null or alternative hypothesis? How do you know?**

Solution:
a) Define:
Population 1 = Males in southern California
Population 2 = Females in southern California

Then the parameters of interest are:

p_1 = the population proportion of males in southern California who surf

p_2 = the population proportion of females in southern California who surf

The random variables of interest are:

$\hat{P}_1$ = the sample proportion of 100 males in southern California who surf

$\hat{P}_2$ = the sample proportion of 100 females in southern California who surf

Verify that it is appropriate to use the *Z*-distribution by checking the conditions hold for both samples.

Population 1: Males in southern California
1. There are $n_1 = 100$ trials.
2. The trials are independent because they come from a random sample.
3. We are interested in finding 'a male in southern California who surfs', so this is a *success*, and finding 'a male in southern California who does not surf' is a *failure*.
4. We do not know the actual value of p_1, but we will assume it is constant.

So for the sample from Population 1 the experiment is Binomial.

Population 2: Females in southern California
1. There are $n_2 = 100$ trials.
2. The trials are independent because they come from a random sample.
3. We are interested in finding 'a female in southern California who surfs', so this is a *success*, and finding 'a female in southern California who does not surf' is a *failure*.
4. We do not know the actual value of p_2, but we will assume it is constant.

So for the sample from Population 2 the experiment is Binomial.

We also need to verify the sample size is large enough to define the distribution of $\hat{P_1}$ and $\hat{P_2}$ as Normal. Since the values of p_1 and p_2 are unknown, we use the value of $\hat{p}_1$ and $\hat{p}_2$ observed in the samples.

For males in southern California:

$$n\hat{p}_1 = 100\left(\frac{33}{100}\right) \qquad n(1-\hat{p}_1) = 1000\left(1-\frac{33}{100}\right)$$
$$= 33 \qquad\qquad\qquad = 67$$

Since both of these values are at least 10, we can define the distribution of $\hat{P_1}$ as Normal

For females in southern California:

$$n\hat{p}_2 = 100\left(\frac{27}{100}\right) \qquad n(1-\hat{p}_2) = 100\left(1-\frac{27}{100}\right)$$
$$= 27 \qquad\qquad\qquad = 73$$

Since both of these values are at least 10, we can define the distribution of $\hat{P_2}$ as Normal

Thus, the conditions required to use the Z-distribution have been satisfied.

Next, set up the hypotheses.

The claim is that $p_1 > p_2$. Since this is a statement of inequality, it is the alternative hypothesis.

The complementary statement to the claim is $p_1 \leq p_2$, and since this is a statement of equality, it is the null hypothesis.

Thus, we write the hypotheses and identify the claim:

$$H_0: \ p_1 \le p_2 \qquad\qquad H_A: \ p_1 > p_2 \ \ (\text{claim})$$

Solution: b) The mean of $\hat{P}_1 - \hat{P}_2$ is $p_1 - p_2$, and since we assume that the null hypothesis is true, this implies that $p_1 = p_2$, and hence, $p_1 - p_2 = 0$. The standard deviation of $\hat{P}_1 - \hat{P}_2$ is:

$$\text{Standard deviation of } \hat{P}_1 - \hat{P}_2: \ \sqrt{\overline{p}(1-\overline{p})\left(\frac{1}{n_1} + \frac{1}{n_2}\right)}$$

where n_1 and n_2 are the sample sizes taken from the two populations, and $\overline{p}$, read 'p-bar', is found by dividing the *total* number of successes in the two samples by the *total* number of trials. Thus, $\overline{p}$ is:

$$\overline{p} = \frac{x_1 + x_2}{n_1 + n_2} = \frac{33 + 27}{100 + 100} = 0.3$$

So the standard deviation of $\hat{P}_1 - \hat{P}_2$ is:

$$\sqrt{\overline{p}(1-\overline{p})\left(\frac{1}{n_1} + \frac{1}{n_2}\right)} = \sqrt{(0.3)(1-0.3)\left(\frac{1}{100} + \frac{1}{100}\right)} = 0.0648$$

The difference in the sample proportions is:

$$\hat{p}_1 - \hat{p}_2 = \frac{33}{100} - \frac{27}{100} = 0.06$$

The distribution of $\hat{P}_1 - \hat{P}_2$ is shown below, with the observed sample difference marked.

$$\hat{P}_1 - \hat{P}_2 \text{ is N}(0, 0.0648)$$

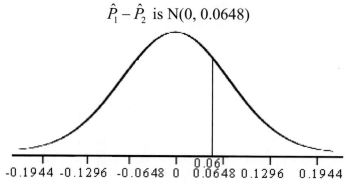

-0.1944 -0.1296 -0.0648 0   0.0648 0.1296   0.1944

As we see, the sample difference observed is more than 0. In order to decide whether this supports the null hypothesis, we first compute a test statistic:

$$z = \frac{0.06 - 0}{0.0648} = 0.93$$

Solution: c) When the sign in the alternative is '>', the p-value is defined to be the area *above* the test statistic. Therefore, the p-value for this test is as shown below:

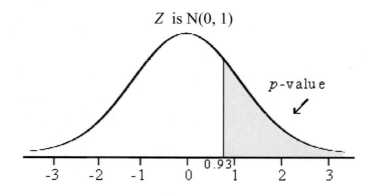

Z is N(0, 1)

This area is found in the Standard Normal table.

$$p - \text{value} = P(Z > 0.93)$$
$$= 1 - 0.8238$$
$$= 0.1762$$

Solution: d) In the example, we were told to use a 5% significance level. So there is enough evidence to reject the null if we observe a p-value that is *less* than 0.05, and there is *not* have enough evidence to reject the null if we observe a p-value that is *more* than 0.05. The p-value for the test is 0.1762, which is *more* than the significance level. Therefore, there is *not* enough evidence to reject the null hypothesis.

Solution: e) The final step in hypothesis testing is to state the conclusion. This means we need to address the original claim. Does the data support the claim, or does it not? Recall the hypotheses for this example:

$$H_0: \ p_1 \leq p_2 \qquad\qquad H_A: \ p_1 > p_2 \ \text{(claim)}$$

Since the decision was to *not* reject the null, the data supports the null, which is *not* the claim. Therefore, at a 5% significance level, we can conclude that the proportion of males in southern California that surf is not higher than the proportion of females in southern California that surf.

Example 8:   Suppose you collect data to test the following hypotheses:

$$H_0: \; p_1 = p_2 \;\; \text{(claim)} \qquad\qquad H_A: \; p_1 \neq p_2$$

Which of the following confidence intervals constructed from the data supports the claim?
A: (0.0634, 0.1152)
B: (-0.1152, 0.0634)
C: (-0.1152, -0.0634)

STOP AND THINK!

The claim is that the two population proportions are equal. Which confidence interval supports this claim?

Solution: Confidence interval B supports the claim because it contains 0.

■

Example 9:   Suppose you conduct a hypothesis test using $\alpha = 0.01$ and conclude that $p_1 < p_2$. Which of the following p-values would lead you to such a decision?
A: 0.2313
B: 0.0487
C: 0.0026

STOP AND THINK!

What were the null and alternative hypotheses tested?

Solution: The conclusion is that $p_1 < p_2$. This is the alternative hypothesis since it does not contain equality. Therefore, $p_1 \geq p_2$ is the null hypothesis. The p-value for the test provided enough evidence for us to reject the null hypothesis. Since $\alpha = 0.01$, the p-value for the test must be less than 0.01. This means the p-value is 0.0026, which is choice C.

■

Example 10: Suppose you conduct a hypothesis test, and reject the null hypothesis at a 5% significance level.
   a) Is it necessarily true that there is enough evidence to reject the null at a 1% significance level?
   b) Is it necessarily true that there is enough evidence to reject the null at a 10% significance level?

> **STOP AND THINK!**
>
> If you reject the null hypothesis at a 5% significance level, is the *p*-value less than 0.05 or greater than 0.05?

Solution: a) The *p*-value for the test is less than 0.05. But it is not necessarily true that the *p*-value will be less than 0.01. Therefore, it is not necessarily true that there is enough evidence to reject the null hypothesis if we use a 1% significance level.

Solution: b) Since the *p*-value for the test is less than 0.05, it is definitely less than 0.10. Therefore, it is necessarily true that there is enough evidence to reject the null hypothesis if we use a 10% significance level.

LESSON 8.3 EXERCISES
MORE PRACTICE IN SOLVING INFERENCE PROBLEMS

1. In a random sample of 300 male American college students, it was found that 28 were fluent in a foreign language. In a random sample of 500 female American college students, it was found that 50 were fluent in a foreign language. A college administrator wants to determine whether there is any difference between the two populations
   a) Define Population 1 and Population 2.
   b) Identify the parameter of interest.
   c) Identify the random variable of interest.
   d) Determine the appropriate distribution for the analysis.
   e) Find a 95% confidence interval for the difference between the two population proportions.
   f) Interpret the confidence interval you found in part (e).
   g) Is there a difference between the two population proportions? Use the confidence interval you found in part e to support your decision.

2. Westfield County Community College students were randomly selected to be part of a survey. Of the 420 female students, 105 said they watch the Super Bowl, whereas 500 of the 680 male students said they watch the Super Bowl. Consider the female students as Population 1, and the male students as Population 2. The 95% confidence interval for the difference between the population proportions of female and male students at Westfield County Community College who watch the Super Bowl is $(-0.5383, -0.4322)$. From this confidence interval, can we conclude that a higher proportion of American men watch the Super Bowl compared to American women? Explain.

3. Two lake resorts kept a record of the number of their boats that leaked on a particular week. At the fishing resort, 3 out of 25 boats leaked. At the water skiing resort, 4 out of 22 boats leaked. Can we use the Z-distribution to compare the population proportion of leaky boats at the two resorts? Explain.

4. A paper-making company, Reams & Reams, has a plant in Ontario and another in Illinois. In a random sample of 200 workers at the Illinois plant, it was found that 65 would take an early retirement package if it was offered. In a random sample of 250 workers at the Ontario plant, it was found that 95 would take an early retirement package if it was offered. The CEO of Reams & Reams is thinking of offering such a package to the Illinois plant, because he claims it has a lower proportion of workers that would take the offer. Test the CEO's claim at a 5% significance level.
   a) Define Population 1 and Population 2.
   b) Determine the appropriate distribution to use.
   c) Define the parameter and random variable of interest.
   d) State the null and alternative hypotheses, and identify the claim.
   e) Calculate the test statistic.
   f) Determine the p-value.
   g) State your decision.
   h) State your conclusion.

5. In a random sample of 300 customers at the Castle Café it was found that 30% had eaten there on a previous occasion. In a survey of 200 customers at the Windmill Diner, it was found that 45% had eaten there on a previous occasion. Test the claim that there is no difference in the proportions of customers who have previously eaten at the Castle Café and the Windmill Diner. Use $\alpha = 0.01$
   a) Define Population 1 and Population 2.
   b) Determine the appropriate distribution to use.
   c) Define the parameter and random variable of interest.
   d) State the null and alternative hypotheses, and identify the claim.
   e) Calculate the test statistic.
   f) Determine the p-value.
   g) State your decision.
   h) State your conclusion.

ANSWERS

LESSON 8.3 EXERCISES

MORE PRACTICE IN SOLVING INFERENCE PROBLEMS

Below are the answers to the exercises for Unit 8, Lesson 8.3.
For full solutions, please refer to the CD included with this textbook.

1. a) Population 1 = Male American college students
    Population 2 = Female American college students
    b) p_1 = the population proportion of male American college students who are fluent in a foreign language
    p_2 = the population proportion of female American college students who are fluent in a foreign language
    The parameter of interest is $p_1 - p_2$.
    c) $\hat{P}_1$ = the sample proportion of 300 male American college students who are fluent in a foreign language
    $\hat{P}_2$ = the sample proportion of 500 female American college students who are fluent in a foreign language
    The random variable of interest is $\hat{p}_1 - \hat{p}_2$.
    d) Conditions are satisfied to use the Z-distribution.
    e) (-0.0488, 0.0354)
    f) With 95% confidence, the difference between the population proportions of male and female American college students that are fluent in a foreign language is between -0.0488 and 0.0354.
    g) The interval indicates that the proportions are the same for the two populations.

2. No, because the sample is not representative of all Americans, just of students at Westfield County Community College. We cannot generalize the conclusions to other populations.

3. No, it is not appropriate to use the Z-distribution because there is not a large enough sample size from either population.

4. a) Population 1 = Workers at Illinois plant
        Population 2 = Workers at Ontario plant
    b) Conditions are satisfied to use the Z-distribution.
    c) The parameters of interest are:
        p_1 = the population proportion of workers at Illinois plant that would take an early retirement package if offered
        p_2 = the population proportion of workers at Ontario plant that would take an early retirement package if offered
        The random variables of interest are:
        $\hat{P}_1$ = the sample proportion of 200 workers at Illinois plant that would take an early retirement package if offered
        $\hat{P}_2$ = the sample proportion of 250 workers at Ontario plant that would take an early retirement package if offered
    d) H_0: $p_1 \geq p_2$ H_A: $p_1 < p_2$ (claim)
    e) $z = -1.21$
    f) $p - \text{value} = 0.1131$
    g) There is not enough evidence to reject the null hypothesis.
    h) There is not enough evidence to support the claim that a lower proportion of workers would take the early retirement plan at the Illinois plant.

5. a) Population 1 = Customers at Castle Café
        Population 2 = Customers at Windmill Diner
    b) Conditions are satisfied to use the Z-distribution.
    c) The parameters of interest are:
        p_1 = the population proportion of customers at the Castle Café that have eaten there on a previous occasion
        p_2 = the population proportion of customers at Windmill Diner that have eaten there on a previous occasion
        The random variables of interest are:
        $\hat{P}_1$ = the sample proportion of 300 customers at the Castle Café that have eaten there on a previous occasion
        $\hat{P}_2$ = the sample proportion of 200 customers at the Windmill Diner that have eaten there on a previous occasion
    d) H_0: $p_1 = p_2$ (claim) H_A: $p_1 \neq p_2$
    e) $z = -3.42$
    f) $p - \text{value} = 0.0006$
    g) There is enough evidence to reject the null hypothesis.
    h) There is not enough evidence to support the claim that the two population proportions are the same.

AVOIDING
COMMON MISTAKES

☺ A common mistake is to mix up the data from the two populations. To avoid this, always begin the problem by clearly defining Population 1 and Population 2.

☺ Other common mistakes are to include sample values or point estimates in your hypotheses. **THIS IS WRONG!!!!!** The claim drives your hypothesis, and the claim is based on the parameter you are trying to learn about, and NOT on the sample data. Setting up your hypotheses right is the key, do not do it incorrectly.

☺ Always verify which distribution you should use *before* computing any confidence intervals or conducting any hypothesis testing. If you use the wrong distribution, you are solving the problem incorrectly.

☺ If you add $\hat{p}_1$ and $\hat{p}_2$, this does *not* equal $\overline{p}$.

UNIT 8 SUMMARY

- $\hat{p}_1 - \hat{p}_2$ is the *point estimate* of $p_1 - p_2$

- Confidence Interval for the Difference between two Population Proportions:

  difference between two sample proportions $\pm$ *margin of error*

- Check the Following Conditions:

  Use the *Z*-distribution for the analysis if all of the following are true for *both* samples:

  ☐ All four Binomial criteria are met in the experiment.
  1. There is a fixed number of trials: n_1 for Population 1 and n_2 for Population 2
  2. The trials are independent
  3. The outcome of each trial is a success or a failure
  4. The proportion of success remains constant from trial to trial

  ☐ The sample size is sufficiently large to define the distribution of $\hat{P}$ as Normal. This is true if:

  $$n_1 p_1 \geq 10 \text{ and } n_1(1 - p_1) \geq 10$$
  $$n_2 p_2 \geq 10 \text{ and } n_2(1 - p_2) \geq 10$$

  but since the value of p_1 and p_2 is unknown, use $\hat{p}_1$ and $\hat{p}_2$.

- A Confidence Interval for the Difference between Two Population Proportions using the *Z*-distribution is:

$$\left(\hat{p}_1 - \hat{p}_2 \right) \pm z \sqrt{\frac{\hat{p}_1(1 - \hat{p}_1)}{n_1} + \frac{\hat{p}_2(1 - \hat{p}_2)}{n_2}}$$

  ☐ $\hat{p}_1$ is the sample proportion of successes observed from Population 1
  ☐ $\hat{p}_2$ is the sample proportion of successes observed from Population 2
  ☐ z is a value obtained from the last row of the *t*-table and is based on the confidence level.
  ☐ n_1 is the sample size from Population 1
  ☐ n_2 is the sample size from Population 2

- The null hypothesis must contain a sign of equality. The alternative hypothesis must contain a sign of inequality.

- Hypothesis testing is always done under the assumption that the *null* hypothesis is true.

- *z*-Test Statistic for Comparing Two Population Proportions

$$z = \frac{\left(\hat{p}_1 - \hat{p}_2\right) - \left(p_1 - p_2\right)}{\sqrt{\bar{p}\left(1-\bar{p}\right)\left(\dfrac{1}{n_1} + \dfrac{1}{n_2}\right)}}$$

- To determine the *p*-value, first look at the sign in the alternative hypothesis:
  - If the sign is '<', then the *p*-value for the test is the area *below* the test statistic.
  - If the sign is '>', then the *p*-value for the test is the area *above* the test statistic.
  - If the sign is '≠', then the *p*-value for the test is the area *below* the negative value of the test statistic *plus* the area *above* the positive value of the test statistic.

- Deciding Whether to Reject H$_0$
  - If the *p*-value is smaller than the significance level α, there is enough evidence to reject the null hypothesis.
  - Otherwise, there is not enough evidence to reject the null hypothesis.

SELF-ASSESSMENT QUIZ

1. A survey determined that in a random sample of 216 women, 72 bought ibuprofen as their pain reliever of choice. In a random sample of 204 men, 102 bought aspirin as their pain reliever of choice. A pharmaceutical company wants to determine whether there is any difference between the two populations
   a) Define Population 1 and Population 2.
   b) Identify the parameter of interest.
   c) Identify the random variable of interest.
   d) Determine the appropriate distribution for the analysis.
   e) Find a 95% confidence interval for the difference between the two population proportions.
   f) Interpret the confidence interval you found in part e.
   g) Is there a difference between the two population proportions? Use the confidence interval you found in part e to support your decision.

2. A random sample of 150 UCSB male students and 200 UCSB female students were asked if they plan to take summer school this year. 78 males and 122 females said they plan to take summer school this year. The following hypotheses are tested, resulting in a p-value of 0.09.
$$H_0:\ p_1 = p_2 \text{ (claim)} \qquad H_A:\ p_1 \neq p_2$$
   a) Is there enough evidence to support the claim? Use $\alpha = 0.05$.
   b) Which of the following confidence intervals supports the conclusion from the hypothesis test?
   A: (-0.1947, 0.0147)
   B: (-0.063, -0.024)
   C: (0.045, 0.072)

3. Sunny Farms produces free-range eggs. They are concerned about the number of boxes of eggs that are broken during transit. They can either use Kinkeggs or FedEggs to deliver their eggs to stores across California. In a random sample of 144 boxes of eggs delivered by Kinkeggs, 18 boxes of eggs were broken during transit. In a random sample of 240 boxes of eggs delivered by FedEggs, 20 were found to be defective. Test the claim that a higher proportion of eggs that are broken during transit by Kinkeggs. Use $\alpha = 0.05$.
   a) Define Population 1 and Population 2.
   b) Determine the appropriate distribution to use.
   c) Define the parameters and random variables of interest.
   d) State the null and alternative hypotheses, and identify the claim.
   e) Calculate the test statistic.
   f) Determine the p-value.
   g) State your decision.
   h) State your conclusion.

ANSWERS

SELF-ASSESSMENT QUIZ

Below are the answers to the exercises for Unit 8, Self-Assessment Quiz. For full solutions, please refer to the CD included with this textbook.

1. a) Population 1 = Women
      Population 2 = Men
   b) p_1 = the population proportion of women who use ibuprofen as their pain reliever of choice
      p_2 = the population proportion of men who use ibuprofen as their pain reliever of choice
      The parameter of interest is $p_1 - p_2$.
   c) $\hat{P}_1$ = the sample proportion of 216 women who use ibuprofen as their pain reliever of choice
      $\hat{P}_2$ = the sample proportion of 204 men who use ibuprofen as their pain reliever of choice
      The random variable of interest is $\hat{p}_1 - \hat{p}_2$.
   d) Conditions are satisfied to use the Z-distribution.
   e) (-0.2598, -0.0736)
   f) With 95% confidence, the difference between the population proportions of women and men who use ibuprofen as their pain reliever of choice is between -0.2598 and -0.0736.
   g) The interval indicates that the proportions are different for the two populations. Since the interval contains only negative values, this means that $p_1 < p_2$. So we can conclude that a higher proportion of men use ibuprofen as their pain reliever of choice.

2. a) There is not enough evidence to reject the null hypothesis since the p-value is larger than the significance level. Thus, there is evidence to support the claim that the population proportions of male and female UCSB students that plan to take summer school this year are the same.
   b) Confidence interval A: (-0.1947, 0.0147) supports the results of the hypothesis test, because this is the only interval that contains 0, which indicates there is no difference in the two population proportions.

3.   a)   Population 1 = Boxes of eggs transported by Kinkeggs
   Population 2 = Boxes of eggs transported by FedEggs
    b)   Conditions are satisfied to use the Z-distribution.
    c)   The parameters of interest are:

        p_1 = the population proportion of boxes of eggs broken by Kinkeggs

        p_2 = the population proportion of boxes of eggs broken by FedEggs

        The random variables of interest are:

        $\hat{P}_1$ = the sample proportion of 144 boxes of eggs broken by Kinkeggs

        $\hat{P}_2$ = the sample proportion of 240 boxes of eggs broken by FedEggs

    d) H_0: $p_1 \le p_2$ H_A: $p_1 > p_2$ (claim)
    e) $z = 1.32$
    f) $p - \text{value} = 0.0934$
    g)   There is not enough evidence to reject the null hypothesis.
    h)   There is not enough evidence to support the claim that a higher proportion of eggs are broken by Kinkeggs.

Unit 9
Correlation between Two Variables

Lesson 9.1 Scatterplots
Exercises for Lesson 9.1
Answers to Exercises for Lesson 9.1

Lesson 9.2 Correlation Coefficient and Coefficient of Determination
Exercises for Lesson 9.2
Answers to Exercises for Lesson 9.2

Lesson 9.3 More Practice in Solving Correlation Problems
Exercises for Lesson 9.3
Answers to Exercises for Lesson 9.3

Avoiding Common Mistakes
Unit 9 Summary
Self-Assessment Quiz
Answers to Self-Assessment Quiz

LESSON 9.1
SCATTERPLOTS

9.1.1 INTRODUCTION

In Units 9 and 10 we continue our study of inferential statistics by looking at the association between two quantitative variables. Using both graphical and numerical summaries, we can establish what type of association exists.

9.1.2 EXPLANATORY AND RESPONSE VARIABLES

A medical practitioner is interested in the association between height and weight of newborns. It is believed that the height of a newborn helps to explain or predict the weight of a newborn. In order to distinguish between these two variables we introduce the following terms: the *response variable*, Y, which in this example is 'weight' and the *explanatory variable*, X, which in this example is 'height'.

Explanatory versus Response Variables:

An *explanatory variable* (X) explains or predicts the behavior of the response variable. The *explanatory variable* is also called the *independent variable*.

A *response variable* (Y) is the variable you want to predict. The *response variable* is also called the *dependent variable*.

To explore the association between height and weight of newborns, we first collect data on newborns, recording their height and weight. Having collected the data, the first stage in the analysis is to plot or graph the data. We do this using a scatterplot.

9.1.3 SCATTERPLOTS

We draw a scatterplot because it is easier to identify a trend or association by looking at a graph than by looking at the raw data.

A *scatterplot* is a graph of two quantitative variables.

The horizontal axis represents the values of X, the explanatory variable.
The vertical axis represents the values of Y, the response variable.

In the study of newborns, the heights and weights of 50 newborns were recorded. A scatterplot representing the data is shown in Figure 9.1 where each pair of values (X, Y) is represented by a dot.

Figure 9.1

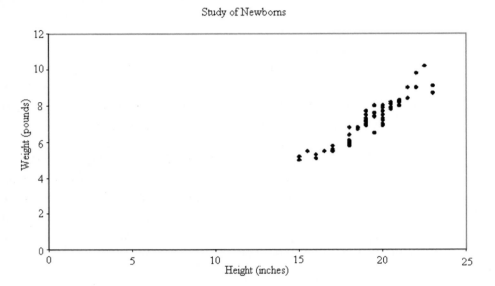

In the above scatterplot, we see that as height increases, weight increases and so there is an association between these two variables. The pattern of the data is approximately a straight line, and so the trend is linear. Next we decide whether this association is positive or negative.

The Association between Two Quantitative Variables X and Y:

Positive if X values increase as Y values increase.

Negative if X values increase as Y values decrease.

Look at the scatterplot in Figure 9.1. Is the association positive or negative?

STOP AND THINK!

How are the Y values changing as the X values increase?

The association between two quantitative variables is positive; as height increases, weight increases.

If the points in a scatterplot all fall on a straight line, then for the current example, all newborns of a particular height would have the same weight. Even though this is not the case, we can still detect a linear pattern in the scatterplot. However, not all scatterplots will show a linear pattern. In Figure 9.2 are some examples that indicate non-linear relationships:

Figure 9.2

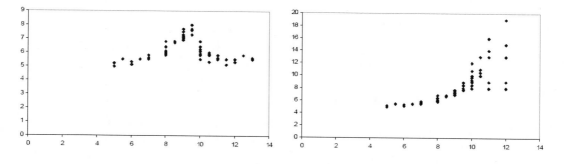

In the above plots, we see that there is a trend in the data, but it is best described by a curve rather than a straight line. Such data is non-linear.

It is also possible to get data that indicates there is no association between two quantitative variables, linear or non-linear. In this case, the scatterplot shows no indication of any trend in the data. See for example, the scatterplot in Figure 9.3.

Figure 9.3

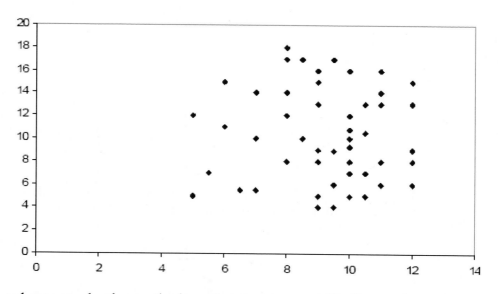

In order to apply the methods and concepts we will discuss in Unit 10, it is necessary to establish that there is a linear association between the explanatory and response variables. If the data appear non-linear, then the analysis is outside the scope of this book. If there appears to be *no* association, then the analysis cannot proceed. Thus it is good practice to graph the data, so we get some idea of whether the association between the variables is linear.

In Lesson 9.2 we will learn how to measure the strength and direction of a linear association.

LESSON 9.1 EXERCISES
SCATTERPLOTS

1. Identify the response and explanatory variables for each of the following situations:
   a) A college dean is interested in the association between GPA and hours spent in the library.
   b) A researcher is interested in height climbed each day by a mountaineer and the time taken.
   c) A medical practitioner wants to determine whether there is any association between the number of cigarettes a person smokes each day and the person's systolic blood pressure.

2. Does the scatterplot below indicate a linear association, a non-linear association or no association? If a linear association is indicated, say whether it is positive or negative.

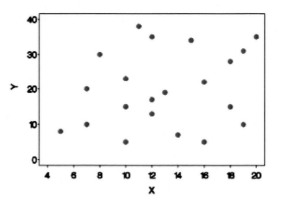

3. Does the scatterplot below indicate a linear association, a non-linear association or no association? If a linear association is indicated, say whether it is positive or negative.

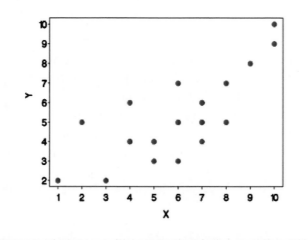

4. Does the scatterplot below indicate a linear association, a non-linear association or no association? If a linear association is indicated, say whether it is positive or negative.

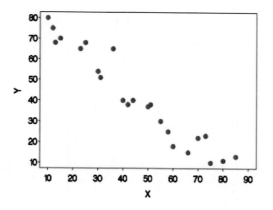

ANSWERS
LESSON 9.1 EXERCISES
SCATTERPLOTS

Below are the answers to the exercises for Unit 9, Lesson 9.1.
For full solutions, please refer to the CD included with this textbook.

1. a) Explanatory variable: Hours spent in the library
        Response variable: GPA
    b) Explanatory variable: Height climbed by mountaineer each day
        Response variable: Time taken to reach height
    c) Explanatory variable: Number of cigarettes a person smokes each day
        Response variable: Person's systolic blood pressure

2. No association.

3. Positive, linear association.

4. Negative, linear association.

LESSON 9.2
CORRELATION COEFFICIENT AND COEFFICIENT OF DETERMINATION

9.2.1   **INTRODUCTION**

Having made the scatterplot for the data and determined that a linear association is appropriate, we now learn how to compute the correlation coefficient r and the coefficient of determination r^2. These provide useful measures about the relationship between the variables X and Y.

9.2.2   **CORRELATION COEFFICIENT**

The correlation coefficient measures the linear association between the explanatory and response variables. The information provided by a correlation coefficient is supported by the scatterplot. It is a useful measure because its interpretation is not as subjective as that of a graph.

Correlation Between Two Quantitative Variables

The value of r is between -1 and 1.

The sign of the correlation coefficient establishes the direction of the linear association.

The Direction of the Linear Association

- If the correlation coefficient is *positive*, then there is a *positive linear association* between X and Y.
- If the correlation coefficient is *negative*, then there is a *negative linear association* between X and Y.

The value of the correlation coefficient establishes the strength of the linear association.

Lesson 9.2: Correlation Coefficient and Coefficient of Determination

The Strength of the Linear Association:

- A correlation coefficient of 0 indicates that there is *no linear association* between X and Y.

- The *closer the value* of the correlation coefficient is to 0, the *weaker* the linear association between X and Y.

- The *closer the value* of the correlation coefficient is to -1 or 1, the *stronger* the linear association between X and Y.

- If the correlation coefficient equals -1 or 1, then there is *perfect* correlation between X and Y. This only happens if all the data fall on a straight line.

Suppose that in the study of newborns introduced in Lesson 9.1, the correlation coefficient was 0.941.

STOP AND THINK!

What is the *strength* and *direction* of the linear association between a newborn's height and weight?

Since the correlation coefficient is *positive* and *close to 1*, there is a positive and strong linear association between a newborn's height and weight.

The correlation coefficient is computed using the following formula:

Correlation between Two Variables

$$r = \frac{1}{n-1} \frac{\sum\limits_{\text{for all x,y}} (x - \overline{x})(y - \overline{y})}{s_x s_y}$$

where
- n represents the number of (x, y) pairs.

- $\sum\limits_{\text{for all x,y}} (x - \overline{x})(y - \overline{y})$ is a measure of the variability between X and Y.

- s_x represents the standard deviation of the explanatory variable X.

$$s_x = \sqrt{\frac{\sum\limits_{\text{for all x}} (x - \overline{x})^2}{n-1}}$$

- s_y represents the standard deviation of the response variable Y.

$$s_y = \sqrt{\frac{\sum\limits_{\text{for all y}} (y - \overline{y})^2}{n-1}}$$

As you can imagine, calculations using this formula are very tedious to do by hand because of all the summations. To make the computations easier and allow you to focus on understanding the concepts involved in this lesson, you will be provided with all the necessary summations. The following example illustrates this.

Example: Values of two variables obtained from a survey are recorded below.
X = the number of cigarettes smoked per day
Y = the number of minutes until a person runs out of breath while exercising

x	3	7	9	12	6	2	10
y	20	14	12	7	17	25	13

Given the following additional information:

$$\bar{x} = 7 \qquad \sum_{\text{for all x}} (x - \bar{x})^2 = 80$$

$$\bar{y} = 16 \qquad \sum_{\text{for all y}} (y - \bar{y})^2 = 196 \qquad \sum_{\text{for all x,y}} (x - \bar{x})(y - \bar{y}) = -120$$

Question 1
What is the correlation coefficient?

Solution: The formula to compute the correlation coefficient is:

$$r = \frac{1}{n-1} \frac{\displaystyle\sum_{\text{for all x,y}} (x - \bar{x})(y - \bar{y})}{s_x s_y}$$

We see from the data that n = 7. To compute r given the information, we first need to compute the standard deviations s_x and s_y.

$$s_x = \sqrt{\frac{\displaystyle\sum_{\text{for all x}} (x - \bar{x})^2}{n-1}} = \sqrt{\frac{80}{7-1}} = 3.6515$$

$$s_y = \sqrt{\frac{\displaystyle\sum_{\text{for all y}} (y - \bar{y})^2}{n-1}} = \sqrt{\frac{196}{7-1}} = 5.7155$$

The correlation coefficient is:

$$r = \left(\frac{1}{7-1}\right) \frac{-120}{(3.6515)(5.7155)}$$

$$= -0.9583$$

Lesson 9.2: Correlation Coefficient and Coefficient of Determination

> **Question 2**
> Interpret the correlation coefficient with respect to the variables in the model.

Solution: The correlation coefficient is *negative* and close to -1, so the linear relationship between the number of cigarettes a person smokes each day and the time it takes them to run out of breath while exercising is *strong* and *negative*.

■

It is important to understand that a strong linear association between X and Y does not imply that X causes Y.

> Correlation does not imply causation.

In the previous example, we found a strong, negative correlation between the number of cigarettes a person smokes each day and the time it takes them to run out of breath while exercising. However, we cannot conclude that smoking *causes* a person to run out of breath faster.

9.2.3   COEFFICIENT OF DETERMINATION

The coefficient of determination is a measure of the amount of variation in the response variable that is explained by the explanatory variable. The coefficient of determination r^2 is found by squaring the correlation coefficient. Given a value of the coefficient of determination, we are able to describe the proportion of the variability in Y that is explained by X.

> **Coefficient of Determination**
>
> ■ The coefficient of determination is found by squaring the correlation coefficient, thus it is always between 0 and 1.
>
> ■ The value of the coefficient of determination tells you what proportion of the variability in Y is explained by X.
>
> ■ If the coefficient of determination is 0, then X does not explain any of the variability in Y. This only happens when the correlation coefficient is 0.
>
> ■ If the coefficient of determination is 1, then X explains all of the variability in Y. This only happens when the correlation coefficient is either -1 or 1.

Consider again the study of heights and weights of newborns. It is not true that all newborns weigh the same amount. So there is variability in the weights of newborns. Part of the reason why newborns do not all weigh the same is because they are not all the same height. So the height of a newborn helps explain *part* of the variation in the weights of newborns. We know that there must be other factors contributing to the weight because the association is not perfectly linear. Recall that the correlation coefficient for this study was $r = 0.941$, therefore the coefficient of determination is:

$$r^2 = 0.941^2 = 0.885$$

So 88.5% of the variability in the weights of newborns is explained by the heights of newborns. This means 11.5% of the variability in the weights of newborns is explained by other factors.

LESSON 9.2 EXERCISES
CORRELATION COEFFICIENT AND COEFFICIENT OF DETERMINATION

1. A random sample of 100 adult males were measured and weighed. You are provided with the following information calculated from the data:

X = height of an adult male (inches)
Y = weight of an adult male (pounds)

$\bar{x} = 70$ $\qquad \sum_{\text{for all x}} (x - \bar{x})^2 = 18$

$\bar{y} = 197$ $\qquad \sum_{\text{for all y}} (y - \bar{y})^2 = 3108$ $\qquad \sum_{\text{for all x,y}} (x - \bar{x})(y - \bar{y}) = 223$

   a) Find the correlation coefficient between the height and weight of adult males.
   b) Explain carefully the meaning of the value you obtain for the correlation coefficient.
   c) Find the coefficient of determination.
   d) Interpret the value of the coefficient of determination with respect to the variables in the model.

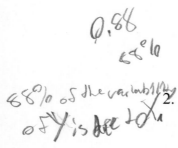

0.88

88^e 10

88% of the variability of Y is due to X

2. Say you wanted to predict the full grown height of a child based on how tall they are at birth. A scatterplot of the data reveals the relationship is distinctly non-linear. If you were to compute the correlation coefficient for the data, what would you expect the value to be? (Think about it.)

3. If you were to predict the number of kids in a family based on the annual household income (thousands of dollars), you would see that the relationship is negative.
   a) Explain what it means that the relationship between family size and income is negative.
   b) The coefficient of determination is 0.53. Interpret what this means with respect to the variables in the problem.
   c) What would be the correlation coefficient? What additional information does this give you?

ANSWERS

LESSON 9.2 EXERCISES

CORRELATION COEFFICIENT AND COEFFICIENT OF DETERMINATION

Below are the answers to the exercises for Unit 9, Lesson 9.2.
For full solutions, please refer to the CD included with this textbook.

1. a) $r = 0.9428$
   b) The linear relationship between an adult male's height and weight is positive and strong.
   c) $r^2 = 0.8889$
   d) 88.89% of the variability in the weight of adult males is explained by their height.

2. $r = 0$

3. a) As the annual household income increases, the number of kids in the family decreases.
   b) 53% of the variability in family size (number of kids) can be explained by the family's annual household income.
   c) $r = -0.728$
   This tells us that there is a strong, negative association between the number of kids in a family and the family's annual household income.

LESSON 9.3
MORE PRACTICE IN CORRELATION PROBLEMS

In this lesson we look at some more examples with full solutions. You are encouraged to work through these problems yourself if you need extra practice.

Example 1:   Identify the response and explanatory variables for the following situation:

A University professor has noticed that some of his best students regularly visit the library. The professor wants to determine whether there is any significant relationship between the grades on his final and hours spent in the library that quarter.

> STOP AND THINK!
>
> **Which variable helps explain the other variable?**

Solution: How much time students spend in the library may help explain their grades on a final exam, so:

Explanatory variable: Hours spend in the library that quarter
Response variable: Grades on the professor's final exam
■

Example 2:   Identify the response and explanatory variables for the following situation:

A store manager is interested in finding out whether there is a linear association between average monthly temperature and monthly revenue from ice cream sales.

> STOP AND THINK!
>
> **Which variable helps explain the other variable?**

Solution: The average monthly temperature may help explain the monthly revenue from ice
              cream sales, so:
              Explanatory variable: Average monthly temperature
              Response variable: Monthly revenue from ice cream sales
              ■

Example 3:   Does the scatterplot below indicate a linear association, a non-linear association
              or no association? If a linear association is indicated, say whether it is positive or
              negative.

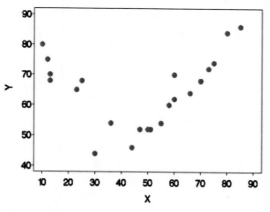

STOP AND THINK!

Does a straight line fit the data well?

Solution: This is an example of a non-linear association. The two variable appear to be
              associated but in a non-linear way.
              ■

Example 4:   Does the scatterplot below indicate a linear association, a non-linear association
              or no association? If an association is indicated, say whether it is positive or
              negative.

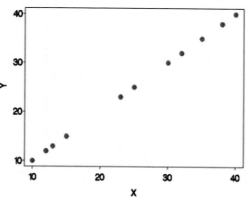

> **STOP AND THINK!**
>
> **Does a straight line fit the data well?**

Solution: This is an example of a perfect linear association. The points fall in a perfectly straight line, and indicate a positive association.

■

Example 5:   Students at UCSB timed themselves to see how long it would take them to bike across campus (in minutes). They also recorded their weight (in pounds). A model was fit to the data, in the hopes that their weight would be a good predictor of their time. The correlation coefficient is 0.7114.
Use this information to answer the following questions:
a) What is the response variable?
b) What is the explanatory variable?
c) Interpret the correlation coefficient with respect to the variables in the model.
d) What is the coefficient of determination? Interpret it with respect to the variables in the model.
e) Can we say that if a UCSB student gained weight, this would *cause* him to ride their bike across campus slower? Explain.

> **STOP AND THINK!**
>
> **What information is provided in the problem?**
>
> **How do you interpret the correlation coefficient?**
>
> **How do you find and interpret the coefficient of determination?**

Solution: a) The response variable is:
            Y = the time it takes a UCSB student to ride their bike across campus (in minutes)

Solution: b) The explanatory variable is:
            X = weight of UCSB student (in pounds)

Solution: c) The correlation coefficient is 0.7114.
            This tells us that the linear association between the time it takes a UCSB student to cross campus on their bike and their weight is strong and positive.

Solution: d) The coefficient of determination is found by squaring the correlation coefficient:

$$r^2 = (0.7114)^2 = 0.5061$$

This tells us that 50.61% of the variability in the time it takes to a UCSB student to cross campus on a bike is explained by the student's weight.

Solution: e) Even though the two variables are correlated, this does not mean that that gaining weight will *cause* a UCSB student's time to increase. Just because two variables are associated does not mean one causes the other to happen.

■

Example 6:   Suppose the correlation between two quantitative variables is 0. What could we do to determine whether this means there is no association at all between the two variables, or that the association is non-linear?

STOP AND THINK!

What is another tool that provides information on the association between two quantitative variables?

Solution: Correlations are helpful, but it is important to always graph the data with a scatterplot in order to get a visual picture of the association. By looking at the scatterplot, you could judge whether a non-linear association may exist, or whether it appears there is no association at all between the two variables.

■

Example 7:   Suppose that you are interested in predicting the cost of a diamond. The correlation between the cost of a diamond and its size is 0.7, and the correlation between the cost of a diamond and its clarity is 0.65. Which explanatory variable, size or clarity, explains more of the variation in the cost of diamonds?

STOP AND THINK!

What measure do we need to calculate?

Solution: From the correlations, we can compute the coefficient of determination between the cost of a diamond and each explanatory variable. This will tell us what percent of the variation in the cost of a diamond each is explaining.

For the association between the cost of a diamond and its size:

$$r^2 = (0.7)^2 = 0.49$$

For the association between the cost of a diamond and its clarity:

$$r^2 = (0.65)^2 = 0.4225$$

So the size of a diamond explains a higher percentage of the variation in cost than the clarity.

■

Example 8: Suppose in your family, every man was married to a woman who was 3 years younger than him. What would the correlation coefficient be between the age of a husband and his wife's age for your family? (Think about it).

> **STOP AND THINK!**
>
> **Try drawing a scatterplot to visualize the scenario.**

Solution: A scatterplot for this scenario is shown below.

As we see, the correlation is perfectly linear and positive, so in your family, the correlation between a husband's age and his wife's age is 1.

■

Example 9: A random sample of 700 university students was asked about their drinking habits (drinks per week) and their GPA. You are provided with the following information calculated from the data:

X = Drinking habits (drinks per week)
Y = GPA

$$\bar{x} = 5.2 \qquad \sum_{\text{for all } x} (x - \bar{x})^2 = 448$$

$$\bar{y} = 2.8 \qquad \sum_{\text{for all } y} (y - \bar{y})^2 = 11 \qquad \sum_{\text{for all } x,y} (x - \bar{x})(y - \bar{y}) = -56$$

a) Find the correlation coefficient between the number of drinks per week and GPA of university students.

b) Explain carefully the meaning of the value you obtain for the correlation coefficient.

c) Find the coefficient of determination.

d) Interpret the value of the coefficient of determination with respect to the variables in the model.

STOP AND THINK!

What formulas are needed?

What is the interpretation of a correlation coefficient?

What is the interpretation of a coefficient of determination?

Solution: a)   The formula to compute the correlation coefficient is:

$$r = \frac{1}{n-1} \frac{\sum\limits_{\text{for all x,y}} (x - \bar{x})(y - \bar{y})}{s_x s_y}$$

We see from the data that $n = 700$. To compute r given the information, we first need to compute the standard deviations s_x and s_y.

$$s_x = \sqrt{\frac{\sum\limits_{\text{for all x}} (x - \bar{x})^2}{n-1}} = \sqrt{\frac{448}{700-1}} = 0.8006$$

$$s_y = \sqrt{\frac{\sum\limits_{\text{for all y}} (y - \bar{y})^2}{n-1}} = \sqrt{\frac{11}{700-1}} = 0.1254$$

The correlation coefficient is:

$$r = \left(\frac{1}{700-1}\right)\frac{-56}{(0.8006)(0.1254)}$$

$$= -0.7980$$

Solution: b)   The correlation coefficient is close to -1, indicating that there is a strong, negative association between a university student's drinking habits and GPA.

Solution: c) The coefficient of determination is found by squaring the correlation coefficient:

$$r^2 = \left(-0.7980\right)^2 = 0.6368$$

Solution: d) The coefficient of determination indicates that 63.68% of the variation in university students' GPA can be explained by their drinking habits.

■

Example 10: Suppose that for the data plotted in the graph below, the coefficient of determination is 0.74. What is the correlation coefficient?

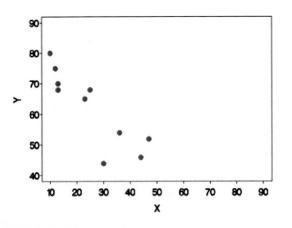

> **STOP AND THINK!**
>
> **The scatterplot indicates a negative association. Does this mean the correlation coefficient is positive or negative?**

Solution: The correlation coefficient is the square-root of the coefficient of determination. However, the sign must match the direction of the association. When you take the square-root of a number with your calculator, it only returns the positive root. But there is also a negative root. We must decide the sign of the correlation coefficient based on the information provided by the scatterplot. Since there is a negative association:

$$r = -\sqrt{r^2} = -\sqrt{0.74} = -0.8602$$

So the interpretation of the correlation coefficient is that there is a strong, negative association between the two variables, which we can see from the scatterplot.

LESSON 9.3 EXERCISES
MORE PRACTICE IN SOLVING CORRELATION PROBLEMS

1. Identify the response and explanatory variables for the following situation: A researcher is interested in determining the association between crop yield (per hectare) and the amount of fertilizer applied (per hectare).

2. Identify the response and explanatory variables for the following situation: A realtor wants to investigate the association between house price (in thousands of dollars) and house floor-plan size (in square feet).

3. Does the scatterplot below indicate a linear association, a non-linear association or no association? If a linear association is indicated, say whether it is positive or negative.

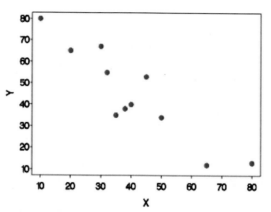

4. Does the scatterplot below indicate a linear association, a non-linear association or no association? If a linear association is indicated, say whether it is positive or negative.

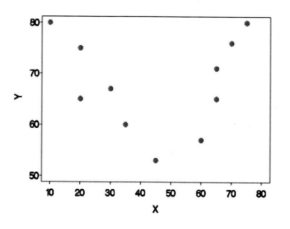

5. Which of the following values represents a strong positive correlation?

   A: $r = -1.0002$
   B: $r = 1.0002$
   C: $r = 0.0002$
   D: $r = -0.9992$
   E: $r = 0.9992$

ANSWERS
LESSON 9.3 EXERCISES
MORE PRACTICE IN SOLVING CORRELATION PROBLEMS

Below are the answers to the exercises for Unit 9, Lesson 9.3.
For full solutions, please refer to the CD included with this textbook.

1. Explanatory variable: Amount of fertilizer applied (per hectare)
   Response variable: Crop yield (per hectare)

2. Explanatory variable: House floor-plan size (in square feet)
   Response variable: House price (in thousands of dollars)

3. Negative, linear association.

4. Non-linear association.

5. E: $r = 0.9992$ represents a strong, positive correlation

AVOIDING
COMMON MISTAKES

☺ Do not confuse the correlation coefficient r with the coefficient of determination r^2. They are related but different measures.

☺ If the problem does not do it for you, clearly identify which variable is the explanatory and which is the response so that you do not mix them up.

☺ If a scatterplot indicates a positive association between two quantitative variables, the correlation coefficient must be positive.

☺ If a scatterplot indicates a negative association between two variables, the correlation coefficient must be negative.

UNIT 9 SUMMARY

- An *explanatory variable* (*X*) explains or predicts the behavior of the response variable. The *explanatory variable* is also called the *independent variable*.

- A *response variable* (*Y*) is the variable you want to predict. The *response variable* is also called the *dependent variable*.

- A *scatterplot* is a graph of two quantitative variables. The horizontal axis represents the values of *X*, the explanatory variable. The vertical axis represents the values of *Y*, the response variable.

- The association between two quantitative variables X and Y is *positive* if *X* values increase as *Y* values increase.

- The association between two quantitative variables *X* and *Y* is *negative* if *X* values increase as *Y* values decrease.

- The value of correlation coefficient *r* is between –1 and 1.

- If the correlation coefficient is *positive*, then there is a *positive linear association* between *X* and *Y*.

- If the correlation coefficient is *negative*, then there is a *negative linear association* between *X* and *Y*.

- A correlation coefficient of 0 indicates that there is *no linear association* between *X* and *Y*.

- The *closer the value* of the correlation coefficient is to 0, the *weaker* the linear association between *X* and *Y*.

- The *closer the value* of the correlation coefficient is to –1 or 1, the *stronger* the linear association between *X* and *Y*.

- If the correlation coefficient equals -1 or 1, then there is *perfect* correlation between *X* and *Y*. This only happens if all the data fall on a straight line.

- The correlation coefficient is calculated as follows:

$$r = \frac{1}{n-1} \frac{\sum\limits_{\text{for all x,y}} (x-\overline{x})(y-\overline{y})}{s_x s_y}$$

  - n represents the number of (x, y) pairs.

  - $\sum\limits_{\text{for all x,y}} (x-\overline{x})(y-\overline{y})$ is a measure of the variability between X and Y.

  - s_x represents the standard deviation of the explanatory variable X.

$$s_x = \sqrt{\frac{\sum\limits_{\text{for all x}} (x-\overline{x})^2}{n-1}}$$

  - s_y represents the standard deviation of the response variable Y.

$$s_y = \sqrt{\frac{\sum\limits_{\text{for all y}} (y-\overline{y})^2}{n-1}}$$

- Correlation does not imply causation.

- The coefficient of determination is found by squaring the correlation coefficient, thus it is always between 0 and 1.

- The value of the coefficient of determination tells you what proportion of the variability in Y is explained by X.

- If the coefficient of determination is 0, then X does not explain any of the variability in Y. This only happens when the correlation coefficient is 0.

- If the coefficient of determination is 1, then X explains all of the variability in Y. This only happens when the correlation coefficient is either -1 or 1.

SELF-ASSESSMENT QUIZ

1. Identify the response and explanatory variables for the following situation: A nutritionist wants to investigate the association between the amount of fat (in grams) consumed each week by American children and their body weight.

2. Identify the response and explanatory variables for the following situation: The tourist board was to find out whether there is an association between monthly precipitation (in inches) and monthly number of visitors to Yosemite.

3. Does the scatterplot below indicate a linear association, a non-linear association or no association? If an association is indicated, say whether it is positive or negative.

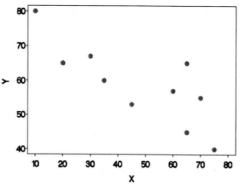

negative linear

4. Which of the following values *cannot* be a correlation coefficient?
   A: $r = -0.0002$
   B: $r = 0.0002$
   C: $r = -0.2$
   D: $r = -1.0002$
   E: $r = 0.9002,$

5. A nutritionist wants to investigate the association between the amount of fat (in grams) consumed each day by American 10 year old girls, and their Body Mass Index (BMI). The following data was collected for a sample of 100 girls.

   X = amount of fat (in grams) consumed each day by American 10 year old girls.
   Y = Body Mass Index (BMI) of American 10 year old girls.

   Given following additional information
   $$\bar{x} = 81 \qquad \sum_{\text{for all x}} (x-\bar{x})^2 = 882$$
   $$\bar{y} = 20 \qquad \sum_{\text{for all y}} (y-\bar{y})^2 = 80 \qquad \sum_{\text{for all x,y}} (x-\bar{x})(y-\bar{y}) = 225$$

a) Find the correlation coefficient between the variables.
b) Explain carefully the meaning of the value you obtain for the correlation coefficient.
c) Find the coefficient of determination.
d) Interpret the value of the coefficient of determination with respect to the variables in the model.

6. A study was conducted to determine whether there is any association between body weight and the time taken to run a mile. The statistician responsible for the analysis reported that the correlation coefficient was low and positive. What can you conclude?

$$S_x = \sqrt{\frac{\sum (x - \bar{x})^2}{n-1}} = \sqrt{\frac{862}{99}} = 2.9848$$

$$S_y = \sqrt{\frac{\sum (y - \bar{y})^2}{n-1}} = \sqrt{\frac{80}{99}} = 0.8989$$

5a) $r = \frac{1}{n-1} \frac{\sum\limits_{\text{all } x} (x - \bar{x})(y - \bar{y})}{S_x S_y}$

$= \frac{1}{99} \frac{225}{(2.9848)(0.8989)}$

$r = 0.8471$

b) There is a strong positive correlation between grams of fat consumed per day and BMI.

c) $r^2 = 0.8471^2 = 0.7175$

d) 71.75% of the variability of r has to do with grams of fat consumed per day.

6) There is a small positive linear correlation between body weight and mile times. Therefore, heavier runners have longer mile times than lighter runners.

ANSWERS
SELF-ASSESSMENT QUIZ

Below are the answers to the exercises for Unit 9, Self-Assessment Quiz. For full solutions, please refer to the CD included with this textbook.

1. Explanatory variable: Amount of fat consumed each week (in grams)
   Response variable: Body weight

2. Explanatory variable: Monthly precipitation (in inches)
   Response variable: Monthly number of visitors

3. Negative, linear association.

4. D: $r = -1.0002$

5. a) $r = 0.8470$
   b) There is a strong, positive association between a 10 year old American girl's fat consumption and BMI.
   c) $r^2 = 0.7175$
   d) 71.57% of the variation in the BMI of 10-year-old American girls is explained by their fat consumption.

6. We can conclude that heavier runners tend to take longer to run a mile than lighter runners. However, the association is not very strong.

UNIT 10
SIMPLE LINEAR REGRESSION

Lesson 10.1 Determining the Best-Fitting Line
Exercises for Lesson 10.1
Answers to Exercises for Lesson 10.1

Lesson 10.2 Confidence Interval for the Slope
Exercises for Lesson 10.2
Answers to Exercises for Lesson 10.2

Lesson 10.3 More Practice in Solving Simple Linear Regression Problems
Exercises for Lesson 10.3
Answers to Exercises for Lesson 10.3

Avoiding Common Mistakes
Unit 10 Summary
Self-Assessment Quiz
Answers to Self-Assessment Quiz

LESSON 10.1
DETERMINING THE BEST-FITTING LINE

10.1.1   **INTRODUCTION**
Having established that there is a significant linear association between two quantitative variables, using the techniques described in Unit 9, the next stage in the analysis is to find the line that best fits the data.

10.1.2   **THE LINE OF BEST FIT**
Consider again the scatter plot for the data on newborns, shown in Figure 10.1.

Figure 10.1

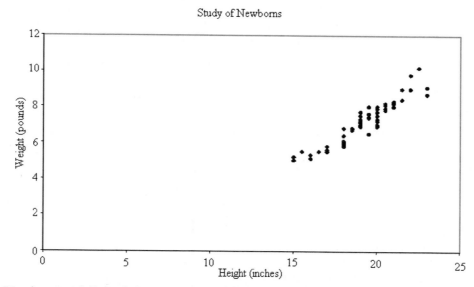

Having established that there is a linear association between the two variables, we now find the *best* straight line that models the data. It is hard to know where to draw the best-fitting line on the scatterplot. So instead of drawing the line by hand, we describe a technique for finding the equation of the straight line that best fits the data. This line is called the least-squares regression line and, as we will see later, it can be used to predict values of the response variable.

The general equation for a straight line involves a slope and an intercept. The method of simple linear regression finds these in a different way to that of high school algebra. In a statistical study we will not usually have data that fall on a straight line, and so we cannot find the slope of the line simply by finding the slope between any two points. Instead, all the values of the data to find the *best* line.

Linear Regression for a Population

The least-squares regression line for an explanatory variable and a response variable is:

$$y = \beta_0 + \beta_1 x$$

β_0 represents the y-intercept of the population of interest

β_1 represents the slope of the population of interest

In the above equation β_0 and β_1 are parameters because they are about the population of interest. However, when we are studying a population we usually do not know the values of the parameters of interest. So we use the sample statistics b_0 and b_1, calculated from sample data, to estimate the parameters β_0 and β_1.

Linear Regression for a Sample

The least-squares regression line for an explanatory variable and a response variable is:

$$\hat{y} = b_0 + b_1 x$$

b_0 represents the y-intercept of the sample data.

b_1 represents the slope of the sample data.

To calculate b_0 and b_1, the formulas given below are used.

Slope and Intercept

$$b_1 = \frac{\sum_{\text{For all x,y}} (x-\bar{x})(y-\bar{y})}{\sum_{\text{For all x}} (x-\bar{x})^2}$$

$$b_0 = \bar{y} - b_1\bar{x}$$

Example: Recall the following example from Lesson 9.2.
Values of two variables obtained from a survey are recorded below.
X = the number of cigarettes smoked per day
Y = the number of minutes until a person runs out of breath while exercising

x	3	7	9	12	6	2	10
y	20	14	12	7	17	25	13

Given the following additional information:

$\bar{x} = 7$ $\qquad \displaystyle\sum_{\text{for all x}} (x - \bar{x})^2 = 80$

$\bar{y} = 16$ $\qquad \displaystyle\sum_{\text{for all y}} (y - \bar{y})^2 = 196$ $\qquad \displaystyle\sum_{\text{for all x,y}} (x - \bar{x})(y - \bar{y}) = -120$

Question
What is the least-squares regression line?

Solution: To find the regression equation, first calculate b_1, the slope of the regression line.

$$b_1 = \frac{\displaystyle\sum_{\text{For all x,y}} (x - \bar{x})(y - \bar{y})}{\displaystyle\sum_{\text{For all x}} (x - \bar{x})^2} = \frac{-120}{80} = -1.5$$

Next, find b_0.

$$\begin{aligned} b_0 &= \bar{y} - b_1\bar{x} \\ &= 16 - (-1.5)(7) \\ &= 26.5 \end{aligned}$$

So the least squares regression equation is:

$$\hat{y} = 26.5 - 1.5x$$

In the next lesson we show how to determine whether the slope is significant and how to use the regression line to make predictions.

LESSON 10.1 EXERCISES
DETERMINING THE BEST-FITTING LINE

1. Given the following least squares regression line, is the slope positive or negative? What is the value of the y-intercept?

$$\hat{y} = 23 + 17x$$

2. A professor is interested in the association between the number of hours her students study each week and their final grades. The following data were collected and recorded for 50 of her students:

$\bar{x} = 9 \qquad \sum_{\text{For all x}} (x - \bar{x})^2 = 98$

$\bar{y} = 77 \qquad \sum_{\text{For all y}} (y - \bar{y})^2 = 580 \qquad \sum_{\text{For all x,y}} (x - \bar{x})(y - \bar{y}) = 200$

 a) What is the explanatory variable?
 b) What is the response variable?
 c) Find the least-squares regression equation.

3. The number of sea kayaks sold daily by Sirius Kayaks the daily high temperatures (in degrees Fahrenheit) were recorded for 120 days. The information below was calculated from the data.

$\bar{x} = 5 \qquad \sum_{\text{For all x}} (x - \bar{x})^2 = 46$

$\bar{y} = 60 \qquad \sum_{\text{For all y}} (y - \bar{y})^2 = 826 \qquad \sum_{\text{For all x,y}} (x - \bar{x})(y - \bar{y}) = 186$

 a) What is the explanatory variable?
 b) What is the response variable?
 c) Find the least-squares regression equation.

ANSWERS
LESSON 10.1 EXERCISES
DETERMINING THE BEST-FITTING LINE

Below are the answers to the exercises for Unit 10, Lesson 10.1.
For full solutions, please refer to the CD included with this textbook.

1. The slope is positive, and the y-intercept is 23.

2. a) X = Hours students study
    b) Y = Final grade
    c) $\hat{y} = 58.6327 + 2.0408x$

3. a) X = Daily high temperature (in degrees Fahrenheit)
    b) Y = Number of sea kayaks sold daily
    c) $\hat{y} = 39.7826 + 4.0435x$

LESSON 10.2
CONFIDENCE INTERVAL FOR THE SLOPE

10.2.1

INTRODUCTION

Once we have found the regression line, we can check whether it fits the data well. If it does, the regression line can be used to make predictions.

10.2.2

DETERMINING IF THE SLOPE IS SIGNIFICANT

The slope computed from the data is a statistic, and so the slope will differ from sample to sample. Even though the values may differ, what we are primarily concerned with is whether or not they indicate that the slope for the population is significant. The reason for this concern is that regression finds the straight line that best fits all the points, but even the 'best-fitting' line may not fit the data well. So we use the sample slope b_1 to determine whether the regression line *actually* fits the data better than a horizontal line, which has a slope of 0.

Deciding if the Slope is Significant

If the data indicate that the slope of the population β_1 is 0, then the population slope is *not* significant, and hence X is *not* a useful predictor of Y.

If the data indicate that the slope of the population β_1 is *not* 0, then the population slope *is* significant, and hence X *is* a useful predictor of Y.

We have a claim about the slope of the population, in which we want to find if it is equal to 0 or not. The value of β_1 is estimated by constructing a confidence interval using the *t*-distribution.

> ## Confidence Interval for β_1
>
> The formula for constructing the confidence interval is:
>
> $$b_1 \pm t(SE_{b_1})$$
>
> where:
>
> - b_1 represents the slope of the sample
> - t is a value obtained from the t-table, based on the confidence level and $n-2$ degrees of freedom
> - SE_{b_1} represents the standard error of b_1
>
> If the confidence interval contains 0, this indicates that $\beta_1 = 0$ and hence the slope is not significant, thus X is not a useful predictor of Y.
>
> If the confidence interval does not contain 0, this indicates that $\beta_1 \neq 0$ and hence the slope is significant, thus X is a useful predictor of Y.

Consider the study introduced in Lesson 9.2, relating the number of cigarettes a person smokes each day to the time it takes them to run out of breath while exercising. In Lesson 10.1, we found the slope was −1.5. Suppose the standard error was 0.023. To construct a 95% confidence interval, we need the appropriate t-value with $n-2$ degrees of freedom. Since the sample size is 7, the degrees of freedom are 5. So the appropriate t-value is 2.571 and thus we apply the formula:

$$b_1 \pm t(SE_{b_1}) = -1.5 \pm 2.571(0.023)$$
$$= -1.5 \pm 0.059$$

The confidence interval for the slope is (−1.559, −1.441). Since the confidence interval does not contain 0, this indicates that the slope is significant. So, the number of cigarettes a person smokes each day is a useful predictor of how long it will take them to run out of breath while exercising.

10.2.3   USING THE REGRESSION EQUATION FOR PREDICTION

Consider again the study of newborns discussed in Section 10.1.2. Using a computer, the least-squares regression equation was found to be:

$$\hat{y} = -4.3 + 0.6x$$

This indicates that the y-intercept is −4.3 and the slope is 0.6. Graphing the best-fitting line (using a computer program) we get the graph in Figure 10.2:

Figure 10.2

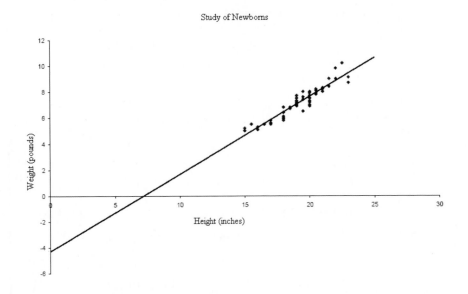

Suppose we want to predict the weight of a newborn given a height of 20 inches. Since a value for the explanatory variable is given, we can substitute this in the regression equation:

$$\hat{y} = -4.3 + 0.6x$$
$$= -4.3 + 0.6(20)$$
$$= 7.7$$

So the predicted weight of a newborn of height 20 inches is 7.7 pounds.

A certain amount of caution must be exercised when using the regression equation to predict values. For example, it makes no sense to enter a negative value for the height of a newborn. It also makes no sense to enter a height of 50 inches, since no data is available for newborns of this height. This leads us to a very important rule in regression:

> A regression line should only be used for interpretation and prediction ***within*** the range of data collected for the explanatory variable.

Since the data for newborns only includes heights from 15 to 23 inches, as shown in Figure 10.2, this means that the regression line found from this data is only informative for this range of heights.

LESSON 10.2 EXERCISES
CONFIDENCE INTERVAL FOR THE SLOPE

1. Professor Levi wants to predict the scores on his final exam from the scores on his midterm exam. He determines the regression equation is:

$$\hat{y} = 28.545 + 0.716x$$

The standard error of the slope is 0.035. There were 23 students included in the sample, whose scores on the midterm exam ranged from 40 to 100, and scores on the final exam ranged from 50 to 100.
a) Construct a 95% confidence interval for the slope.
b) Interpret the confidence interval found in part (a).
c) Is the slope significant? Explain.
d) Suppose a student takes Professor Levi's midterm and earns a 30. Can the regression equation be used to predict this student's final exam grade? Explain.

2. A university wants to predict a student's GPA from the number of hours the student works each week.   100 students are sampled, and the regression equation obtained from the data is:

$$\hat{y} = 3.76 - 0.0249x$$

The standard error of the slope is 0.004.
a) Construct a 95% confidence interval for the slope.
b) Interpret the confidence interval found in part (a).
c) Is the slope significant? Explain.
d) Predict the GPA of a university student who works 15 hours per week.

ANSWERS

LESSON 10.2 EXERCISES

CONFIDENCE INTERVAL FOR THE SLOPE

Below are the answers to the exercises for Unit 10, Lesson 10.2.
For full solutions, please refer to the CD included with this textbook.

1. a) (0.6432, 0.7888)
    b) We can be 95% confident that the population slope is between 0.6432 and 0.7888.
    c) Yes, the slope is significant because the confidence interval does not contain 0. So midterm scores are a good predictor of final exam scores for Professor Levi's tests.
    d) No, because a midterm score of 30 is outside the range of the midterm scores used to obtain the regression equation.

2. a) (−0.0328, −0.017)
    b) We can be 95% confident that the population slope is between −0.0328 and −0.017.
    c) Yes, the slope is significant because the confidence interval does not contain 0. So the weekly hours a student works is a good predictor of their GPA.
    d) $\hat{y} = 3.39$

LESSON 10.3
MORE PRACTICE IN SIMPLE LINEAR REGRESSION PROBLEMS

In this lesson we look at some more examples with full solutions. You are encouraged to work through these problems yourself if you need extra practice.

Example 1: A social worker is interested in the association between parent income (in thousands of dollars) and how many years of school their child completes. The following data were collected and recorded for 100 families:

$$\bar{x} = 60 \qquad \sum_{\text{For all x}} (x - \bar{x})^2 = 35,448$$

$$\bar{y} = 11.6 \qquad \sum_{\text{For all y}} (y - \bar{y})^2 = 2,518 \qquad \sum_{\text{For all x,y}} (x - \bar{x})(y - \bar{y}) = 9,217$$

a) What is the explanatory variable?
b) What is the response variable?
c) Find the least-squares regression equation.

STOP AND THINK!

Which variable is helping to explain the other?

How do you compute the slope?

How do you compute the y-intercept?

Solution: a) Since the parent income explains the years of schooling for the child, the explanatory variable is X = parent income (in thousands of dollars).

Solution: b) Since the years of schooling for the child depends on the parent income, the response variable is Y = years of schooling for the child.

Solution: c) To find the regression equation, first calculate b_1, the slope of the regression line.

$$b_1 = \frac{\displaystyle\sum_{\text{For all x,y}} (x-\bar{x})(y-\bar{y})}{\displaystyle\sum_{\text{For all x}} (x-\bar{x})^2} = \frac{9,217}{35,448} = 0.26$$

Next, find b_0.

$$b_0 = \bar{y} - b_1\bar{x}$$
$$= 11.6 - (0.26)(60)$$
$$= -4$$

So the least squares regression equation is:

$$\hat{y} = -4 + 0.26x$$

■

Example 2:   Suppose that you obtain a regression equation $\hat{y} = -4.177 + 0.2785x$ which predicts a restaurant server's tip from the total bill. Which of the following is a possible value of correlation coefficient resulting from the analysis?
A: $r = -0.23$
B: $r = 0.23$

STOP AND THINK!

What do we know about the association between these two variables if the slope is positive?

Solution: Since the slope is positive, the association between a server's tip and the total bill have a positive association. Therefore, the correlation coefficient must be positive, so B: $r = 0.23$ is a possible value.

■

Example 3:   It is commonly believed that SAT scores help predict college freshman GPA. Suppose at a particular university, the regression equation is:

$$\hat{y} = 2.6 + 0.0006x$$

What is the interpretation of the value of the slope?

STOP AND THINK!

What does the slope measure?
Which variable is the explanatory and which is the response?

Solution: The explanatory variable is the SAT scores, and the response variable is the college freshman GPA. The slope measures how much the response variable changes with every one-unit increase in the explanatory variable. Thus, if the slope is 0.0006, this means that for every extra point earned on the SAT, the predicted college GPA will increase by 0.0006 points.

∎

Example 4: Suppose you collect data on 1,000 adult females and obtain the following regression equation between their height (in inches) and weight (in pounds).

$$\hat{y} = -185.26 + 5.132x$$

Which of the following confidence intervals supports the claim that the slope is significant? Explain your answer.
A: (5.092, 5.1712)
B: (-1.14, 11.404)

STOP AND THINK!

What does it mean for the slope to be significant?

What value do you look for in the intervals to make your decision?

Solution: If the slope is significant, that means that the slope in the population is not equal to 0. Therefore, a confidence interval that supports this claim is one that does *not* contain 0. So confidence interval A: (5.092, 5.1712) indicates that the slope is significant.

∎

Example 5: Recall Example 5 from Lesson 9.3. Students at UCSB timed themselves to see how long it would take them to bike across campus (in minutes). They also recorded their weight (in pounds). A model was fit to the data, in the hopes that their weight would be a good predictor of their time. Their results were as follows:
- The best fitting line was determined to be $\hat{y} = 6.2567 + 0.0498x$
- The correlation coefficient is 0.7114
- The confidence interval for the slope is (0.0106, 0.0890)

Use this information to answer the following questions:
a) What is the value of the slope? Explain what this indicates with respect to the variables in the model.
b) What is the value of the y-intercept?
c) Is a UCSB student's weight a good predictor of their time? Explain.

Solution: a) The slope is $b_1 = 0.0498$

The slope is positive, which means that as the weight of UCSB students increases, the time it takes them to ride their bike across campus increases. In other words, heavier students tend to be able to take more time to cross campus. The fact that the value of the slope is 0.0498 tells us that for every extra pound a UCSB student weighs, it is predicted they will take an extra 0.0498 minutes to cross campus on their bike.

Solution: b) The y-intercept is $b_0 = 6.2567$

Solution: c) To answer this question, refer to the confidence interval for the slope. Since it does not contain 0, this tells us that a UCSB student's weight is a good predictor of their time to cross campus on a bike.

Example 6:   Which of the following is true based on the scatterplot below?
A: The correlation coefficient is positive and the slope is negative.
B: The correlation coefficient is negative and the slope is negative.
C: The correlation coefficient is positive and the slope is positive.
D: The correlation coefficient is negative and the slope is positive.

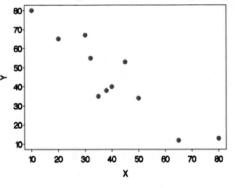

Solution: The scatterplot indicates a negative association. This means both the correlation coefficient *and* the slope must be negative. So the answer is B.

◼

Example 7: Consider the following regression equation, obtained from a sample size of 50:

$$\hat{y} = 3.8 - 0.277x$$

The standard error of the slope is 0.39.
a) Construct a 95% confidence interval for the slope.
b) Is the slope significant? Explain.
c) Suppose you wanted to conduct a hypothesis test to determine if the slope is significant. The hypotheses to test are:

H_0: $\beta_1 = 0$ H_A: $\beta_1 \neq 0$ (claim)

From the results of the confidence interval, which hypothesis is supported by the data? Explain.

STOP AND THINK!

What are the degrees of freedom?

What is the *t*-value?

Does the interval indicate that the population slope is equal to 0?

Solution: a) To construct a 95% confidence interval, we need the appropriate *t*-value with $n - 2$ degrees of freedom. Since the sample size is 50, the degrees of freedom are 48. So the appropriate *t*-value is 2.011 and thus we apply the formula:

$$b_1 \pm t(SE_{b_1}) = -0.277 \pm 2.011(0.39)$$
$$= -0.277 \pm 0.784$$

The confidence interval for the slope is (−1.061, 0.507).

Solution: b) Since the confidence interval does contain 0, this indicates that the slope is *not* significant.

Solution: c) Since we concluded the slope is not significant, this means that $\beta_1 = 0$. Therefore, the data supports the null hypothesis.

◼

Example 8: Suppose you construct a confidence interval for the slope of a regression line, but it is much wider than you want it to be. Will increasing or decreasing the confidence level result in a narrower interval? Explain.

> **STOP AND THINK!**
>
> **How does the confidence level affect the width of the interval?**

Solution: Increasing the confidence level makes the interval wider. Therefore, to construct a narrower confidence interval, you would want to decrease the confidence.

■

Example 9: Tonya is interested in predicting how fast she can run a mile from the current temperature. She obtains the regression equation, and constructs the following 95% confidence interval for the slope of the regression line (1.45, 2.06). Should she use the regression equation she obtained to make predictions? Explain.

> **STOP AND THINK!**
>
> **When is it appropriate to use a regression equation to make predictions?**

Solution: Yes, Tonya should use the regression equation she obtained to make predictions because the confidence interval indicates that the slope is significant.

■

Example 10: Ages and IQ scores of 100 individuals age 20 to 40 are obtained to derive the regression equation predicting a person's IQ score from a person's age.

$$\hat{y} = 56.053 + 1.553x$$

Can the regression equation be used to predict the IQ score of a 13 year old? Explain.

> **STOP AND THINK!**
>
> **Was any data collected on 13 year olds?**

Solution: A regression equation should only be used for prediction within the range of the data for the explanatory variable. Since the regression equation was obtained for people 20 to 40 years old, it should not be used to predict the IQ of a 13 year old.

■

LESSON 10.3 EXERCISES
MORE PRACTICE IN SOLVING SIMPLE LINEAR REGRESSION PROBLEMS

1. Ten towns were the subject of a study to determine the association between the number of stores selling liquor in their downtown areas and the number of DUI arrests downtown during one month. The data and summary information is provided below.

x	0	5	6	5	11	9	10	3	7	4
y	40	50	55	64	73	75	88	25	20	10

$\bar{x} = 6$ $\quad \sum_{\text{For all x}} (x - \bar{x})^2 = 102$

$\bar{y} = 50$ $\quad \sum_{\text{For all y}} (y - \bar{y})^2 = 6,024$ $\quad \sum_{\text{For all x,y}} (x - \bar{x})(y - \bar{y}) = 513$

   a) What is the explanatory variable?
   b) What is the response variable?
   c) Find the least-squares regression equation.
   d) If the standard error of the slope is 0.37, construct a 95% confidence interval for the population slope.
   e) Is the slope significant?

2. Given the following least squares regression line, is the slope positive or negative? What is the value of the intercept?

$$\hat{y} = 3 - 10x$$

3. Jim and Michele love to go wine tasting. On a recent wine tasting trip, they learn that there is a negative association between the cost of a bottle of wine and the number of bottles produced by the winery. Which of the following is a possible value for the slope of the regression line?
   A: $b_1 = 3.4$
   B: $b_1 = 0$
   C: $b_1 = -5.2$

ANSWERS

LESSON 10.3 EXERCISES

MORE PRACTICE IN SOLVING SIMPLE LINEAR REGRESSION PROBLEMS

Below are the answers to the exercises for Unit 10, Lesson 10.3.
For full solutions, please refer to the CD included with this textbook.

1. a) X = the number of stores selling liquor in the downtown areas
   b) Y = the number of DUI arrests downtown
   c) $\hat{y} = 19.8235 + 5.0294x$
   d) (4.1762, 5.8826)
   e) The slope is significant.

2. The slope is positive. The y-intercept is 3.

3. C: $b_1 = -5.2$

AVOIDING COMMON MISTAKES

☺ Think carefully about which is the explanatory variable and which is the response variable.

☺ Confidence intervals for the slope use the t-distribution with $n-2$ degrees of freedom.

☺ Do not use the regression equation to make predictions for values of the explanatory variable outside the range of the collected data.

UNIT 10 SUMMARY

- Linear Regression for a Population

  The least-squares regression line for an explanatory variable and a response variable is:

  $$y = \beta_0 + \beta_1 x$$

  - β_0 represents the y-intercept of the population of interest

  - β_1 represents the slope of the population of interest

- Linear Regression for a Sample

  The least-squares regression line for an explanatory variable and a response variable is:

  $$\hat{y} = b_0 + b_1 x$$

  - b_0 represents the y-intercept of the sample data.

  - b_1 represents the slope of the sample data.

- The formula to calculate the slope is:

  $$b_1 = \frac{\displaystyle\sum_{\text{For all x,y}} (x - \bar{x})(y - \bar{y})}{\displaystyle\sum_{\text{For all x}} (x - \bar{x})^2}$$

- The formula to calculate the y-intercept is:

  $$b_0 = \bar{y} - b_1 \bar{x}$$

- Deciding if the slope is significant:
  - If the data indicate that the slope of the population β_1 is 0, then the population slope is *not* significant, and hence X is *not* a useful predictor of Y.

  - If the data indicate that the slope of the population β_1 is *not* 0, then the population slope *is* significant, and hence X *is* a useful predictor of Y.

- Confidence Interval for β_1:

  $$b_1 \pm t(SE_{b_1})$$

  - b_1 represents the slope of the sample
  - t is a value obtained from the t-table, based on the confidence level and $n - 2$ degrees of freedom
  - SE_{b_1} represents the standard error of b_1

- If the confidence interval for the slope contains 0, this indicates that $\beta_1 = 0$ and hence the slope is not significant, thus X is not a useful predictor of Y.

- If the confidence interval for the slope does not contain 0, this indicates that $\beta_1 \neq 0$ and hence the slope is significant, thus X is a useful predictor of Y.

- A regression line should only be used for interpretation and prediction *within* the range of data collected for the explanatory variable

SELF-ASSESSMENT QUIZ

1. Researchers found that the association between the number of hours of sleep that a student has the night before an examination and his performance in the examination, can be modeled by the following regression equation.

$$\hat{y} = 45 + 5.5x$$

In this study, the number of hours a student slept ranged from 0 hours to 10 hours. The standard error of the slope is 0.245 and there were 75 students in the sample.
a) Construct a 95% confidence interval for the population slope. Is the slope significant? Explain.
b) Can you use this regression equation to predict the examination score for a student who slept 6 hours the night before the examination? If so, calculate the predicted score. If not, explain why not.
c) Can you use this regression equation to predict the examination score for a student who slept 12 hours the night before the examination? If so, calculate the predicted score. If not, explain why not.

2. Given the following least squares regression line, is the slope positive or negative? What is the value of the intercept? Would the correlation coefficient be positive or negative?

$$\hat{y} = 102 - 6x$$

3. Highway Patrol is interested in finding the association between the lowest temperature on a spring day and the number of calls for assistance they receive. The following summary information is provided from data collected over a period of 30 days.

$$\bar{x} = 5.5 \qquad \sum_{\text{For all x}} (x - \bar{x})^2 = 427.5$$

$$\bar{y} = 59 \qquad \sum_{\text{For all y}} (y - \bar{y})^2 = 4,570 \qquad \sum_{\text{For all x,y}} (x - \bar{x})(y - \bar{y}) = 1330$$

a) What is the explanatory variable?
b) What is the response variable?
c) Find the least-squares regression equation.

ANSWERS
SELF-ASSESSMENT QUIZ

Below are the answers to the exercises for Unit 10, Self-Assessment Quiz. For full solutions, please refer to the CD included with this textbook.

1. a) (5.0117, 5.9883)
    The slope is significant because the confidence interval does not contain 0.
    b) $\hat{y} = 78$
    c) No, because it is outside the range of the data collected for the explanatory variable.

2. The slope is negative. The y-intercept is 102. The correlation coefficient would be negative.

3. a) X = Lowest temperature on a spring day
    b) Y = Number of calls for assistance made to the Highway Patrol
    c) $\hat{y} = 41.8889 + 3.1111x$

APPENDIX

Binomial Table

Standard Normal Table

t-Table

							p						
n	x	0.1	0.2	0.25	0.3	0.4	0.5	0.6	0.7	0.75	0.8	0.9
1	0	0.9000	0.8000	0.7500	0.7000	0.6000	0.5000	0.4000	0.3000	0.2500	0.2000	0.1000
	1	0.1000	0.2000	0.2500	0.3000	0.4000	0.5000	0.6000	0.7000	0.7500	0.8000	0.9000
2	0	0.8100	0.6400	0.5625	0.4900	0.3600	0.2500	0.1600	0.0900	0.0625	0.0400	0.0100
	1	0.1800	0.3200	0.3750	0.4200	0.4800	0.5000	0.4800	0.4200	0.3750	0.3200	0.1800
	2	0.0100	0.0400	0.0625	0.0900	0.1600	0.2500	0.3600	0.4900	0.5625	0.6400	0.8100
3	0	0.7290	0.5120	0.4219	0.3430	0.2160	0.1250	0.0640	0.0270	0.0156	0.0080	0.0010
	1	0.2430	0.3840	0.4219	0.4410	0.4320	0.3750	0.2880	0.1890	0.1406	0.0960	0.0270
	2	0.0270	0.0960	0.1406	0.1890	0.2880	0.3750	0.4320	0.4410	0.4219	0.3840	0.2430
	3	0.0010	0.0080	0.0156	0.0270	0.0640	0.1250	0.2160	0.3430	0.4219	0.5120	0.7290
4	0	0.6561	0.4096	0.3164	0.2401	0.1296	0.0625	0.0256	0.0081	0.0039	0.0016	0.0001
	1	0.2916	0.4096	0.4219	0.4116	0.3456	0.2500	0.1536	0.0756	0.0469	0.0256	0.0036
	2	0.0486	0.1536	0.2109	0.2646	0.3456	0.3750	0.3456	0.2646	0.2109	0.1536	0.0486
	3	0.0036	0.0256	0.0469	0.0756	0.1536	0.2500	0.3456	0.4116	0.4219	0.4096	0.2916
	4	0.0001	0.0016	0.0039	0.0081	0.0256	0.0625	0.1296	0.2401	0.3164	0.4096	0.6561
5	0	0.5905	0.3277	0.2373	0.1681	0.0778	0.0313	0.0102	0.0024	0.0010	0.0003	
	1	0.3281	0.4096	0.3955	0.3602	0.2592	0.1563	0.0768	0.0284	0.0146	0.0064	0.0005
	2	0.0729	0.2048	0.2637	0.3087	0.3456	0.3125	0.2304	0.1323	0.0879	0.0512	0.0081
	3	0.0081	0.0512	0.0879	0.1323	0.2304	0.3125	0.3456	0.3087	0.2637	0.2048	0.0729
	4	0.0005	0.0064	0.0146	0.0284	0.0768	0.1563	0.2592	0.3602	0.3955	0.4096	0.3281
	5		0.0003	0.0010	0.0024	0.0102	0.0313	0.0778	0.1681	0.2373	0.3277	0.5905
6	0	0.5314	0.2621	0.1780	0.1176	0.0467	0.0156	0.0041	0.0007	0.0002	0.0001	
	1	0.3543	0.3932	0.3560	0.3025	0.1866	0.0938	0.0369	0.0102	0.0044	0.0015	0.0001
	2	0.0984	0.2458	0.2966	0.3241	0.3110	0.2344	0.1382	0.0595	0.0330	0.0154	0.0012
	3	0.0146	0.0819	0.1318	0.1852	0.2765	0.3125	0.2765	0.1852	0.1318	0.0819	0.0146
	4	0.0012	0.0154	0.0330	0.0595	0.1382	0.2344	0.3110	0.3241	0.2966	0.2458	0.0984
	5	0.0001	0.0015	0.0044	0.0102	0.0369	0.0938	0.1866	0.3025	0.3560	0.3932	0.3543
	6		0.0001	0.0002	0.0007	0.0041	0.0156	0.0467	0.1176	0.1780	0.2621	0.5314
7	0	0.4783	0.2097	0.1335	0.0824	0.0280	0.0078	0.0016	0.0002	0.0001		
	1	0.3720	0.3670	0.3115	0.2471	0.1306	0.0547	0.0172	0.0036	0.0013	0.0004	
	2	0.1240	0.2753	0.3115	0.3177	0.2613	0.1641	0.0774	0.0250	0.0115	0.0043	0.0002
	3	0.0230	0.1147	0.1730	0.2269	0.2903	0.2734	0.1935	0.0972	0.0577	0.0287	0.0026
	4	0.0026	0.0287	0.0577	0.0972	0.1935	0.2734	0.2903	0.2269	0.1730	0.1147	0.0230
	5	0.0002	0.0043	0.0115	0.0250	0.0774	0.1641	0.2613	0.3177	0.3115	0.2753	0.1240
	6		0.0004	0.0013	0.0036	0.0172	0.0547	0.1306	0.2471	0.3115	0.3670	0.3720
	7			0.0001	0.0002	0.0016	0.0078	0.0280	0.0824	0.1335	0.2097	0.4783
8	0	0.4305	0.1678	0.1001	0.0576	0.0168	0.0039	0.0007	0.0001			
	1	0.3826	0.3355	0.2670	0.1977	0.0896	0.0313	0.0079	0.0012	0.0004	0.0001	
	2	0.1488	0.2936	0.3115	0.2965	0.2090	0.1094	0.0413	0.0100	0.0038	0.0011	
	3	0.0331	0.1468	0.2076	0.2541	0.2787	0.2188	0.1239	0.0467	0.0231	0.0092	0.0004
	4	0.0046	0.0459	0.0865	0.1361	0.2322	0.2734	0.2322	0.1361	0.0865	0.0459	0.0046
	5	0.0004	0.0092	0.0231	0.0467	0.1239	0.2188	0.2787	0.2541	0.2076	0.1468	0.0331
	6		0.0011	0.0038	0.0100	0.0413	0.1094	0.2090	0.2965	0.3115	0.2936	0.1488
	7		0.0001	0.0004	0.0012	0.0079	0.0313	0.0896	0.1977	0.2670	0.3355	0.3826
	8				0.0001	0.0007	0.0039	0.0168	0.0576	0.1001	0.1678	0.4305

n	x	0.1	0.2	0.25	0.3	0.4	p 0.5	0.6	0.7	0.75	0.8	0.9
9	0	0.3874	0.1342	0.0751	0.0404	0.0101	0.0020	0.0003				
	1	0.3874	0.3020	0.2253	0.1556	0.0605	0.0176	0.0035	0.0004	0.0001		
	2	0.1722	0.3020	0.3003	0.2668	0.1612	0.0703	0.0212	0.0039	0.0012	0.0003	
	3	0.0446	0.1762	0.2336	0.2668	0.2508	0.1641	0.0743	0.0210	0.0087	0.0028	0.0001
	4	0.0074	0.0661	0.1168	0.1715	0.2508	0.2461	0.1672	0.0735	0.0389	0.0165	0.0008
	5	0.0008	0.0165	0.0389	0.0735	0.1672	0.2461	0.2508	0.1715	0.1168	0.0661	0.0074
	6	0.0001	0.0028	0.0087	0.0210	0.0743	0.1641	0.2508	0.2668	0.2336	0.1762	0.0446
	7		0.0003	0.0012	0.0039	0.0212	0.0703	0.1612	0.2668	0.3003	0.3020	0.1722
	8			0.0001	0.0004	0.0035	0.0176	0.0605	0.1556	0.2253	0.3020	0.3874
	9					0.0003	0.0020	0.0101	0.0404	0.0751	0.1342	0.3874
10	0	0.3487	0.1074	0.0563	0.0282	0.0060	0.0010	0.0001				
	1	0.3874	0.2684	0.1877	0.1211	0.0403	0.0098	0.0016	0.0001			
	2	0.1937	0.3020	0.2816	0.2335	0.1209	0.0439	0.0106	0.0014	0.0004	0.0001	
	3	0.0574	0.2013	0.2503	0.2668	0.2150	0.1172	0.0425	0.0090	0.0031	0.0008	
	4	0.0112	0.0881	0.1460	0.2001	0.2508	0.2051	0.1115	0.0368	0.0162	0.0055	0.0001
	5	0.0015	0.0264	0.0584	0.1029	0.2007	0.2461	0.2007	0.1029	0.0584	0.0264	0.0015
	6	0.0001	0.0055	0.0162	0.0368	0.1115	0.2051	0.2508	0.2001	0.1460	0.0881	0.0112
	7		0.0008	0.0031	0.0090	0.0425	0.1172	0.2150	0.2668	0.2503	0.2013	0.0574
	8		0.0001	0.0004	0.0014	0.0106	0.0439	0.1209	0.2335	0.2816	0.3020	0.1937
	9				0.0001	0.0016	0.0098	0.0403	0.1211	0.1877	0.2684	0.3874
	10					0.0001	0.0010	0.0060	0.0282	0.0563	0.1074	0.3487
11	0	0.3138	0.0859	0.0422	0.0198	0.0036	0.0005					
	1	0.3835	0.2362	0.1549	0.0932	0.0266	0.0054	0.0007				
	2	0.2131	0.2953	0.2581	0.1998	0.0887	0.0269	0.0052	0.0005	0.0001		
	3	0.0710	0.2215	0.2581	0.2568	0.1774	0.0806	0.0234	0.0037	0.0011	0.0002	
	4	0.0158	0.1107	0.1721	0.2201	0.2365	0.1611	0.0701	0.0173	0.0064	0.0017	
	5	0.0025	0.0388	0.0803	0.1321	0.2207	0.2256	0.1471	0.0566	0.0268	0.0097	0.0003
	6	0.0003	0.0097	0.0268	0.0566	0.1471	0.2256	0.2207	0.1321	0.0803	0.0388	0.0025
	7		0.0017	0.0064	0.0173	0.0701	0.1611	0.2365	0.2201	0.1721	0.1107	0.0158
	8		0.0002	0.0011	0.0037	0.0234	0.0806	0.1774	0.2568	0.2581	0.2215	0.0710
	9			0.0001	0.0005	0.0052	0.0269	0.0887	0.1998	0.2581	0.2953	0.2131
	10					0.0007	0.0054	0.0266	0.0932	0.1549	0.2362	0.3835
	11						0.0005	0.0036	0.0198	0.0422	0.0859	0.3138
12	0	0.2824	0.0687	0.0317	0.0138	0.0022	0.0002					
	1	0.3766	0.2062	0.1267	0.0712	0.0174	0.0029	0.0003				
	2	0.2301	0.2835	0.2323	0.1678	0.0639	0.0161	0.0025	0.0002			
	3	0.0852	0.2362	0.2581	0.2397	0.1419	0.0537	0.0125	0.0015	0.0004	0.0001	
	4	0.0213	0.1329	0.1936	0.2311	0.2128	0.1208	0.0420	0.0078	0.0024	0.0005	
	5	0.0038	0.0532	0.1032	0.1585	0.2270	0.1934	0.1009	0.0291	0.0115	0.0033	
	6	0.0005	0.0155	0.0401	0.0792	0.1766	0.2256	0.1766	0.0792	0.0401	0.0155	0.0005
	7		0.0033	0.0115	0.0291	0.1009	0.1934	0.2270	0.1585	0.1032	0.0532	0.0038
	8		0.0005	0.0024	0.0078	0.0420	0.1208	0.2128	0.2311	0.1936	0.1329	0.0213
	9		0.0001	0.0004	0.0015	0.0125	0.0537	0.1419	0.2397	0.2581	0.2362	0.0852
	10				0.0002	0.0025	0.0161	0.0639	0.1678	0.2323	0.2835	0.2301
	11					0.0003	0.0029	0.0174	0.0712	0.1267	0.2062	0.3766
	12						0.0002	0.0022	0.0138	0.0317	0.0687	0.2824

n	x	0.1	0.2	0.25	0.3	0.4	p 0.5	0.6	0.7	0.75	0.8	0.9
13	0	0.2542	0.0550	0.0238	0.0097	0.0013	0.0001					
	1	0.3672	0.1787	0.1029	0.0540	0.0113	0.0016	0.0001				
	2	0.2448	0.2680	0.2059	0.1388	0.0453	0.0095	0.0012	0.0001			
	3	0.0997	0.2457	0.2517	0.2181	0.1107	0.0349	0.0065	0.0006	0.0001		
	4	0.0277	0.1535	0.2097	0.2337	0.1845	0.0873	0.0243	0.0034	0.0009	0.0001	
	5	0.0055	0.0691	0.1258	0.1803	0.2214	0.1571	0.0656	0.0142	0.0047	0.0011	
	6	0.0008	0.0230	0.0559	0.1030	0.1968	0.2095	0.1312	0.0442	0.0186	0.0058	0.0001
	7	0.0001	0.0058	0.0186	0.0442	0.1312	0.2095	0.1968	0.1030	0.0559	0.0230	0.0008
	8		0.0011	0.0047	0.0142	0.0656	0.1571	0.2214	0.1803	0.1258	0.0691	0.0055
	9		0.0001	0.0009	0.0034	0.0243	0.0873	0.1845	0.2337	0.2097	0.1535	0.0277
	10			0.0001	0.0006	0.0065	0.0349	0.1107	0.2181	0.2517	0.2457	0.0997
	11				0.0001	0.0012	0.0095	0.0453	0.1388	0.2059	0.2680	0.2448
	12					0.0001	0.0016	0.0113	0.0540	0.1029	0.1787	0.3672
	13						0.0001	0.0013	0.0097	0.0238	0.0550	0.2542
14	0	0.2288	0.0440	0.0178	0.0068	0.0008	0.0001					
	1	0.3559	0.1539	0.0832	0.0407	0.0073	0.0009	0.0001				
	2	0.2570	0.2501	0.1802	0.1134	0.0317	0.0056	0.0005				
	3	0.1142	0.2501	0.2402	0.1943	0.0845	0.0222	0.0033	0.0002			
	4	0.0349	0.1720	0.2202	0.2290	0.1549	0.0611	0.0136	0.0014	0.0003		
	5	0.0078	0.0860	0.1468	0.1963	0.2066	0.1222	0.0408	0.0066	0.0018	0.0003	
	6	0.0013	0.0322	0.0734	0.1262	0.2066	0.1833	0.0918	0.0232	0.0082	0.0020	
	7	0.0002	0.0092	0.0280	0.0618	0.1574	0.2095	0.1574	0.0618	0.0280	0.0092	0.0002
	8		0.0020	0.0082	0.0232	0.0918	0.1833	0.2066	0.1262	0.0734	0.0322	0.0013
	9		0.0003	0.0018	0.0066	0.0408	0.1222	0.2066	0.1963	0.1468	0.0860	0.0078
	10			0.0003	0.0014	0.0136	0.0611	0.1549	0.2290	0.2202	0.1720	0.0349
	11				0.0002	0.0033	0.0222	0.0845	0.1943	0.2402	0.2501	0.1142
	12					0.0005	0.0056	0.0317	0.1134	0.1802	0.2501	0.2570
	13					0.0001	0.0009	0.0073	0.0407	0.0832	0.1539	0.3559
	14						0.0001	0.0008	0.0068	0.0178	0.0440	0.2288
15	0	0.2059	0.0352	0.0134	0.0047	0.0005						
	1	0.3432	0.1319	0.0668	0.0305	0.0047	0.0005					
	2	0.2669	0.2309	0.1559	0.0916	0.0219	0.0032	0.0003				
	3	0.1285	0.2501	0.2252	0.1700	0.0634	0.0139	0.0016	0.0001			
	4	0.0428	0.1876	0.2252	0.2186	0.1268	0.0417	0.0074	0.0006	0.0001		
	5	0.0105	0.1032	0.1651	0.2061	0.1859	0.0916	0.0245	0.0030	0.0007	0.0001	
	6	0.0019	0.0430	0.0917	0.1472	0.2066	0.1527	0.0612	0.0116	0.0034	0.0007	
	7	0.0003	0.0138	0.0393	0.0811	0.1771	0.1964	0.1181	0.0348	0.0131	0.0035	
	8		0.0035	0.0131	0.0348	0.1181	0.1964	0.1771	0.0811	0.0393	0.0138	0.0003
	9		0.0007	0.0034	0.0116	0.0612	0.1527	0.2066	0.1472	0.0917	0.0430	0.0019
	10		0.0001	0.0007	0.0030	0.0245	0.0916	0.1859	0.2061	0.1651	0.1032	0.0105
	11			0.0001	0.0006	0.0074	0.0417	0.1268	0.2186	0.2252	0.1876	0.0428
	12				0.0001	0.0016	0.0139	0.0634	0.1700	0.2252	0.2501	0.1285
	13					0.0003	0.0032	0.0219	0.0916	0.1559	0.2309	0.2669
	14						0.0005	0.0047	0.0305	0.0668	0.1319	0.3432
	15							0.0005	0.0047	0.0134	0.0352	0.2059
16	0	0.1853	0.0281	0.0100	0.0033	0.0003						
	1	0.3294	0.1126	0.0535	0.0228	0.0030	0.0002					
	2	0.2745	0.2111	0.1336	0.0732	0.0150	0.0018	0.0001				
	3	0.1423	0.2463	0.2079	0.1465	0.0468	0.0085	0.0008				
	4	0.0514	0.2001	0.2252	0.2040	0.1014	0.0278	0.0040	0.0002			
	5	0.0137	0.1201	0.1802	0.2099	0.1623	0.0667	0.0142	0.0013	0.0002		
	6	0.0028	0.0550	0.1101	0.1649	0.1983	0.1222	0.0392	0.0056	0.0014	0.0002	
	7	0.0004	0.0197	0.0524	0.1010	0.1889	0.1746	0.0840	0.0185	0.0058	0.0012	
	8	0.0001	0.0055	0.0197	0.0487	0.1417	0.1964	0.1417	0.0487	0.0197	0.0055	0.0001
	9		0.0012	0.0058	0.0185	0.0840	0.1746	0.1889	0.1010	0.0524	0.0197	0.0004
	10		0.0002	0.0014	0.0056	0.0392	0.1222	0.1983	0.1649	0.1101	0.0550	0.0028
	11			0.0002	0.0013	0.0142	0.0667	0.1623	0.2099	0.1802	0.1201	0.0137
	12				0.0002	0.0040	0.0278	0.1014	0.2040	0.2252	0.2001	0.0514
	13					0.0008	0.0085	0.0468	0.1465	0.2079	0.2463	0.1423
	14					0.0001	0.0018	0.0150	0.0732	0.1336	0.2111	0.2745
	15						0.0002	0.0030	0.0228	0.0535	0.1126	0.3294
	16							0.0003	0.0033	0.0100	0.0281	0.1853

n	x	0.1	0.2	0.25	0.3	0.4	0.5	0.6	0.7	0.75	0.8	0.9
17	0	0.1668	0.0225	0.0075	0.0023	0.0002						
	1	0.3150	0.0957	0.0426	0.0169	0.0019	0.0001					
	2	0.2800	0.1914	0.1136	0.0581	0.0102	0.0010	0.0001				
	3	0.1556	0.2393	0.1893	0.1245	0.0341	0.0052	0.0004				
	4	0.0605	0.2093	0.2209	0.1868	0.0796	0.0182	0.0021	0.0001			
	5	0.0175	0.1361	0.1914	0.2081	0.1379	0.0472	0.0081	0.0006	0.0001		
	6	0.0039	0.0680	0.1276	0.1784	0.1839	0.0944	0.0242	0.0026	0.0005	0.0001	
	7	0.0007	0.0267	0.0668	0.1201	0.1927	0.1484	0.0571	0.0095	0.0025	0.0004	
	8	0.0001	0.0084	0.0279	0.0644	0.1606	0.1855	0.1070	0.0276	0.0093	0.0021	
	9		0.0021	0.0093	0.0276	0.1070	0.1855	0.1606	0.0644	0.0279	0.0084	0.0001
	10		0.0004	0.0025	0.0095	0.0571	0.1484	0.1927	0.1201	0.0668	0.0267	0.0007
	11		0.0001	0.0005	0.0026	0.0242	0.0944	0.1839	0.1784	0.1276	0.0680	0.0039
	12			0.0001	0.0006	0.0081	0.0472	0.1379	0.2081	0.1914	0.1361	0.0175
	13				0.0001	0.0021	0.0182	0.0796	0.1868	0.2209	0.2093	0.0605
	14					0.0004	0.0052	0.0341	0.1245	0.1893	0.2393	0.1556
	15					0.0001	0.0010	0.0102	0.0581	0.1136	0.1914	0.2800
	16						0.0001	0.0019	0.0169	0.0426	0.0957	0.3150
	17							0.0002	0.0023	0.0075	0.0225	0.1668
18	0	0.1501	0.0180	0.0056	0.0016	0.0001						
	1	0.3002	0.0811	0.0338	0.0126	0.0012	0.0001					
	2	0.2835	0.1723	0.0958	0.0458	0.0069	0.0006					
	3	0.1680	0.2297	0.1704	0.1046	0.0246	0.0031	0.0002				
	4	0.0700	0.2153	0.2130	0.1681	0.0614	0.0117	0.0011				
	5	0.0218	0.1507	0.1988	0.2017	0.1146	0.0327	0.0045	0.0002			
	6	0.0052	0.0816	0.1436	0.1873	0.1655	0.0708	0.0145	0.0012	0.0002		
	7	0.0010	0.0350	0.0820	0.1376	0.1892	0.1214	0.0374	0.0046	0.0010	0.0001	
	8	0.0002	0.0120	0.0376	0.0811	0.1734	0.1669	0.0771	0.0149	0.0042	0.0008	
	9		0.0033	0.0139	0.0386	0.1284	0.1855	0.1284	0.0386	0.0139	0.0033	
	10		0.0008	0.0042	0.0149	0.0771	0.1669	0.1734	0.0811	0.0376	0.0120	0.0002
	11		0.0001	0.0010	0.0046	0.0374	0.1214	0.1892	0.1376	0.0820	0.0350	0.0010
	12			0.0002	0.0012	0.0145	0.0708	0.1655	0.1873	0.1436	0.0816	0.0052
	13				0.0002	0.0045	0.0327	0.1146	0.2017	0.1988	0.1507	0.0218
	14					0.0011	0.0117	0.0614	0.1681	0.2130	0.2153	0.0700
	15					0.0002	0.0031	0.0246	0.1046	0.1704	0.2297	0.1680
	16						0.0006	0.0069	0.0458	0.0958	0.1723	0.2835
	17						0.0001	0.0012	0.0126	0.0338	0.0811	0.3002
	18							0.0001	0.0016	0.0056	0.0180	0.1501
19	0	0.1351	0.0144	0.0042	0.0011	0.0001						
	1	0.2852	0.0685	0.0268	0.0093	0.0008						
	2	0.2852	0.1540	0.0803	0.0358	0.0046	0.0003					
	3	0.1796	0.2182	0.1517	0.0869	0.0175	0.0018	0.0001				
	4	0.0798	0.2182	0.2023	0.1491	0.0467	0.0074	0.0005				
	5	0.0266	0.1636	0.2023	0.1916	0.0933	0.0222	0.0024	0.0001			
	6	0.0069	0.0955	0.1574	0.1916	0.1451	0.0518	0.0085	0.0005	0.0001		
	7	0.0014	0.0443	0.0974	0.1525	0.1797	0.0961	0.0237	0.0022	0.0004		
	8	0.0002	0.0166	0.0487	0.0981	0.1797	0.1442	0.0532	0.0077	0.0018	0.0003	
	9		0.0051	0.0198	0.0514	0.1464	0.1762	0.0976	0.0220	0.0066	0.0013	
	10		0.0013	0.0066	0.0220	0.0976	0.1762	0.1464	0.0514	0.0198	0.0051	
	11		0.0003	0.0018	0.0077	0.0532	0.1442	0.1797	0.0981	0.0487	0.0166	0.0002
	12			0.0004	0.0022	0.0237	0.0961	0.1797	0.1525	0.0974	0.0443	0.0014
	13			0.0001	0.0005	0.0085	0.0518	0.1451	0.1916	0.1574	0.0955	0.0069
	14				0.0001	0.0024	0.0222	0.0933	0.1916	0.2023	0.1636	0.0266
	15					0.0005	0.0074	0.0467	0.1491	0.2023	0.2182	0.0798
	16					0.0001	0.0018	0.0175	0.0869	0.1517	0.2182	0.1796
	17						0.0003	0.0046	0.0358	0.0803	0.1540	0.2852
	18							0.0008	0.0093	0.0268	0.0685	0.2852
	19							0.0001	0.0011	0.0042	0.0144	0.1351

n	x	0.1	0.2	0.25	0.3	0.4	p 0.5	0.6	0.7	0.75	0.8	0.9
20	0	0.1216	0.0115	0.0032	0.0008							
	1	0.2702	0.0576	0.0211	0.0068	0.0005						
	2	0.2852	0.1369	0.0669	0.0278	0.0031	0.0002					
	3	0.1901	0.2054	0.1339	0.0716	0.0123	0.0011					
	4	0.0898	0.2182	0.1897	0.1304	0.0350	0.0046	0.0003				
	5	0.0319	0.1746	0.2023	0.1789	0.0746	0.0148	0.0013				
	6	0.0089	0.1091	0.1686	0.1916	0.1244	0.0370	0.0049	0.0002			
	7	0.0020	0.0545	0.1124	0.1643	0.1659	0.0739	0.0146	0.0010	0.0002		
	8	0.0004	0.0222	0.0609	0.1144	0.1797	0.1201	0.0355	0.0039	0.0008	0.0001	
	9	0.0001	0.0074	0.0271	0.0654	0.1597	0.1602	0.0710	0.0120	0.0030	0.0005	
	10		0.0020	0.0099	0.0308	0.1171	0.1762	0.1171	0.0308	0.0099	0.0020	
	11		0.0005	0.0030	0.0120	0.0710	0.1602	0.1597	0.0654	0.0271	0.0074	0.0001
	12		0.0001	0.0008	0.0039	0.0355	0.1201	0.1797	0.1144	0.0609	0.0222	0.0004
	13			0.0002	0.0010	0.0146	0.0739	0.1659	0.1643	0.1124	0.0545	0.0020
	14				0.0002	0.0049	0.0370	0.1244	0.1916	0.1686	0.1091	0.0089
	15					0.0013	0.0148	0.0746	0.1789	0.2023	0.1746	0.0319
	16					0.0003	0.0046	0.0350	0.1304	0.1897	0.2182	0.0898
	17						0.0011	0.0123	0.0716	0.1339	0.2054	0.1901
	18						0.0002	0.0031	0.0278	0.0669	0.1369	0.2852
	19							0.0005	0.0068	0.0211	0.0576	0.2702
	20								0.0008	0.0032	0.0115	0.1216

Standard Normal Table
Negative Z-scores

The probabilities given in this table represent the area to the LEFT of the z-score.
The area to the RIGHT of a z-score = 1 – the area to the LEFT of the z-score.

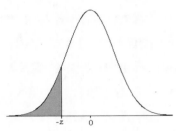

z	0.00	0.01	0.02	0.03	0.04	0.05	0.06	0.07	0.08	0.09
-3.4	0.0003	0.0003	0.0003	0.0003	0.0003	0.0003	0.0003	0.0003	0.0003	0.0002
-3.3	0.0005	0.0005	0.0005	0.0004	0.0004	0.0004	0.0004	0.0004	0.0004	0.0003
-3.2	0.0007	0.0007	0.0006	0.0006	0.0006	0.0006	0.0006	0.0005	0.0005	0.0005
-3.1	0.0010	0.0009	0.0009	0.0009	0.0008	0.0008	0.0008	0.0008	0.0007	0.0007
-3.0	0.0013	0.0013	0.0013	0.0012	0.0012	0.0011	0.0011	0.0011	0.0010	0.0010
-2.9	0.0019	0.0018	0.0018	0.0017	0.0016	0.0016	0.0015	0.0015	0.0014	0.0014
-2.8	0.0026	0.0025	0.0024	0.0023	0.0023	0.0022	0.0021	0.0021	0.0020	0.0019
-2.7	0.0035	0.0034	0.0033	0.0032	0.0031	0.0030	0.0029	0.0028	0.0027	0.0026
-2.6	0.0047	0.0045	0.0044	0.0043	0.0041	0.0040	0.0039	0.0038	0.0037	0.0036
-2.5	0.0062	0.0060	0.0059	0.0057	0.0055	0.0054	0.0052	0.0051	0.0049	0.0048
-2.4	0.0082	0.0080	0.0078	0.0075	0.0073	0.0071	0.0069	0.0068	0.0066	0.0064
-2.3	0.0107	0.0104	0.0102	0.0099	0.0096	0.0094	0.0091	0.0089	0.0087	0.0084
-2.2	0.0139	0.0136	0.0132	0.0129	0.0125	0.0122	0.0119	0.0116	0.0113	0.0110
-2.1	0.0179	0.0174	0.0170	0.0166	0.0162	0.0158	0.0154	0.0150	0.0146	0.0143
-2.0	0.0228	0.0222	0.0217	0.0212	0.0207	0.0202	0.0197	0.0192	0.0188	0.0183
-1.9	0.0287	0.0281	0.0274	0.0268	0.0262	0.0256	0.0250	0.0244	0.0239	0.0233
-1.8	0.0359	0.0351	0.0344	0.0336	0.0329	0.0322	0.0314	0.0307	0.0301	0.0294
-1.7	0.0446	0.0436	0.0427	0.0418	0.0409	0.0401	0.0392	0.0384	0.0375	0.0367
-1.6	0.0548	0.0537	0.0526	0.0516	0.0505	0.0495	0.0485	0.0475	0.0465	0.0455
-1.5	0.0668	0.0655	0.0643	0.0630	0.0618	0.0606	0.0594	0.0582	0.0571	0.0559
-1.4	0.0808	0.0793	0.0778	0.0764	0.0749	0.0735	0.0721	0.0708	0.0694	0.0681
-1.3	0.0968	0.0951	0.0934	0.0918	0.0901	0.0885	0.0869	0.0853	0.0838	0.0823
-1.2	0.1151	0.1131	0.1112	0.1093	0.1075	0.1056	0.1038	0.1020	0.1003	0.0985
-1.1	0.1357	0.1335	0.1314	0.1292	0.1271	0.1251	0.1230	0.1210	0.1190	0.1170
-1.0	0.1587	0.1562	0.1539	0.1515	0.1492	0.1469	0.1446	0.1423	0.1401	0.1379
-0.9	0.1841	0.1814	0.1788	0.1762	0.1736	0.1711	0.1685	0.1660	0.1635	0.1611
-0.8	0.2119	0.2090	0.2061	0.2033	0.2005	0.1977	0.1949	0.1922	0.1894	0.1867
-0.7	0.2420	0.2389	0.2358	0.2327	0.2296	0.2266	0.2236	0.2206	0.2177	0.2148
-0.6	0.2743	0.2709	0.2676	0.2643	0.2611	0.2578	0.2546	0.2514	0.2483	0.2451
-0.5	0.3085	0.3050	0.3015	0.2981	0.2946	0.2912	0.2877	0.2843	0.2810	0.2776
-0.4	0.3446	0.3409	0.3372	0.3336	0.3300	0.3264	0.3228	0.3192	0.3156	0.3121
-0.3	0.3821	0.3783	0.3745	0.3707	0.3669	0.3632	0.3594	0.3557	0.3520	0.3483
-0.2	0.4207	0.4168	0.4129	0.4090	0.4052	0.4013	0.3974	0.3936	0.3897	0.3859
-0.1	0.4602	0.4562	0.4522	0.4483	0.4443	0.4404	0.4364	0.4325	0.4286	0.4247
-0.0	0.5000	0.4960	0.4920	0.4880	0.4840	0.4801	0.4761	0.4721	0.4681	0.4641

Standard Normal Table
Positive Z-scores

The probabilities given in this table represent the area to the LEFT of the z-score.
The area to the RIGHT of a z-score = 1 − the area to the LEFT of the z-score.

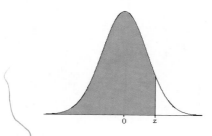

z	0.00	0.01	0.02	0.03	0.04	0.05	0.06	0.07	0.08	0.09
0.0	0.5000	0.5040	0.5080	0.5120	0.5160	0.5199	0.5239	0.5279	0.5319	0.5359
0.1	0.5398	0.5438	0.5478	0.5517	0.5557	0.5596	0.5636	0.5675	0.5714	0.5753
0.2	0.5793	0.5832	0.5871	0.5910	0.5948	0.5987	0.6026	0.6064	0.6103	0.6141
0.3	0.6179	0.6217	0.6255	0.6293	0.6331	0.6368	0.6406	0.6443	0.6480	0.6517
0.4	0.6554	0.6591	0.6628	0.6664	0.6700	0.6736	0.6772	0.6808	0.6844	0.6879
0.5	0.6915	0.6950	0.6985	0.7019	0.7054	0.7088	0.7123	0.7157	0.7190	0.7224
0.6	0.7257	0.7291	0.7324	0.7357	0.7389	0.7422	0.7454	0.7486	0.7517	0.7549
0.7	0.7580	0.7611	0.7642	0.7673	0.7704	0.7734	0.7764	0.7794	0.7823	0.7852
0.8	0.7881	0.7910	0.7939	0.7967	0.7995	0.8023	0.8051	0.8078	0.8106	0.8133
0.9	0.8159	0.8186	0.8212	0.8238	0.8264	0.8289	0.8315	0.8340	0.8365	0.8389
1.0	0.8413	0.8438	0.8461	0.8485	0.8508	0.8531	0.8554	0.8577	0.8599	0.8621
1.1	0.8643	0.8665	0.8686	0.8708	0.8729	0.8749	0.8770	0.8790	0.8810	0.8830
1.2	0.8849	0.8869	0.8888	0.8907	0.8925	0.8944	0.8962	0.8980	0.8997	0.9015
1.3	0.9032	0.9049	0.9066	0.9082	0.9099	0.9115	0.9131	0.9147	0.9162	0.9177
1.4	0.9192	0.9207	0.9222	0.9236	0.9251	0.9265	0.9279	0.9292	0.9306	0.9319
1.5	0.9332	0.9345	0.9357	0.9370	0.9382	0.9394	0.9406	0.9418	0.9429	0.9441
1.6	0.9452	0.9463	0.9474	0.9484	0.9495	0.9505	0.9515	0.9525	0.9535	0.9545
1.7	0.9554	0.9564	0.9573	0.9582	0.9591	0.9599	0.9608	0.9616	0.9625	0.9633
1.8	0.9641	0.9649	0.9656	0.9664	0.9671	0.9678	0.9686	0.9693	0.9699	0.9706
1.9	0.9713	0.9719	0.9726	0.9732	0.9738	0.9744	0.9750	0.9756	0.9761	0.9767
2.0	0.9772	0.9778	0.9783	0.9788	0.9793	0.9798	0.9803	0.9808	0.9812	0.9817
2.1	0.9821	0.9826	0.9830	0.9834	0.9838	0.9842	0.9846	0.9850	0.9854	0.9857
2.2	0.9861	0.9864	0.9868	0.9871	0.9875	0.9878	0.9881	0.9884	0.9887	0.9890
2.3	0.9893	0.9896	0.9898	0.9901	0.9904	0.9906	0.9909	0.9911	0.9913	0.9916
2.4	0.9918	0.9920	0.9922	0.9925	0.9927	0.9929	0.9931	0.9932	0.9934	0.9936
2.5	0.9938	0.9940	0.9941	0.9943	0.9945	0.9946	0.9948	0.9949	0.9951	0.9952
2.6	0.9953	0.9955	0.9956	0.9957	0.9959	0.9960	0.9961	0.9962	0.9963	0.9964
2.7	0.9965	0.9966	0.9967	0.9968	0.9969	0.9970	0.9971	0.9972	0.9973	0.9974
2.8	0.9974	0.9975	0.9976	0.9977	0.9977	0.9978	0.9979	0.9979	0.9980	0.9981
2.9	0.9981	0.9982	0.9982	0.9983	0.9984	0.9984	0.9985	0.9985	0.9986	0.9986
3.0	0.9987	0.9987	0.9987	0.9988	0.9988	0.9989	0.9989	0.9989	0.9990	0.9990
3.1	0.9990	0.9991	0.9991	0.9991	0.9992	0.9992	0.9992	0.9992	0.9993	0.9993
3.2	0.9993	0.9993	0.9994	0.9994	0.9994	0.9994	0.9994	0.9995	0.9995	0.9995
3.3	0.9995	0.9995	0.9995	0.9996	0.9996	0.9996	0.9996	0.9996	0.9996	0.9997
3.4	0.9997	0.9997	0.9997	0.9997	0.9997	0.9997	0.9997	0.9997	0.9997	0.9998

t-table

Confidence Levels

Degrees of Freedom	90%	95%	98%	99%
1	6.314	12.706	31.821	63.657
2	2.920	4.303	6.965	9.925
3	2.353	3.182	4.541	5.841
4	2.132	2.776	3.747	4.604
5	2.015	2.571	3.365	4.032
6	1.943	2.447	3.143	3.707
7	1.895	2.365	2.998	3.499
8	1.860	2.306	2.896	3.355
9	1.833	2.262	2.821	3.250
10	1.812	2.228	2.764	3.169
11	1.796	2.201	2.718	3.106
12	1.782	2.179	2.681	3.055
13	1.771	2.160	2.650	3.012
14	1.761	2.145	2.624	2.977
15	1.753	2.131	2.602	2.947
16	1.746	2.120	2.583	2.921
17	1.740	2.110	2.567	2.898
18	1.734	2.101	2.552	2.878
19	1.729	2.093	2.539	2.861
20	1.725	2.086	2.528	2.845
21	1.721	2.080	2.518	2.831
22	1.717	2.074	2.508	2.819
23	1.714	2.069	2.500	2.807
24	1.711	2.064	2.492	2.797
25	1.708	2.060	2.485	2.787
26	1.706	2.056	2.479	2.779
27	1.703	2.052	2.473	2.771
28	1.701	2.048	2.467	2.763
29	1.699	2.045	2.462	2.756
30	1.697	2.042	2.457	2.750
31	1.696	2.040	2.453	2.744
32	1.694	2.037	2.449	2.738
33	1.692	2.035	2.445	2.733
34	1.691	2.032	2.441	2.728
35	1.690	2.030	2.438	2.724
36	1.688	2.028	2.434	2.719
37	1.687	2.026	2.431	2.715
38	1.686	2.024	2.429	2.712
39	1.685	2.023	2.426	2.708
40	1.684	2.021	2.423	2.704
41	1.683	2.020	2.421	2.701
42	1.682	2.018	2.418	2.698
43	1.681	2.017	2.416	2.695
44	1.680	2.015	2.414	2.692
45	1.679	2.014	2.412	2.690
46	1.679	2.013	2.410	2.687
47	1.678	2.012	2.408	2.685
48	1.677	2.011	2.407	2.682
49	1.677	2.010	2.405	2.680
50	1.676	2.009	2.403	2.678

Confidence Levels

Degrees of Freedom	90%	95%	98%	99%
51	1.675	2.008	2.402	2.676
52	1.675	2.007	2.400	2.674
53	1.674	2.006	2.399	2.672
54	1.674	2.005	2.397	2.670
55	1.673	2.004	2.396	2.668
56	1.673	2.003	2.395	2.667
57	1.672	2.002	2.394	2.665
58	1.672	2.002	2.392	2.663
59	1.671	2.001	2.391	2.662
60	1.671	2.000	2.390	2.660
61	1.670	2.000	2.389	2.659
62	1.670	1.999	2.388	2.657
63	1.669	1.998	2.387	2.656
64	1.669	1.998	2.386	2.655
65	1.669	1.997	2.385	2.654
66	1.668	1.997	2.384	2.652
67	1.668	1.996	2.383	2.651
68	1.668	1.995	2.382	2.650
69	1.667	1.995	2.382	2.649
70	1.667	1.994	2.381	2.648
71	1.667	1.994	2.380	2.647
72	1.666	1.993	2.379	2.646
73	1.666	1.993	2.379	2.645
74	1.666	1.993	2.378	2.644
75	1.665	1.992	2.377	2.643
76	1.665	1.992	2.376	2.642
77	1.665	1.991	2.376	2.641
78	1.665	1.991	2.375	2.640
79	1.664	1.990	2.374	2.640
80	1.664	1.990	2.374	2.639
81	1.664	1.990	2.373	2.638
82	1.664	1.989	2.373	2.637
83	1.663	1.989	2.372	2.636
84	1.663	1.989	2.372	2.636
85	1.663	1.988	2.371	2.635
86	1.663	1.988	2.370	2.634
87	1.663	1.988	2.370	2.634
88	1.662	1.987	2.369	2.633
89	1.662	1.987	2.369	2.632
90	1.662	1.987	2.368	2.632
91	1.662	1.986	2.368	2.631
92	1.662	1.986	2.368	2.630
93	1.661	1.986	2.367	2.630
94	1.661	1.986	2.367	2.629
95	1.661	1.985	2.366	2.629
96	1.661	1.985	2.366	2.628
97	1.661	1.985	2.365	2.627
98	1.661	1.984	2.365	2.627
99	1.660	1.984	2.365	2.626
500	1.648	1.965	2.334	2.586
1000	1.646	1.962	2.330	2.581
z-values	**1.645**	**1.96**	**2.326**	**2.576**

Note: *z*-values are in this row: